NUCLEAR REACTOR EXPERIMENTS

ARGONNE NATIONAL LABORATORY

*Operated by the University of Chicago
for the United States Atomic Energy Commission*

CONTRIBUTORS

ADER, M.
ARMSTRONG, R. H.
BAIRD, J. E.
BARNES, A. H.
BRYANT, H.
CHIESNA, T. H.
DRALEY, J. E.
FIRESTONE, R. F.
FRIDDLE, R. J.
GAST, F. B.
GORDON, S.
GROTENHUIS, M.
HART, E. J.
HIBDON, C.
HOAG, J. B.
KELBER, C. N.
KRAUSE, D. P.
KUCZEN, K. D.
LARSEN, R. R.
LENNOX, D. H.
LONDON, A. L.
MACDONNELL, D. M.

MAYER, W. J.
McCORKLE, W. H.
MURPHY, W. F.
NATALE, J. V.
PATTERSON, D. R.
PAWLICKI, G. S.
RABOY, S.
REED, G. W.
RHODE, R.
RINGO, G. R.
ROSS, L. E.
RYLANDER, E. W.
SCHILTZ, R. J.
SHOEMAKER, V. H.
SMITH, A. B.
SPINRAD, B. I.
STEVENS, H. C.
SWANK, R. K.
SWOPE, H. G.
TRAIL, C. C.
VARTERESSIAN, K. A.
YOUNGQUIST, C. H.

NUCLEAR REACTOR EXPERIMENTS

BY THE STAFF OF

U, S, ARGONNE NATIONAL LABORATORY

Operated by the University of Chicago
for the United States Atomic Energy Commission

J. BARTON HOAG

Editor and Contributor

D. VAN NOSTRAND COMPANY, INC.

PRINCETON, NEW JERSEY

TORONTO   LONDON

NEW YORK

D. VAN NOSTRAND COMPANY, INC.
120 Alexander St., Princeton, New Jersey (*Principal office*)
257 Fourth Avenue, New York 10, New York

D. VAN NOSTRAND COMPANY, LTD.
358, Kensington High Street, London, W.14, England

D. VAN NOSTRAND COMPANY (Canada), LTD.
25 Hollinger Road, Toronto 16, Canada

FOREWORD

DURING wartime, the education and training of personnel on the government's atomic energy project were essential to our defense effort. In the postwar era, further efforts on the part of those serving the government were needed to disseminate information and orient teachers to the newer developments in nuclear science. Then the broad expansion of peacetime atomic energy development created still more demand for educational activity on the part of the major AEC contractors.

When President Eisenhower's Atoms for Peace program was inaugurated, the Atomic Energy Commission established a school of nuclear science and engineering at the Argonne National Laboratory to serve both national and international interests. More than one-half of the students come from abroad.

The purpose of the school is to advance nuclear science, including nuclear engineering education, throughout the world. It is appropriate, then, that books and manuals based on the courses given at Argonne be published so that the experience gained here may be more universally applied. To this end, the Laboratory offers this manual and trusts that it will serve a purpose meriting the efforts of contributors and the editor.

Argonne National Laboratory
February 1958

NORMAN HILBERRY

PREFACE

THIS is a laboratory book for instruction in the field of nuclear science and engineering.

The theory of nuclear reactors starts with the production and properties of elementary "particles" such as neutrons and gamma rays, and their interactions with atomic nuclei of varied structure and stability. The theory continues with the release of energy by fission and of the chain reaction which multiplies these energies to practical importance. It considers the slowing down of neutrons, from their "birth" at fast, fission energies, to thermal or room-temperature values, and also their diffusion among the atoms of solids, liquids, and gases, their reflection from various materials, and their absorption, scattering, and transmission as they pass through matter. Also it "keeps the books" on the number of neutrons, from their birth at fission to their final absorption.

From these theories come equations for the size and mass of the fissile uranium and of the moderating or slowing-down material that make up the core of a critical nuclear reactor; the heat then produced and, of utmost importance, the methods of control of the power developed; as well as changes with time when the controls, the temperature or the pressure are altered; and the effect of internally produced "poisons" which develop with continued use of the reactor.

Certain constants and parameters of nuclear reactors can be calculated from the theories—and they can also be measured by methods set forth in this book. There is a continual interplay between theory and measurement in the growth of this new science and technology. Among the quantities to be considered there are: cross sections of neutron interactions with matter, thermal diffusion lengths, slowing-down lengths, mean-free-paths, neutrons per fission, fast fission factor, resonance escape probability, thermal utilization factor, leakage and disadvantage factor.

The list may be continued to include: reflector savings; moderating ratio, slowing-down and diffusion times, delayed neutron time and the generation time. For the reactor itself there is the flux distribution and buckling, the extrapolated distance, reactivity, period, temperature coefficient, burn-up, conversion factor, breeding ratio, power output, power distribution in the core and shield, etc.

The problems of an operating reactor include much more, such as: the heat transfer and removal, fluid flow, bulk shielding, control and safety instrumentation, the containment building, turbines of more or less conventional design, electrical generators. Of especial importance, there is the protection of personnel from the various radiations.

But this is not the whole story. To get the "fuel," one must start at the mine. The ore must be concentrated and converted to metal. There are isotope separation processes; plutonium production and the purification, handling, and heat and mechanical treatment of the fuel; its physical metallurgy, alloying, changes under intense bombardment by neutrons and gamma rays, fission fragment recoil, fabrication and cladding of heterogeneous reactor fuel plates, aqueous and metal solutions of the fuel for homogeneous reactors, as well as corrosion and decomposition effects.

Then, after the "burn-up" of the fuel in the reactor, there is need for the separation of the unfissioned material from the new fuel which has been bred and from the "waste" or fission products. This involves: dissolution, solvent extraction, coprecipitation, ion exchange, fractional distillation, pulse columns, etc., all with large quantities of dangerously radioactive materials. There is the problem of the final use, or the disposal, of the radioactive "waste" products. Finally, there is the refabrication of the unfissioned fuel into proper form for reinsertion in the reactor.

Here, then, is a dynamic challenge for the scientist or the engineer who has been trained in a specialty—mechanical, electrical, chemical, or physical—to broaden his horizon. A multitude of experiences over the past years have demonstrated that the specialist *must* have at least a rough knowledge of the whole field before he can work effectively with other specialists as a member of a nuclear reactor team.

As a consequence of this experience, the present book contains a wide diversity of experiments. These have been organized by the editor to emphasize particular ideas or concepts rather than to follow the traditional departmental or divisional schemes.

This book, as a whole, is a product of the Argonne National Laboratory (ANL) the successor to the Metallurgical Laboratory whose men, at the University of Chicago, were the first to accomplish a nuclear chain reaction. ANL was the first to make electricity from "atomic energy," to make a heavy water reactor, a boiling water reactor, and one which, demonstrably, bred more fuel than it consumed. The aggressive ideas, drive, and administration of Dr. Walter H. Zinn and Dr. Norman Hilberry contributed greatly to these developments.

For the most part, the experiments in this book have been written by ANL staff members who created or helped create the work they describe. The editor (who started his work in this field by separating radon from carnotite and measuring its half-life in 1919) has served to unify the diverse experiments, reduce overlapping discussions, and add a section here and there for the benefit of the beginner. No claim is made for completeness in such a rapidly growing technology.

This instruction was fully launched under the auspices of President Eisenhower's Atoms for Peace program, when the International School of Nuclear Science and Engineering was established in 1955 at the Argonne National Laboratory, where there existed the necessary qualified personnel and magnificent equipment. It has received a full measure of support from the U. S. Atomic Energy Commission.

The editor, who helped launch the school as Associate Director in 1955, believes that this book will bring closer the day when nuclear energy will truly add to the material peacetime benefits for humanity throughout the world.

New London, Connecticut
January 1958

J. BARTON HOAG
Captain, U. S. Coast Guard

ACKNOWLEDGMENTS*

A BOOK such as this, which involves so many specialties, has obviously received the help of many people. In addition to Dr. W. H. Zinn and Dr. N. Hilberry, E. W. Rylander, S. McLain and those mentioned in the text, the forty-four contributors also wish to express their gratitude to:

1. The Division of Reactor Development, U.S.A.E.C: especially J. F. Kaufmann.
2. The Division Directors, Argonne National Laboratory: A. H. Barnes, Reactor Engineering; T. Brill, Electronics; J. F. Ege, Jr., Industrial Hygiene and Safety; F. G. Foote, Metallurgy; R. C. Goertz, Remote Control Engineering; S. Lawroski, Chemical Engineering; W. M. Manning, Chemistry; W. H. McCorkle, Director, Reactor Operations; J. E. Rose, Radiological Physics; R. G. Taecker, International School of Nuclear Science and Engineering, L. A. Turner, Physics; H. D. Young, Technical Information.
3. Keen interest and help have also been provided by: Rita Birkey, Sec.; D. E. Dalquest, Graphic Arts; D. S. Manson, Site Administration; J. H. Martens, Information Division; J. H. McKinley, Business Manager; Ann Rea, Sec.; P. R. Shlemon, Legal; D. C. Sternberg, Site Administration; D. F. Wood, Assistant Business Manager; as well as by Central Shops, Security Division, Special Materials and the Health Division.
4. The Editor wishes to thank Vice Admiral A. C. Richmond, Commandant, U. S. Coast Guard, and Rear Admirals R. J. Mauerman and F. A. Leamy, Superintendents, U.S.C.G. Academy for permission to work with the U. S. Atomic Energy Commission and the Argonne National Laboratory; as well as J. J. Flaherty, formerly Manager, Chicago Operations Office, AEC, for efforts in this liaison.
5. Mr. John H. Martens of the Information Division of the Argonne National Laboratories has been of great assistance during the publishing stages of the book.

* This incomplete list might well serve as a guide to the extensive organization needed to prosecute a program in nuclear reactor research and development.

SPECIAL ACKNOWLEDGMENTS

ELMER W. RYLANDER

Executive Assistant, Education, Laboratory Director's Office, Argonne National Laboratory, who vigorously *expedited* the initial planning, construction, and installation of a majority of the experiments of the International School of Nuclear Science and Engineering, in addition to his direct contribution to the material on the exponential assemblies.

STUART McLAIN

Formerly Associate Director, Argonne National Laboratory, who lent unstintingly of his time in the initial planning of the experiments in Nuclear Engineering.

CONTENTS

Chapter 1

SOME BASIC INFORMATION

INTRODUCTION

By J. B. HOAG, ANL, International School of Nuclear Science and Engineering*

The organization of this book is such that the simpler, less radioactive, and less costly experiments are considered first. The first chapter gives briefly some of the basic or elementary information that is common knowledge for the rest of the book. The second chapter deals with the detection and measurement of the basic radiations. Then, for several chapters, there are details of the measurements of the physical constants and parameters which enter into the design of nuclear reactors, using first a moderator assembly, then a subcritical assembly, and finally, a critical or operating reactor. Next come experiments to measure the static and kinetic characteristics of an operating reactor; these are followed by heat transfer loops for the study of the removal of heat from the reactor. The remainder of the book treats of the metallurgical preparation of fuel elements, the corrosion and radiation damage in a reactor, the handling of radioactive materials in a "hot" laboratory, and finally the separation of the "burned" and "unburned" fuels from each other and from the plutonium which has been produced during the reactor's operation.

PRIMARY PARTICLES

The primary particles of interest in nuclear reactor work are:

(1) *Alpha particles*, α or $_2He^4$. These are helium nuclei. Their mass is approximately 4 atomic mass units (oxygen-sixteen is $16.000 \cdots$) and their electrical charge, which is positive, is two electronic units. They are relatively easily absorbed—by a few centimeters of standard air, a thick sheet of paper, or a thin sheet of aluminum. As they pass through a gas, they produce a large number of ions per cm of path, i.e., they are good ionizers; they travel along straight paths until near the end of their range.

(2) *Beta particles*, β^- or $_-\beta^0$, are electrons ejected from the nucleus of an atom. Their mass is 1/1838 that of the lightest atom, hydrogen, and their

---

* A given author's work continues in this book until the next contributor's name appears.

electrical charge is negative and equal to one electronic unit $(1.60 \times 10^{-19}$ coulombs). They are moderately easily absorbed—by a few millimeters of lead. They pass through a gas along curved trajectories with frequent small deflections, and they produce a moderate amount of ionization. Certain artificially produced radioactive substances emit **positrons,** β^+ or $_+\beta^0$. These are the same as the more familiar electrons, but carry a positive charge; they are sometimes referred to as positive electrons.

(3) *Gamma rays,* γ, are electromagnetic radiations of very short wave length, like X-rays, traveling with the speed of light. Their ionization is relatively small and comes about by an indirect process wherein they give up energy to electrons which in turn do the ionizing. They are penetrating—requiring, say, a foot of iron for their absorption. The denser the material, the more readily absorbed the gamma rays.

(4) *Neutrons,* n or $_0n^1$, are noncharged particles of mass nearly equal to that of the proton or hydrogen nucleus. Since they are electrically neutral, they do not interact by means of electrical forces with the charged parts of atoms. Hence, they cause essentially no ionization and are very penetrating. However, by collision with atomic nuclei they may suffer appreciable loss of kinetic energy and be slowed down, especially by the lighter atoms. When slowed down —say, to thermal energies around 0.025 ev (electron volts)—they are readily absorbed, for example, by cadmium or boron. Thermal neutrons have a high probability of causing the fission of uranium-235 atoms.

Dualism. According to the quantum theory, the gamma rays not only have an electromagnetic wave character but also act as discrete particles. They may be thought of as a packet of waves. These "quanta" are called *photons* and each has an energy $E = h\nu$ and momentum $p = h\nu/c = h/\lambda$, where E is in ergs, h is Planck's constant $(6.55 \times 10^{-27}$ erg · sec), ν is their frequency in vibrations per second $(= c/\lambda$, where λ is their wave length in cm), p is in gram · cm per sec, and c is the speed of light $(3 \times 10^{10}$ cm/sec). Conversely, each of the particles acts, under appropriate conditions, not as a particle but as a wave, with a wave length given by the De Broglie equation $\lambda = h/mv = h/p$, where m is their mass in grams and v is their velocity in cm/sec.

THE SIMPLE DECAY LAW

Let n be the number of atoms of parent radioactive substance present at time t. During a very short time interval, Δt, a certain number of these, Δn, will disintegrate, with the emission of a radiation (alpha, beta, or gamma) to become "daughter" atoms. The chance or probability of disintegration is then given by $-\Delta n/n$, the negative sign indicating a decrease in the number of parent atoms.

The *decay or transformation constant,* λ, is defined as the fraction of atoms disintegrating each second and is a constant for a given radioactive substance, as was proved by Rutherford and Soddy. Then $\lambda \Delta t$ is the fraction of atoms disintegrating in time Δt, which is the probability of disintegration. Hence, in the limit, as $\Delta t \rightarrow 0$,

$$\frac{dn}{n} = -\lambda \, dt. \tag{1-1}$$

For example: Assume $n = 10{,}000$ atoms at the start and that 200 (2 per cent) of these disintegrate in the first second ($\lambda = 0.02$), leaving 9800 parent atoms. During the second second, 2 per cent or 196 of the 9800 atoms disintegrate, leaving 9604 parent atoms, etc. Notice that it is the same *fraction* of atoms that break up during each unit of time, i.e., λ is a constant.

From Equation 1-1, the rate of disintegration, r, is given by

$$\frac{dn}{dt} = -\lambda n = r \tag{1-2}$$

and is seen to be directly proportional to the number of atoms present. For example, in the case of radium-226 ($_{92}Ra^{226}$), $\lambda = 1.39 \times 10^{-11}$. In 1 gram there are $N_0/A = 6.02 \times 10^{23}/226$ atoms, where N_0 = Avogadro's number and A is the gram atomic weight. Hence, the number of disintegrations per second per gram of radium-226 is $\lambda n = 3.7 \times 10^{10}$ dis/(sec)$\cdot$(gram).

The curie is defined as that quantity of radioactive substance in which there occur 3.7×10^{10} disintegrations per second. It need not be radium that is referred to; it can be any radioactive material. It need not be one gram; the active substance may be dispersed in large quantities of nonradioactive material; it is the number of atoms that decay each second that is important. The millicurie (mc) and the microcurie (μc) are smaller units: 1 mc = 10^{-3} c, and has 3×10^7 dis/sec; while 1 μc = 10^{-6} c and has 3×10^4 dis/sec. Another unit of radioactivity occasionally used is the rutherford = 10^6 dis/sec. To determine the activity of a substance in curies, measure the number of disintegrations per second and divide by 3.7×10^{10}. Note that the number of particles radiated when the disintegration occurs need not necessarily equal the number of disintegrations; several radiations are possible in certain cases.

Integration of Equation 1-1 gives $\ln n = -\lambda t +$ constant. When $t = 0$, $n = n_0$ = number of atoms present at the start, and the constant of integration is $\ln n_0$. Then, taking antilogs, the number of parent atoms n present at time t is

$$n = n_0 e^{-\lambda t}, \tag{1-3}$$

where e is the base of the Naperian system of logarithms.

If both sides of this equation are multipled by the number of grams per atom, the total mass M is given as

$$M = M_0 e^{-\lambda t}, \tag{1-4}$$

where M_0 is the mass of the parent material when $t = 0$.

If both sides of Equation 1-3 are multiplied by $-\lambda$, and Equation 1-2 is consulted, it is seen that the rate of disintegration is given by an equation of the same form. Thus

$$r = r_0 e^{-\lambda t}. \tag{1-5}$$

If both sides of the last equation are multipled by the number of particles (n') emitted at each disintegration, then the "activity," $\alpha = n'r$, will be

$$\alpha = \alpha_0 e^{-\lambda t}. \tag{1-6}$$

The radiated particles may be detected by the ions which they produce in passing through the gas in the "detector." Each particle will produce a certain number of ions, each of a certain electrical charge. A percentage of these will be collected by the electrodes of the detector. The detector voltage can be made high enough to collect all of the ions as they are produced (saturation voltage). Thus the output current can be made proportional to the number of particles. Multiplying both sides of Equation 1-6 by the proportionality constant gives the output current reading as

$$\boxed{I = I_0 e^{-\lambda t}} \tag{1-7}$$

These are referred to as measured activities, in contrast to the actual activities given by Equation 1-6. The emitted particles may also be detected by the pulses which they produce in a "counter tube." The number of counts or pulses per unit time is proportional to the activity and hence, again, an equation of the same form results.

The *detection efficiency* K is the ratio of number of particles recorded by the "detector" to the number emitted by the radioactive material in a given time; a quantity which varies from 100 per cent to as little as 1 per cent. K canceled out of Equation 1-7, but must be included for any absolute measurement of activity, i.e.,

$$I = K\alpha. \tag{1-8}$$

A plot of I vs. t gives the exponential decay curve of Fig. 1-1A. If logarithms to the natural base are taken of both sides of Equation 1-7 (or 1-3 through 1-6), one gets

$$\ln I = \ln I_0 + (-\lambda)t, \tag{1-9}$$

which may be compared with the equation of a straight line $y = b + mx$. Hence, if values of $\ln I$ are plotted vertically and values of t horizontally, as in Fig. 1-1B, a straight line results, whose y intercept is $\ln I_0$ and whose slope (negative) is equal to the decay constant, λ. Instead of looking up values of $\ln I$ in tables, semilog paper may be used, as in Fig. 1-1C, where the vertical distances, although labeled in I values, are proportional to $\ln I$.

The number of atoms, hence the mass, the rate of disintegration, and the

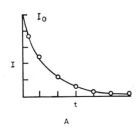 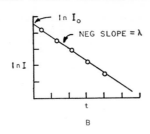 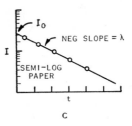

A   B   C

FIG. 1-1. Decay curves.

activity of a radioactive material, decreases to one-half its original value, starting with $t = 0$ at any time along the decay curve, during a period of time called the *half-life*, $T_{1/2}$. Thus $n/n_0 = \frac{1}{2} = e^{-\lambda T_{1/2}}$ or $(\ln 1 - \ln 2) = -\lambda T_{1/2}$. But $\ln 1 = 0$ and $\ln 2 = 0.693$, so that

$$T_{1/2} = 0.693/\lambda \qquad (1\text{-}10)$$

The *average life* of the atoms τ can be shown to be

$$\tau = 1/\lambda \qquad (1\text{-}11)$$

and represents the time for the number of atoms to decay to $1/e$ of their original value, where $e = 2.718 \cdots$, the base of the natural system of logarithms. The half-lives of different radioactive materials vary over a wide range, from a small fraction of a second to billions of years, but there is only one value for a given type of decay. Hence a measurement of $T_{1/2}$ or λ serves in the identification of a radioactive material. As a general rule, those substances with the shorter lives send out the more energetic particles.

In Equation 1-2, we may substitute $\lambda = 0.693/T_{1/2}$. Also, n is equal to the number of atoms present = (number of atoms per gram) (grams) = (number of atoms per mole/gram atomic weight) (grams) = $(N_0/A)m$. Hence the rate of decay is

$$r = \left(\frac{0.693}{T_{1/2}}\right)\left(\frac{N_0}{A}m\right). \qquad (1\text{-}12)$$

Dividing by the number of disintegrations per second gives *curies*, $C = (1.13 \times 10^{13})\ m/AT_{1/2}$. Then the *specific activity*, SA, defined as the activity per gram, is

$$SA = \frac{1.13 \times 10^{13}}{A T_{1/2}} \text{ curies/gram.} \qquad (1\text{-}13)$$

When the material under study contains two radioactive materials, the semilog plot will appear as in Fig. 1-2, where the circles represent experimental points. It is not a single straight line, but curves at first. The decay constant of the longer-lived substance is obtained from the slope of the straight line on the right in the usual manner, as described above. To get the decay constant of the shorter-lived material, extrapolate the straight line backward. At $t = 0$, subtract the value of I (not $\ln I$) of the extrapolated line from the first, meas-

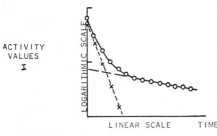

ACTIVITY
VALUES
I

ured I value and plot as x. Repeat at successively later t values to get the "x x x" straight line, whose slope gives the decay constant of the shorter-lived substance. The y intercepts give rela- tive initial activities of the two active materials, as in Fig. 1-3. It is not al- ways easy to draw the straight line correctly through the right-hand ex- perimental points because of statistical fluctuations in their value. The proper line has been found when the "x x x"

FIG. 1-2. Decay curve: Two active sub- stances are present at the same time.

points lie along a straight line. Errors are indicated in Fig. 1-4.

When more than two radioactive substances are present, their decay con- stants are determined by successive subtraction of straight lines, always start- ing from the right. Analytical methods can be used as well as the graphical procedure outlined above.

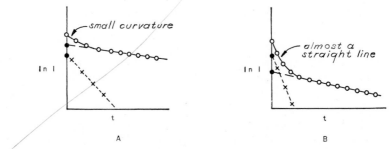

FIG. 1-3. In A, the longer-lived substance has the greater initial activity. In B, the shorter-lived substance is the stronger at the start.

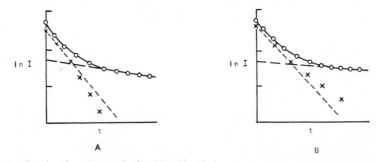

FIG. 1-4. In A, the slope of the long-lived (— —) curve is too steep. In B, the long-lived activity has too low an intensity in the transition region.

NEUTRON INTERACTIONS

Consider a parallel beam, of unit cross section, of neutrons moving with velocity v cm/sec, from left to right, as in Fig. 1-5A. If there are n neutrons in each cubic centimeter, then the number passing in 1 sec through 1 cm^2 perpendicular to the beam is nv. This is called the flux ϕ. In a nuclear reactor, the

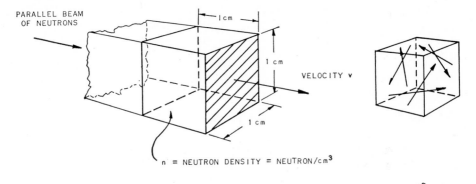

FIG. 1-5.   The neutron flux density or "flux" is $\phi = nv$.

neutrons travel in all directions. Since reactions between the neutrons and the nuclei of atoms are independent of the direction from which the neutrons strike the nuclei, the same terminology is carried over to the reactor, as in Fig. 1-5B. Thus, the *flux density, or flux,* is

$$\phi = nv \tag{1-14}$$

A second interpretation of the flux is: the total length of the paths of all the neutrons in 1 cm^3 traversed in 1 sec. A third interpretation would be: the flux is the number of neutrons incident on 1 cm^2 cross section of target material each second.

The probability that a certain interaction (say, capture or scattering or fission) will take place between 1 neutron and 1 atomic nucleus is called the *microscopic cross section* and is symbolized by σ. This may also be thought of as the effective area (cm^2) of 1 nucleus for 1 neutron for the particular reaction. If there are N nuclei in 1 cm^3 of "target" material, then $N\sigma$ is the effective area of interaction for 1 neutron of all the nuclei in 1 cm^3 and is called the *macroscopic cross section* Σ. Thus

$$\Sigma = N\sigma \tag{1-15}$$

The concept of cross sections is very important in nuclear studies and will be discussed in much greater detail in later chapters.

The total chance of interaction of all the neutrons in a given flux on all the nuclei in 1 cm³ is the *rate of interaction R*. Thus

$$R = \Sigma \phi \qquad (1\text{-}16)$$

a most important equation.

If Σ_f is the cross section for fissions of uranium-235 in 1 cm³ each second by 1 neutron, $\Sigma_f \phi$ is total number of fissions/(cm³)(sec). The number of fissions/sec in a volume V will be $V\Sigma_f \phi$. But 3.1×10^{10} fissions/sec are known to produce 1 watt of power. Hence the *power* developed in a reactor by the fissioning of U^{235} is

$$P = \frac{V\Sigma_f \phi}{3.1 \times 10^{10}} \text{ watts.} \qquad (1\text{-}17)$$

Note that the power developed is directly proportional to the flux.

As a neutron is scattered by nuclei, it follows a zigzag path. It travels, on the average, a certain mean free path λ before undergoing a second scattering. (NOTE: Do not confuse this λ with the decay constant.) If v is the distance a neutron travels in 1 sec, v/λ is the number of interactions (such as a scattering) for 1 neutron in 1 sec. Then, if the neutron density is n, the average number of interactions/cm³ · sec is $R_1 = nv/\lambda$. But nv is the flux ϕ. From Equation 1-16, it follows that the *mean free path is*

$$\lambda = 1/\Sigma \qquad (1\text{-}18)$$

This can also be interpreted as the thickness of material which will reduce the intensity of a neutron beam to $1/e$ (where e = the base of Naperian logarithms) of its original value. Hence the mean free path is also called the *relaxation length*. There are various λ's, corresponding to the various types of interaction, such as absorption, fission, elastic and inelastic collision. When there are several kinds of nuclei present, their cross sections are to be added. Thus $\Sigma = \Sigma_1 + \Sigma_2 + \cdots$ and $\lambda = 1/\Sigma = 1/(\Sigma_1 + \Sigma_2 + \cdots)$. Note that λ is *not* equal to $(1/\Sigma_1 + 1/\Sigma_2 + \cdots)$.

Among the *methods of producing neutrons*, the following interaction is possible.

$$_4\text{Be}^9 + _2\text{He}^4 \rightarrow _6\text{C}^{12} + _0n^1, \qquad (1\text{-}19)$$

which is abbreviated to $\text{Be}^9(\alpha,n)\text{C}^{12}$ and referred to as α,n reaction. This means that when beryllium-9 is bombarded with alpha particles (α) from, say, radium or polonium, high-energy neutrons (n) are emitted and carbon-12 atoms are produced. The subscripts such as 4, 2, etc., in the reaction are the atomic numbers, or nuclear charges, of the elements, and the superscripts are the mass numbers—the nearest integers to the (atomic or) isotopic weights. Note that both sub- and superscripts add up, respectively, to the same value on the left and right side of the equation.

Another source of neutrons is produced as follows. Antimony-123 (42 per cent abundant in natural antimony) is bombarded with neutrons: $Sb^{123}(n,\gamma)Sb^{124}$. The antimony-124 is itself radioactive, with a half-life of 60 days, emitting 1.7-Mev gamma rays (γ). When these gamma rays strike beryllium, the following reaction takes place

$$Be^9 \ (\gamma,n) \ Be^8. \qquad (1\text{-}20)$$

This reaction occurs only if the gamma rays have energy in excess of 1.66 Mev (the threshold). The neutrons emitted in this photo-neutron reaction have an energy of about 25 Kev.

Typical reactions for the *capture of neutrons*—say, for use as the control rods of a reactor—are

$$Cd^{113} \ (n,\gamma) \ Cd^{114}, \qquad (1\text{-}21)$$

$$B^{10} \ (n,\alpha) \ Li^7. \qquad (1\text{-}22)$$

The former is called a *radiative capture* reaction, since neutrons are captured and photons (gamma rays) are radiated. Also, xenon (Xe) has a very high capture cross section for neutrons. Thus

$$Xe^{135} \ (n,\gamma) \ Xe^{136}, \qquad (1\text{-}23)$$

which is one of the serious "poisoning processes" that occur in an operating reactor.

Cobalt-60 is widely used in isotope work for industrial applications, etc. It is made in the reaction

$$Co^{59} \ (n,\gamma) \ Co^{60}. \qquad (1\text{-}24)$$

It has a half-life of 5.27 years and emits weak beta rays (negative electrons), of energy 0.30 Mev, and gamma rays of energies 1.17 and 1.33 Mev.

The following reactions are for the *production* of plutonium (Pu^{239}) from uranium-238 (U^{238}) with the intermediate beta emitter neptunium-239. The half-lives are given in m (minutes), d (days), and y (years).

$$_{92}U^{238} + {_0}n^1 \rightarrow \gamma + {_{92}}U^{239} \xrightarrow[2.3 \text{ m}]{} \beta^- + {_{93}}Np^{239}$$

$$\xrightarrow[2.3 \text{ d}]{} \beta^- + {_{94}}Pu^{239} \xrightarrow[24,000 \text{ y}]{} {_{92}}U^{235} + {_2}He^4. \qquad (1\text{-}25)$$

To make uranium-233 from thorium-232 the following reactions occur:

$$_{90}Th^{232} + {_0}n^1 \rightarrow \gamma + {_{90}}Th^{233} \xrightarrow[23.3 \text{ m}]{} \beta^- + {_{91}}Pa^{233}$$

$$\xrightarrow[27.4 \text{ d}]{} \beta^- + {_{92}}U^{233} \xrightarrow[1.62 \times 10^5 \text{ y}]{} {_{90}}Th^{229} + {_2}He^4. \qquad (1\text{-}26)$$

Tritium (triply heavy hydrogen), H^3, can be made in the following reaction of neutrons on lithium.

$$_3Li^6 + {_0}n^1 \rightarrow {_2}He^4 + {_1}H^3 \qquad (1\text{-}27)$$

Tritium is a β^- emitter (0.189 Mev) and has a half-life of 12.5 years.

ACTIVATION

Let V cm³ of an element be placed in a nuclear reactor and thus subjected to intense neutron bombardment. The new isotope produced by the radiative capture process (n,γ) is itself often radioactive. We now wish to study the rate of formation of this radioactive isotope as it is produced at a steady rate, $V\Sigma_a\phi$, and simultaneously, decays at the rate $-\lambda n$. Thus

$$\text{Net production rate} = \text{Formation rate} + \text{Decay rate}$$

$$\frac{dn}{dt} = V\Sigma_a\phi \qquad -\lambda n. \qquad (1\text{-}28)$$

The n's refer to the number of radioisotope atoms existing at time t in the sample of volume V, starting with zero number at zero time. (Note that λ is used here as the decay constant of the new isotope, not as the mean free path.)

At the start: no new atoms have been formed; there are none to decay. Later: some are formed, some are decaying—the number formed per second exceeding the number decaying per second. Still later: the number forming each second is equal to the number decaying each second. The last-mentioned state is the *saturation condition*. Then, from Equation 1-28, $V\Sigma_a\phi = \lambda n_\infty$, or

$$n_\infty = \frac{V\Sigma_a\phi}{\lambda}. \qquad (1\text{-}29)$$

Substitution of Equation 1-29 in 1-28 gives

$$\frac{dn}{dt} = \lambda n_\infty - \lambda n = \lambda(n_\infty - n).$$

Integration gives

$$-\ln(n_\infty - n) = \lambda t + \text{constant}.$$

When $t = 0$, $n = 0$, i.e., $-\ln n_\infty = \text{constant}$, and

$$\ln\left(\frac{n_\infty - n}{n_\infty}\right) = -\lambda t.$$

Taking antilogs gives

$$n = n_\infty(1 - e^{-\lambda t}) \qquad (1\text{-}30)$$

Multiplying both sides by $(-\lambda)$ gives $(-n\lambda)$, the disintegration rate. Measured activities, I, are proportional to these rates, i.e.,

$$\boxed{I = I_\infty(1 - e^{-\lambda t})} \qquad (1\text{-}31)$$

A plot of activity vs. time is shown in Fig. 1-6.

From Equations 1-8 and 1-29, $n_\infty\lambda = V\Sigma_a\phi = I_\infty/K$. Thus

$$I_\infty = KV\Sigma_a\phi, \qquad (1\text{-}32)$$

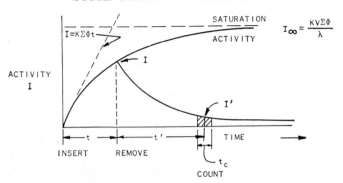

Fig. 1-6. Activation and decay curve of a radioisotope: K = constant; t = time of exposure; t' = wait time; t_c = count time.

where I_x is the measured saturation activity, K is the detector efficiency, V is the volume of the sample in cm³, Σ_a is the macroscopic absorption cross section in cm^{-1}, and ϕ is the neutron flux in neutrons/(cm²) (sec).

The *saturation factor* S is given by

$$S = \frac{I}{I_\infty} = (1 - e^{-\lambda t}) \tag{1-33}$$

and is defined as the activity produced in time t, divided by that produced by exposure to the neutron flux for an infinite time. Then

$$I = KV\Sigma_a\phi S \tag{1-34}$$

Since $\Sigma_a = N\sigma_a$, where N is the number of atoms in 1 cm³ of target material, and NV is the total number of atoms in the irradiated sample; and since $N = N_0 m/A$, where N_0 is Avogadro's number, m is the mass of irradiated material in the sample (density times volume), and A is the gram atomic weight,

$$I = K\frac{N_0 m}{A}\sigma_a\phi S. \tag{1-35}$$

Dividing this by 3.7×10^7 will give the activity in millicuries. Again dividing by the mass m will give the specific activity in mc/gram. The maximum or saturation activity, $\mathcal{Q}_x$, occurs when $S = 1$. Then

$$\mathcal{Q}_\infty = \frac{N_0\sigma_a\phi}{A}m, \quad \text{or} \quad \boxed{I_\infty = \frac{KN_0\sigma_a\phi}{A}m} \tag{1-36}$$

Since $e^x = 1 + x/1 + x^2/2! + x^3/3! + \cdots$, it is seen that in Equation 1-31, $e^{-\lambda t} = 1 - \lambda t + (\lambda t/2)^2 + \cdots$. If λ is very small (or the half-life $T_{1/2}$ is very great), $e^{-\lambda t} \approx (1 - \lambda t)$; the higher terms are negligibly small. Then Equation 1-31 reduces to $I = I_x\lambda t$, as indicated by the sloping dotted line in Fig. 1-6. Using Equation 1-35, we find $I = KN_0\sigma_a\phi m\lambda t/A$. The formation of the radioisotope, in this case, is directly proportional to the (capture) microscopic cross section σ_a of the sample, to the neutron flux ϕ of the reactor, and to the time of exposure t.

Suppose the sample is placed in the neutron flux at the time $t = 0$. The new element begins to form faster than it decays, as shown in Fig 1-6. After t seconds have elapsed, the sample is removed from the flux. It then decays for an interval of time, t', called the "wait time." The activity is then counted, during t_c seconds, and is given by

$$I' = Ie^{-\lambda t'} \tag{1-37}$$

an equation which may be used to calculate the activity I at the time of removal.

I_∞ is given by Equation 1-31 as I/S. Hence

$$\boxed{I_\infty = \frac{I'}{(1 - e^{-\lambda t})e^{-\lambda t'}}} \tag{1-38}$$

an equation which may be used to determine the saturation activity I_∞ from the activity I' measured after an irradiation time t, followed by a wait time t' (measured to the *middle* of the count time) *provided* the time of counting, t_c, is small compared with the half-life $T_{1/2} = 0.693/\lambda$.

When the counting time is appreciable in comparison with $T_{1/2}$, the following equation is to be used:

$$I_\infty = \frac{KC\lambda}{(1 - e^{-\lambda t})e^{-\lambda t''}(1 - e^{-\lambda t_c})}, \tag{1-39}$$

where K is the detection efficiency, C is the total number of counts (proportional to the number of disintegrations) during the counting time t_c (the shaded area in Fig. 1-6), and t'' is the wait time measured from the time of removal of the sample from the neutron flux to the *beginning* of the count time.

From Equation 1-36, it is seen that from the measured saturation activity I_∞ and the mass m (grams) of the irradiated isotope whose gram atomic weight is A, it is possible to compute either the neutron flux ϕ or the microscopic cross section σ_a when the other is known. Note that σ_a so obtained is for a particular radioisotope and a specific radiation (α or β or γ), as detected by a counter of efficiency K. These values of σ_a are known as *activation cross sections*.

THE CADMIUM RATIO

It would be ideal if there existed a neutron filter which would pass all neutrons of energy above a certain value and completely block out all below that cut-off energy. There are no such materials. However, cadmium has a high absorbing ability for neutrons below approximately 0.4 ev, and moderately low cross section for neutrons above this energy, as is seen in Fig. 1-7. Since the

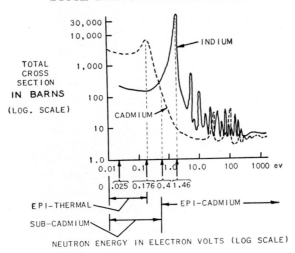

FIG. 1-7.   The total cross sections of cadmium and indium at various energies.

scattering of neutrons by cadmium is only ~7 barns and that for indium is ~2 barns and since these values are essentially constant with neutron energy, the curves in Fig. 1-7 effectively represent the absorption abilities of these materials for neutrons of the energies shown. Note that the peak of resonance for cadmium is large, approximately 7200 barns at 0.176 ev; and that for indium is very large and sharp, over 30,000 barns at 1.46 ev. When indium is exposed to a neutron flux it becomes radioactive, whereas cadmium does not. Other foils that are used are gold, cobalt, and an alloy of Al, Co, and Mn.

By definition, the *cadmium ratio* is the saturated activity of a bare foil $\mathcal{a}_\infty^b$, such as indium, divided by the saturated activity of the foil completely covered with cadmium, $\mathcal{a}_\infty^c$.

$$R_{\text{Cd}} = \frac{\mathcal{a}_\infty^b}{\mathcal{a}_\infty^c}. \tag{1-40}$$

The covered foil responds largely to the flux in its resonance region because the cadmium essentially stops all neutrons below its cut-off and is nearly transparent to neutrons of greater energy, and because contributions to the indium's activity by neutrons of energy above approximately 2 ev are very small in comparison with that in the resonance region. The bare foil, of course, responds to the subcadmium (or to the epithermal) neutrons (see Fig. 1-7) as well as to the epicadmium flux. Thus $\mathcal{a}_\infty^b - \mathcal{a}_\infty^{\text{sub-Cd}} + \mathcal{a}_\infty^{\text{epi-Cd}}$, from which it follows that

$$R_{\text{Cd}} - 1 = \frac{\mathcal{a}_\infty^{\text{sub-Cd}}}{\mathcal{a}_\infty^{\text{epi-Cd}}}. \tag{1-41}$$

Thus, the cadmium ratio (minus one) may be taken as a measure of how well the neutrons are thermalized; the greater the ratio, the greater the degree of thermalization, i.e., the greater the percentage of slow to faster neutrons.

The *cadmium difference* is defined as the saturated activity of a bare foil, minus that of the cadmium-covered foil, or

$$D_{\mathrm{Cd}} = \mathcal{Q}_\infty^b - \mathcal{Q}_\infty^c = \mathcal{Q}_\infty^{\mathrm{sub\text{-}Cd}}, \tag{1-42}$$

which is the activity produced by neutrons whose energies are less than the cut-off of cadmium.

From Equation 1-36 it can be seen that activities are proportional to the cross section σ and to the flux ϕ. Since both σ and ϕ are functions of energy, care must be taken in interpreting the meaning of R_{Cd} and D_{Cd}. Using "averaged" cross sections, one sometimes says that the cadmium ratio is a measure of the "thermal" to the "greater than thermal" fluxes, or that the cadmium difference is a measure of the "thermal" flux.

Let a gold foil be irradiated for a known time in a known thermal flux, ϕ^{th}, whose R_{Cd} is also known, i.e., in a "standard pile." Measure the activity and compute the saturated activity, $\mathcal{Q}_\infty{}^{\mathrm{th}}$, using Equation 1-38 or 1-39. Then k, a constant of proportionality, can be computed from

$$\mathcal{Q}_\infty^{\mathrm{th}} = k\phi^{\mathrm{th}}. \tag{1-43}$$

The same foil is then irradiated in an unknown flux, is "counted," and its saturation activity computed. Then, the unknown flux can be determined by using Equation 1-43 again. If the constant k is known, the foil is said to be a standard foil.

Radiation Units

One roentgen, which is the unit of X- or gamma-ray dose, produces one electrostatic unit—1 esu = 1 statcoulomb = $1/(3 \times 10^9)$ coulombs—of ions of either sign (either positive ions or negative ions, not both) in 0.001293 gram of air (i.e., dry, atmospheric air occupying 1 cm^3 at 0°C, 760 mm of mercury). One roentgen of X- or gamma rays will produce 2.083×10^9 ion pairs in 1 cm^3 of standard air or 1.6×10^{12} ion pairs in 1 gram of standard air. Since it requires 34 ev to create one ion pair in standard air, the roentgen is the radiation dose that will release 87.7 ergs of energy in 1 gram of air.

One rep, or "roentgen equivalent physical," will produce the same number of ion pairs in 1 gram of standard air as does 1 roentgen. The distinction between reps and roentgens is that with reps, the ionizing radiations may be X- or gamma rays or may be electrons, alpha or beta particles, neutrons, or any other ionizing radiation, whereas the roentgen applies only to X and gamma radiations. One rep will result in the absorption in *tissue* of 97.7 ergs/gram. However, both the roentgen and the rep are units of radiation. Absorption units are given on the next page.

Absorption Units

One rad is the unit of absorbed dose. It is the quantity of radiation which will release 100 ergs of energy in 1 gram of tissue. It applies to any radiation— X, gamma, alpha, or beta, electrons, protons, neutrons, etc.

One rem, or "roentgen equivalent man," is the quantity of any type of radiation that will produce the same effect on a biological object as does 1 roentgen of X- or gamma radiation.

Radiation Protection

Dosimetry.* All workers around radioactive materials should take extreme precautions to prevent not only an excess radiation of their bodies or parts thereof, but especially to prevent the entrance of radioactive materials into their bodies. A pocket dosimeter and/or film badge should be worn at all times while working around radioactive materials. Dosimeters and film badges and other portable meters are available on the market; their description and directions for their use can be obtained from the manufacturing companies and need not be repeated here. Some of them measure the dose, D, while others measure the dose-rate, R. If t is the time of exposure,

$$D = Rt, \quad \text{or} \quad D = \int R \, dt. \qquad (1\text{-}44)$$

Maximum Permissible Dosage. *The maximum permissible whole-body dose is 0.3 rem per working week of forty hours.* The maximum permissible amount of material in the body varies greatly with the radioactive material considered.†

For natural uranium, the contact dose rate is 250 mrep/hr. This allows a maximum permissible handling time of 6 hr/day with the bare hands and 12 hr/day with the metal 1 mm distant from the skin, as, for example, when wearing leather gloves.

Safety Practices.‡ Radiation intensity decreases from a point source inversely as the square of the distance. If it is not possible by using distance to reduce the dose rate to a sufficiently low level to accomplish the work in the required time, use shielding. For *gamma rays*, the denser the shield material the better. Lead bricks may be used as temporary shields when the activity is 1 mc or less. The bricks are usually made in rectangular shapes $2'' \times 4'' \times 8''$

---

* R. F. Barker, "General Handbook for Radiation Monitoring," LA 1835 (1954).

† Details will be found in "Permissible Dose from External Sources of Ionizing Radiation," Handbook 59, National Bureau of Standards; and "Maximum Permissible Amounts of Radioisotopes in the Human Body and Maximum Permissible Concentrations in Air and Water," Handbook 52, National Committee on Radiation Protection, National Bureau of Standards (March 1953).

‡ J. R. Novak (Ed.), "Radiation Safety Guide," ANL-5574 (1956).

(approximately 25 lb) or $2'' \times 3'' \times 6''$ (approximately 15 lb). The attenuation of 1-Mev gamma rays through 2 in. of lead is about 30. It is $30 \times 30 = 900$ through 4 in. of lead. Remember, however, that some of these rays scatter from surrounding objects and may come over the top of the lead wall. Always measure the activity with a monitoring meter. For more permanent structures (which are larger) hot-rolled steel plate is very satisfactory because it is structurally strong, less expensive, and the thickness is only increased by about 50 per cent for 1-Mev gamma rays. The attenuation charts of Figs. 1-9 and 1-10 have been found to be useful by radiochemists for laboratory shielding calculations. But, to repeat, always check the activity with a monitoring meter; the scattered radiation may be serious.

For *beta rays*, use sheets of aluminum, plastics such as Lucite, or glass. Microcurie beta samples are sufficiently shielded by the glassware which contains them. Beta rays scatter readily from nearby objects. With *alpha rays*, which are easily absorbed and of short range, the main worry is that they may get into the body. With high-intensity alpha sources, be sure to wear respiratory equipment such as a Scott Air-Pak or a military assault mask.

Neutron sources such as Ra-Be and Sb-Be also emit gamma rays and must be provided with thick lead containers. Neutrons can be slowed down by 1 ft or more of water or paraffin and then captured with a cadmium sheet.

Use rubber gloves and an apron in the laboratory and leave them there, so as not to spread contamination to clean areas. Never use the mouth for pipetting. Do not eat or smoke in the laboratory. Keep radioactive materials off the bare hands. Always wear a dosimeter or pocket chamber.

Keep the work under a hood which has excellent ventilation when dealing with volatile materials and when spraying or spattering is possible. Use a plastic cover on work surfaces and handle the chemicals in a tray in case there should be a spill. Dispose of radioactive waste in special containers. Always keep in mind that there is a dust hazard in handling any radioactive material. Do not contaminate the insides of the counter shield.

Additional precautions are mentioned in the discussions of the experiments of this book, wherever appropriate.

IRRADIATION OF ANTIMONY

By C. H. YOUNGQUIST, ANL, Chemistry Division

As an example of the calculations used in the activation of a substance and of the protection needed for safe transportation of a radioisotope, the case of antimony (Sb) is considered below. This particular example is used because the radioactive antimony emits gamma rays which, striking beryllium, serve as a source of neutrons suitable for the experiments on moderator and subcritical assemblies, as described in Chapters 3 and 4.

A sample of antimony of the dimensions shown in Fig. 1-8 is used. The ball on top of the cylinder is used for gripping with remote handling tools after the activation. The cylinder has a total volume of 1.19 in.³ or 19.5 cm³ and a total weight of 130 grams, of which 58 per cent is Sb^{121} (antimony-121) and 42 per cent is Sb^{123}.

When the two antimony isotopes are irradiated with neutrons in a reactor, they become Sb^{122}, a β emitter with a 2.8 day half-life, and Sb^{124}, with a 60-day half-life, which gives off gamma rays of five different energies,* namely 0.60, 0.65, 0.72, 1.69, and 2.10 Mev. The decay to the ground state involves five beta particle emissions at energies of 0.28 (12 per cent), 0.63 (56 per cent), 1.07 (4 per cent), 1.68 (6 per cent) and 2.39 (22 per cent) Mev. The decay results in an energy loss of 2.90 Mev/atom, divided in some manner between the beta and gamma energies.

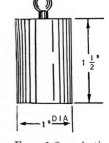

Fig. 1-8. Antimony sample to be irradiated.

It is assumed that the two highest gamma energies are associated with the two lowest beta energies, which account for 12 per cent and 56 per cent of the decay. Furthermore, since the decay scheme is not well defined in the literature, a pessimistic approach is to add these two percentages and assume that all of the high-energy decay is 2.10 Mev. Thus, we have assumed that shielding must be provided against 2.10-Mev gamma rays, representing 68 per cent of the decay of Sb^{124}. Lower energies will not affect the results, nor will the beta decay of Sb^{122}. Therefore, calculations will be made only for the Sb^{123} originally present in the sources to an extent of 42 per cent. Thus, 42 per cent of 130 grams = 54.6 grams of Sb^{123} present in the sample of Fig. 1-8. The total number of atoms = (6.02×10^{23}) $(54.6/123)$ = $2.67 \times 10^{23} = N_t$. When irradiated in a neutron flux ϕ for a time t, the "activity" or number of disintegrations per second is given by

$$r = N_t \sigma_{ac} \phi (1 - e^{-\lambda t}) \text{ dis/sec,} \tag{1-45}$$

where σ_{ac} = activation cross section in cm² $(2.5 \times 10^{-24}$ cm² in this case) and $\lambda = 0.693/T_{1/2}$. Let the sample be left in a flux of 5×10^{12} neutrons/(cm²) (sec) for 60 days. Then, $r = (2.67 \times 10^{23})$ (2.5×10^{-24}) (5×10^{12}) $(1 - e^{-0.693})$ = 1.67×10^{12} dis/sec. However, only 68 per cent of the disintegrations yield sufficiently energetic gamma rays for use in the source. This leaves 1.14×10^{12} dis/sec of high-energy gamma disintegrations. Since 3.7×10^{10} dis/sec is equal to 1 c, the number of curies of high energy or useful gammas is $1.14 \times 10^{12}/3.7 \times 10^{10} = 30.7$ c. A similar calculation will show that if the antimony is irradiated continuously in the same flux for 8 days, the strength of the high-energy gamma-ray emitter will be 5.4 c.

The radiation from a point source is approximated by:†

$$\text{Roentgens/hr, at 1 ft} = 6\,CE \tag{1-46}$$

* Nuclear Science Abstracts, Vol. 9, No. 24b (Dec. 31, 1955).

† S. Peterson et el., "Fundamentals for Nuclear Reactor Engineers," TID-5260 (May 1955).

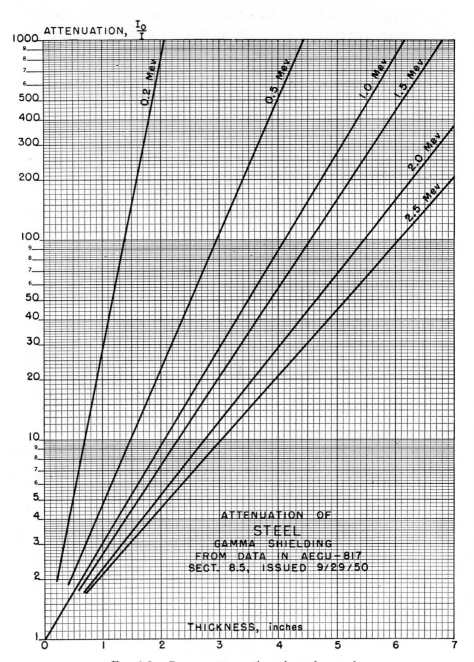

FIG. 1-9. Gamma attenuation chart for steel.

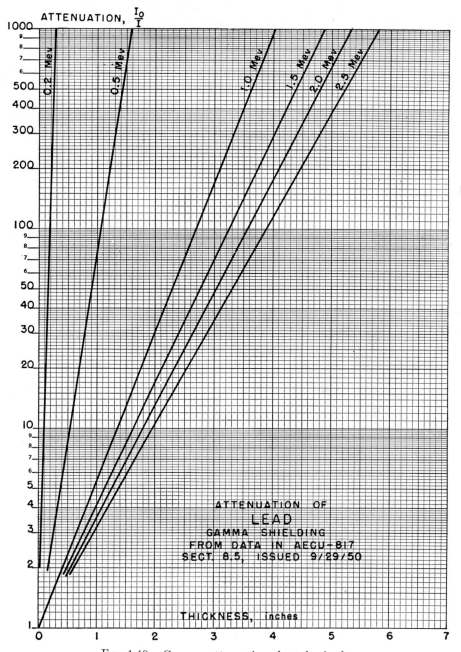

FIG. 1-10. Gamma attenuation chart for lead.

where C = number of curies, E = energy in Mev. For the 5.4-curie antimony source, this gives $6 \times 5.4 \times 2.10 = 68$ r/hr at 1 ft. This radiation must be reduced by a factor of about 10,000 if the antimony is to be transported safely. Fig. 1-10 gives attenuation curves for gamma rays of various energies. An attenuation of 1000 requires approximately 5.4 in. of lead and an attenuation of 10 requires approximately 1.8 in. Therefore, to cut down by a factor of 10,000 will require $(5.4 + 1.8) = 7.2$ in. of lead. This will result in a field of 6.8 mr/hr (milliroentgens per hour) a short distance from the shielding container. Hence, the shipping container should have lead walls about 7½ in. thick. If the container were to house a 50-curie source of this kind, the shielding should be increased by a "tenth value layer," or 1.8 in. of lead, additional, all around. A container of this type is shown in Fig. 4-8.

Chapter 2

NUCLEAR RADIATION DETECTION

INTRODUCTION

By J. B. HOAG, ANL, International School of Nuclear Science and Engineering

Output Voltage Relations. Nuclear radiations, such as alpha, beta, and gamma rays and neutrons, can be detected by the direct or indirect ionization of a gas through which they pass. Alpha and beta rays ionize directly, while gamma rays and neutrons can produce secondary particles which serve to ionize the gas. Gamma rays produce free electrons which cause the ionization. Slow neutrons can be used on boron as in Reaction 1-22 (Chapter 1) to produce alpha particles and lithium nuclei which serve as the direct ionizing agents, or on uranium-235, in which case the fission fragments ionize the gas directly. Slow neutrons may also be detected by measurements of the activity which they induce in foils such as indium or gold (see Fig. 1-6).

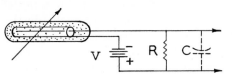

FIG. 2-1. The detection of ionizing radiations.

Consider a tube of gas (say, argon) containing a metal cylinder and a coaxial metal wire, as in Fig. 2-1. When a nuclear radiation passes through the gas, ions are formed and can be drawn to the electrodes by the electrical field established by the voltage V. The central wire acts as the anode (+) to collect electrons, and the cylinder acts as the cathode (−) to collect positive ions. The total charge can be measured in terms of the voltage produced across the resistance R.

The amount Q of charge collected by the electrodes depends on the applied voltage V as shown in Fig. 2-2. The detector tube can be operated in three different ways: as an ionization chamber, as a proportional counter, or as a Geiger-Müller counter, according to the applied voltage.

Details of these three types of counters are given at various places through-

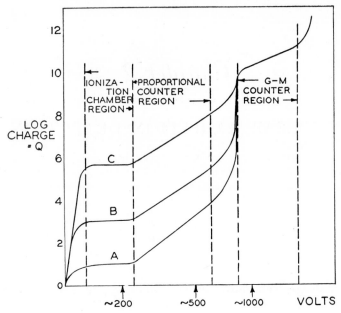

FIG. 2-2. The three operating regions: Curve A is for a weak ionizer such as a gamma ray; B is for intermediate, such as beta particles; and C is for strong ionizers, such as alpha particles.

out this book, wherever their special characteristics are required, but a brief statement concerning each is given immediately below.*

Ionization Chambers. When the voltage applied to the electrodes is in the ionization-chamber region, as indicated in Fig. 2-2, i.e., when a "saturation voltage" is used, all ions created in the gas of the tube are drawn over to the electrodes. Then the electrical charge collected by the electrodes is of constant value, independent of the applied voltage, and is equal to that carried by the primary ion pairs produced in the gas.

When the original ionizing radiations are well spaced in time from each other, and the discharge time through the resistance R of Fig. 2-1 is suitably short, then output voltage pulses are developed across R, one for each ionizing particle. The detector or "sensing element" is then referred to as a *pulse chamber*. An advantage of this type of operation is that it can detect the better

* A few of the many discussions of these detectors and their circuits may be listed here: S. Glasstone, "Nuclear Reactor Engineering," D. Van Nostrand Co., Princeton, N. J. (1955); E. Bleuler and G. J. Goldsmith, "Experimental Nucleonics," Rinehart & Company, Inc., New York (1952); G. Friedlander and J. W. Kennedy, "Introduction to Radiochemistry," John Wiley & Sons, Inc., New York (1949); B. B. Rossi and H. H. Staub, "Ionization Chambers and Counters," McGraw-Hill Book Co., Inc., New York (1949); S. A. Korff, "Electron and Nuclear Counters," D. Van Nostrand Co., Princeton, N. J. (1946); J. B. Hoag and S. A. Korff "Electron and Nuclear Physics," D. Van Nostrand Co., Princeton, N. J. (1948); E. Segre (Ed.), "Experimental Nuclear Physics," Vol. I, John Wiley & Sons, Inc., New York.

ionizers (direct or indirect), such as alpha particles or neutrons alone, even in the presence of considerable numbers of the weaker ionizers (direct or indirect) such as beta and gamma rays.

If, on the other hand, the ionizing events are so closely spaced in time and/or the "time constant" (RC of Fig. 2-1) of the circuit is great, a steady "average" voltage is developed across the resistance R. The instrument is then referred to as an *integrating ionization chamber*.

Ionization chambers are often used as monitors and for radiation surveys. When built with thick walls, they detect the penetrating gamma rays and give on their output meters the dosage rate (milliroentgens per hour, say), not the total dose. When thinner-walled tubes are used, they detect beta-plus-gamma rays, and when very thin or no walls at all are used, they respond to alpha-plus-beta-plus-gamma rays. They may be used for the detection of fast neutrons if the gas is hydrogen, for then protons (hydrogen nuclei), recoiling under neutron impact, will produce the ionization. Recoil protons are also produced if the inner walls of the tube are lined with substances rich in hydrogen such as paraffin or a plastic such as polyethylene. For slow neutrons, a thin coating of boron, particularly of the isotope boron-10, is used on one or both electrodes; or the tube is filled with the gas boron trifluoride (BF_3), when Reaction 1-22 occurs. Or for slow neutrons the electrodes are coated with a compound of uranium-235, and the fission fragments serve as the ionizing radiations.

A "differential" or *compensated chamber* is used to detect neutrons alone when both neutrons and gamma rays are present. The chamber is built with two identical parts, one of which is boron-coated or contains BF_3 and is therefore sensitive to both radiations. The other half does not contain boron and hence is sensitive to gamma rays alone. The outputs from the two parts of the tube are electrically connected so that the gamma current is canceled, leaving a net output proportional to the neutrons alone.

Proportional Counters. As is seen in Fig. 2-2, a radiation detector is operated at a higher voltage in the proportional than in the ionization-chamber region. Under the influence of the higher electrical field in the tube, the primary ions are now able to create additional ions by collision with the gas molecules, as much as ten or more times as many per primary ion. This gas amplification is an advantage, since the sensitivity of the recording equipment or the gain in the electronic amplifier, which follows the detector tube, need not be as great. In addition, the recovery time (see below, page 32) is shorter and much higher counting rates are possible. Another advantage is that it is possible to count radiations of greater ionizing ability in the presence of those of lesser specific ionization by operating at the lower voltages of the proportional region. Then, by operating at higher voltages but staying in the proportional region, both kinds of radiation may be recorded. A disadvantage of operation in the proportional region is the need for great stabilization of the applied voltage, since any change will alter the gas amplification and hence the output. Nevertheless, proportional counters are proving to be of increasing value in reactor work.

In proportional counters, the output pulse produced by each incident nuclear radiation is determined by the motion of the positive ions in the tube rather than by the time constant of the tube and circuits as with an ionization chamber. After the electrons produced by the ionization of the gas have quickly moved to the central wire or anode, the positive ions move at a more leisurely rate toward the outer cylinder or cathode. Thus the voltage pulse rises, as in the dotted line in Fig. 2-3. Following the tube, there is a *differentiating circuit* which has a short time constant (RC). The net result is that the resolving time of a proportional counter and its circuit can be made very short, perhaps only 0.2 microseconds. Hence much faster counting rates are possible. Proportional counters are used for monitoring, especially of neutrons and alpha particles. Weak pulses due to beta or gamma rays can be suppressed by applying sufficient bias voltage to the amplifying or scaling circuits.

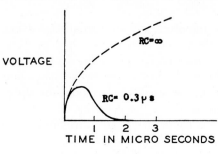

VOLTAGE

RC= ∞

RC= 0.3 µs

TIME IN MICRO SECONDS

Fig. 2-3. Pulse shaping.

Geiger-Müller Counters. When the voltage applied to the radiation detector is in the Geiger region of Fig. 2-2, the ionizing avalanche produced by the primary ionization spreads throughout the tube, with an attendant gas amplification as high as 10^8. The charge collected (and hence the output voltage pulse) is independent of the ionizing ability of the original nuclear radiation which passed through the tube. It is independent of both the nature and the energy of the initial nuclear radiation; that is, each particle which enters the gas produces a pulse of the same size. G-M counters are in wide use for monitoring gamma and beta radiations. After an avalanche of ionizing events has occurred in a G-M tube, with the desirable high value of gas amplification, some means of stopping the discharge is needed. One method is to use sufficiently high resistance (10^9 to 10^{12} ohms) that the voltage drop across it (R in Fig. 2-1) is great enough to lower the net voltage across the tube to its shutoff value. A second commonly used method of stopping the discharge is to add to the customary argon of the tube a small amount of organic vapor such as ethyl alcohol. Then the positive ions do not release electrons when they strike the cathode and the discharge is not perpetuated. When a tube is so filled, it is referred to as a *self-quenching tube*.

Scintillation Counters. For many years, high-energy charged particles such as the alpha particles emitted by a radioactive substance have been studied by the feeble flashes of light which they produce on striking certain fluorescent chemical substances or "phosphors," such as activated zinc sulfide or calcium tungstate. Visual observation of the flashes of light has now been replaced by the use of photomultiplier tubes. The phosphor or scintillator is mounted over the photocathode or sensitive surface of the multiplier tube. Then the flashes of light cause the emission of electrons inside the multiplier. These photo-electrons are accelerated and strike a second, specially prepared surface, which then emits several electrons per primary or incident electron. These in turn are accelerated to a second multiplying surface inside the tube, etc., for as many as ten surfaces or "stages," multiplying the number of electrons each time. The original current of the photocathode, caused by the feeble flash of light, is thus increased many-fold, to give an output current of sufficient size for easy ampli-fication by the usual electronic circuits. High counting rates of gamma rays are possible with scintillometers which consist of the scintillator, photomultiplier tube, and amplifying and registering equipment.

The following material on scintillation counters was contributed by R. K. SWANK, ANL, Physics Division.

Fig. 2-4 shows a scintillator placed in optical contact with the photocathode and surrounded by a reflector to gain in optical efficiency.

A beta particle of 1 Mev energy, when absorbed in a good scintillator, will produce about 30,000 photons of fluores-cent light. If 80 per cent of the light is collected onto the photocathode, about 3000 photoelectrons will be produced. Ten stages of secondary emission ampli-fication will, typically, produce an out-put pulse of the order of 3×10^8 elec-trons. With the usual output capaci-tance of ~ 20 $\mu\mu$f, this results in a volt-age pulse of 2.4 volts. Such a pulse can be fed directly into a scaling circuit. However, to detect lower energy radia-tion, and to generate larger pulses for

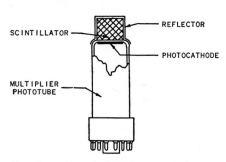

FIG. 2-4. A scintillator mounted on a multiplier phototube.

operating other circuits, a linear amplifier with a gain of about 2000 is usually provided.

Scintillations may be produced in crystals, liquids, plastics, and gases. Of the many materials which are usable, the following have received widespread use:

1. *Sodium iodide single crystals*, NaI(Tl), containing 0.07–0.2 per cent thallium impurity are the most widely used scintillators. Crystals as large as 8 in. in diameter by 8 in. in length have been grown. Because of the large effective mass of such a detector and its excellent transparency to its own fluorescence, it is unsurpassed for the detection of gamma rays. It is also very

useful for measuring gamma-ray energy and discriminating between gamma rays on the basis of energy, making use of the different pulse-amplitude distributions.

2. *Aromatic hydrocarbon liquids* such as toluene, containing fluorescent activators such as *p*-terphenyl or diphenyloxazole are useful because of their low cost, unlimited size, and short pulse duration ($\sim 10^{-9}$ sec).

3. *Aromatic high polymers*, such as polyvinyltoluene, containing activators such as *p*-terphenyl or tetraphenylbutadiene, perform similarly to the liquids.

4. *Anthracene single crystals* are useful for counting beta rays, and for beta-ray spectrometry.

5. *Noble gases* are useful because of their efficiency for counting heavy particles. This property, together with very fast time resolution ($\sim 10^{-9}$ sec) makes these materials ideal for fission counters.

The choice of a scintillation counter over another type will depend on many factors. However, in general, certain properties will be most important:

1. It will detect gamma rays with high efficiency.

2. With sodium iodide, gamma-ray spectrometry is practical.

3. Short resolving time may be achieved, ranging from 10^{-9} sec with liquids and gases to 10^{-7} sec for sodium iodide.

EXPERIMENT 2-1

G-M COUNTER STUDIES

By J. B. Hoag, ANL, International School of Nuclear Science and Engineering

The main points to be brought out in the next two experiments are (1) the voltage applied to a Geiger-Müller counter tube must lie within a certain range of value, called the plateau, and (2) a large number of counts must be made in any activity measurement if accurate results, free from statistical variations, are to be obtained.

(1) **The Operating Voltage.** For the first purpose, a G-M tube is set up, with its voltage supply, amplifier, scaler and mechanical register. A constant source of radiation is placed near the tube. Then the number of counts per unit time is recorded as the voltage applied to the tube is increased. A curve like one of those in Fig. 2-5 will be obtained, the upper one if a stronger source is used or if a weaker source is located closer to the tube. Care should be taken that the counting rate is not so fast that dead-time corrections (see below, page 33) become appreciable. As the voltage is raised, counts will be observed first at the *starting voltage*. Since only the larger pulses are now counted, this voltage depends on the sensitivity of the amplifier used in conjunction with the counter tube. The starting voltage will be lower with a more sensitive amplifier.

At the *Geiger threshold*, as indicated in Fig. 2-5, all the pulses are of the

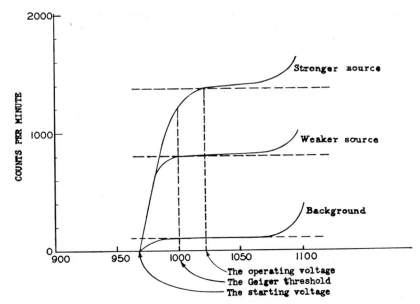

Fɪɢ. 2-5.   Typical G-M counting rate voltage curves. The nearly horizontal parts of the curves are the plateaus.

same size and are counted. At still higher voltages the curve is nearly horizontal, usually for a hundred volts or so. Over this *Geiger plateau,* changes in the voltage do not alter the counting rate appreciably. In order to prolong the life of the tube (internal quenching type) it is advantageous to choose an operating voltage toward the left of the plateau, but sufficiently above the threshold that changes do not drop the operating voltage below the threshold. Usually the operating voltage is set above the threshold approximately one-third the length of the plateau. In practice the plateau is not strictly flat but may rise by, say, 0.1 volt or even 1 volt in 100 volts. Hence, despite the nearly constant counting rate over the plateau, the voltage source should contain a stabilizing circuit. G-M counters should never be operated above the plateau, where a rapid rise in the counting rate occurs, or they will be permanently damaged. When operated properly, the life of a G-M tube is of the order of 10^8 to 10^{10} total counts.

For this experiment, plot a counting-rate voltage curve, specify the range and slope of the plateau, and choose a suitable operating voltage. The radioactive source may be any long-lived substance such as a uranium salt or cobalt-60 ($T_{1/2} = 5.27$ years). Its position with respect to the counter tube is not to be changed once the experiment has been started. With the usual small cylindrical or end-window tubes, the voltage may be increased in steps of 25 volts. At each voltage, take at least several thousand counts. Divide the total number of counts by the total time to get the counting rate.

(2) **Counting-Rate Fluctuations.** The following experiment is concerned with the fluctuations of the counting rate around the average value. Consider a "steady" source, i.e., a finite sample of radioactive material of long life. It will contain a very large number of nuclei, only a few of which will disintegrate in the comparatively short time interval used in counting their emission rate. It is of course impossible to say when any one of these nuclei will disintegrate, but it is possible to determine an average number decaying in unit time (counting rate) either by taking an average of many short-time readings or from a single comparatively long time measurement. Future repetitions of these measurements will yield nearly the same counting rate, but not exactly the same value. In other words, the "steady" source is not quite steady; there

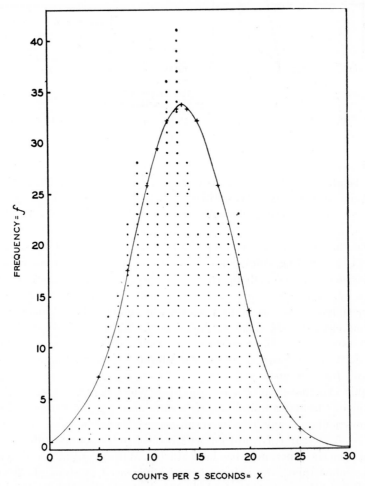

FIG. 2-6. The background counting rate, as measured repeatedly in short time intervals, varies a great deal.

are random fluctuations around the average value which are inherent in the process of emission.

In order to overemphasize the fluctuations, an extreme case will be considered. For the "source" we shall use only the background activity around an unshielded G-M counter tube. This activity is due to cosmic rays and to radioactive substances in the air, the earth, the walls of the room, and the materials out of which the counter itself is constructed. Also, we shall use a comparatively short time interval t—say, five seconds—in which to count the radiations. The number of counts x, observed in this interval, is to be remeasured several hundred times. It will be found to vary greatly—say, 5 counts in the first interval, 22 in the next, then 12, 2, 10, 21, 5, etc. There is, then, great uncertainty in the value of a weak activity when measured over a short time interval.

A frequency-distribution chart is to be plotted as in Fig. 2-6. Each time a given number of counts x is observed in the time interval t (5 sec), a dot is made on the chart. For example, during the 407 ($= n$) measurements shown in the figure, there were 13 times ($= f$, the frequency) when 6 counts per 5-sec interval were obtained. The values of x are seen to run from 2 to 26; the i-th case to be represented by x_i; and the corresponding frequency to be f_i.

The best estimate of the average value from this experimental data is the arithmetic mean, $\bar{x}$, as computed from the equation

$$\bar{x} = \frac{\Sigma(f_i x_i)}{n}, \tag{2-1}$$

where Σ is the summation of all cases from $i = 1$ to k (here $k = 26$) and n is the total number of measurements; i.e.,

$$n = \Sigma(f_i). \tag{2-2}$$

In Fig. 2-6, $\bar{x} = 13.5$ c/sec. The mean counting rate is, then, $r = \bar{x}/t = 13.5/5 = 2.70$ counts per sec.

The second feature of interest is the spread or *dispersion* of the observed counts around the mean. Each value of x differs from the mean $\bar{x}$ by an amount called the deviation, d. For the i-th case,

$$d_i = x_i - \bar{x}. \tag{2-3}$$

Any arithmetic average of these deviations is zero and cannot be used to express the dispersion of the data. However, a meaningful measure of the fluctuations is the root-mean-square deviations from the mean; also called the *standard deviation, s*. For a single measurement, it is given by

$$s_{o1} = \sqrt{\frac{\Sigma(f_i d_i^2)}{n - 1}}. \tag{2-4}$$

When n is greater than 30, the denominator of Equation 2-4 may be taken as n instead of n-1 with reasonable accuracy. The subscript o is used to indicate that the value of s so computed comes from observed data. For the data of Fig. 2-6, $s_{o1} = 4.82$.

If the data fits a Gaussian or normal distribution, as indicated by the bell-shaped curve of the figure, approximately two-thirds (actually 68.26 per cent) of the measurements (x values) would have a smaller deviation from the mean than the standard error or deviation s. Although the standard deviation is the one most commonly used in counting, other errors used in statistical analysis are probable error $= 0.6745\ s$; nine-tenths error $= 1.6449\ s$; ninety-five hundredths error $= 1.9600\ s$; and ninety-nine hundredths error $= 2.5758\ s$. It is equally probable that the deviation from the mean of any one measurement is larger or smaller than the "probable error." Also, 95.44 per cent of the cases lie between plus and minus $2s$, and 99.73 per cent of the cases lie between plus and minus $3s$. It is seen then, that s or some multiple of s is a measure of how close a single future measurement is likely to come to the mean.

It is possible to derive an expression for s from probability theory.* In particular, the Poisson distribution law can be used, since it applies to small samples taken from large populations, i.e., to few disintegrations per unit time from the very large number of nuclei in a radioactive sample. From this theory one obtains as the *expected standard deviation* s_{t1}, of a single measurement

$$s_{t1} \approx \sqrt{\bar{x}}. \qquad (2\text{-}5)$$

With the data of Fig. 2-6, $s_{t1} = 3.67$. The larger value of s (4.82) obtained from the experimental Equation 2-4 indicates that additional fluctuations were present in the apparatus itself, perhaps due to a faulty condenser, pickup from external sparks, etc.

The *standard deviation of the mean*, $s_{\bar{x}}$, is given by

$$s_{\bar{x}} = \frac{s_1}{\sqrt{n}} \approx \sqrt{\frac{\bar{x}}{n}}. \qquad (2\text{-}6)$$

In the example of Fig. 2-6, $s_{\bar{x}} = \sqrt{13.50/407} = 0.180$. The result of the repeated measurements would be reported as $(\bar{x} \pm s_{\bar{x}}) = (13.50 \pm 0.18)$ counts/5 sec. The counting rate r would be

$$r = \frac{\bar{x} \pm \sqrt{\bar{x}/n}}{t} \text{ counts per second}, \qquad (2\text{-}7)$$

which, in this case, is $r = 2.70 \pm 0.036$.

---

*Consult: Rainwater and Wu, Nucleonics, **1**, No. 2, 60 (1947); **2**, No. 1, 42 (1948); Elmore, Nucleonics, **6**, 26 (1950); Ghelardi and Brown, Nucleonics, **1**, No. 1, 58 (1947); G. Friedlander and J. W. Kennedy, "Introduction to Radiochemistry," John Wiley & Sons, Inc., New York (1949), Chapter IX; E. Bleuler and G. J. Goldsmith, "Experimental Nucleonics," Rinehart & Company, Inc. (1952), p. 62; books on statistics such as T. C. Fry, "Probability and Its Engineering Uses"; Worthing and Geffner, "Treatment of Experimental Data"; H. E. Garret, "Statistics in Psychology and Education"; O. W. Eshback, "Handbook of Engineering Fundamentals" 2nd ed., pp. 2-27; and many others.

Suppose, now, that only *one measurement* is made. Let this consist of a large number of counts, N, taken over a long period of time, T. The counting rate of this one measurement will be reported as

$$R = \frac{N \pm \sqrt{N}}{T}. \tag{2-8}$$

Notice that since there is only one measurement, the standard deviation is of necessity given as $\sqrt{N}$ rather than $\sqrt{\overline{N}}$. When N is large, this approximation does not introduce serious error. In the data of Fig. 2-6, a total of 5492 counts were made over a total of 2035 sec. If these had been counted in a single measurement, the result would have been $R_1 = (5492 \pm \sqrt{5492})/2035 = 2.70 \pm 0.036$ counts/sec, as before.

The accuracy or *relative deviation* is given by

$$RD \approx \frac{\sqrt{N}}{N} = \frac{1}{\sqrt{N}}. \tag{2-9}$$

For 100 counts, $RD = 10$ per cent; for 5492 counts, $RD = 1.35$ per cent; for 10,000 counts, $RD = 1$ per cent. Hence, when a single measurement is made, an excessively large number of counts must be made in order to attain high precision.

The standard deviation S of the sum or of a difference of two standard deviations, s_1 and s_2, is

$$S = \sqrt{s_1{}^2 + s_2{}^2}. \tag{2-10}$$

Suppose, for example, that a radioactive sample is now placed near the counter, whose background counting rate was determined as above; $R_b = 2.70 \pm 0.036$. Say 3600 counts are now recorded in 600 sec. Then the total rate due to the sample and the background will be $R_t = 6 \pm 0.1$. The counting rate of the sample will be $6 - 2.7 = 3.3$, and its standard deviation $S = \sqrt{0.1^2 + 0.036^2} = 0.106$. Thus the net counting rate $R_n = 3.3 \pm 0.11$.

In this experiment an unshielded G-M counter tube, operated at its proper voltage, and with its amplifier, is used to obtain the data. A distribution curve like that in Fig. 2-6 is to be plotted and the quantities indicated on Data Sheet 2-1 are to be computed.

Next, place a radioactive sample near the counter tube and determine the total counting due to the sample and background, using Equation 2-8. Then compute the net counting rate and its standard deviation, using Equation 2-10.

Dead Time and Resolving Time.* After a particle has passed through a G-M counter tube, there is a short time interval during which the tube is inactive. Any particle which arrives during this interval will not be counted. Hence

---

* R. T. Myers, "Dead Time of a Geiger-Mueller Tube by the Double-Source Method," J. Chem. Ed., 33, No. 8, 395 (August 1956); E. Bleuler and G. J. Goldsmith, "Experimental Electronics," Rinehart and Company, Inc., New York (1952).

DATA SHEET, 2-1

Counts per 5 sec = x_i	Frequency		$f_i x_i$	Deviations d_i	$f_i d_i$	$f_i d_i^2$
	Tab	f_i				
2	//	2	4	11.5	23	264
⋮	⋮	⋮	⋮	⋮	⋮	⋮
Sums		$\Sigma f_i = n$	$\Sigma f_i x_i$			$\Sigma f_i d_i^2$

Mean $\bar{x}$ = Equations 2-1 and 2-2
Observed std. dev., s_{o1} = Equations 2-3 and 2-4
Expected std. dev., s_{t1} = Equation 2-5
Counting rate, r = Equation 2-7
Relative deviation, RD = Equation 2-9

a correction is needed to the observed or measured counting rate r_m to obtain the true rate r.

The voltage pulse generated by a properly quenched G-M tube is shown at the left in Fig. 2-7. A second particle, entering the counter during the *dead time* t_d will not be recorded. Even particles which arrive a little later may be too weak to be recorded. But still later, particles give increasingly large output amplitudes and may be recorded. Finally, as is shown by the dotted line at the right of Fig. 2-7, the pulse due to a particle is of full amplitude. The *recovery time* t_r extends from the time when a weak pulse could just appear to the time when another pulse of full amplitude is just starting.

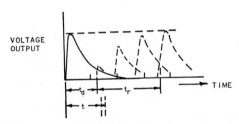

VOLTAGE OUTPUT

FIG. 2-7. The dead time t_d, the recovery time t_r, and the resolving time t of a G-M counter tube.

The *resolving time* t is that between counts that can actually be counted. If a sensitive amplifier is used, the weak pulses immediately following the dead time will be counted and t will be nearly equal to t_d. The resolving time of G-M counters is of the order of 100 or 200 microseconds or less. Thus the maximum counting rate of G-M counters, with their circuits, is about 5000 to 10,000 counts per sec. Since radioactive processes are always subject to statistical variations around a mean rate, it is possible that even at counting rates lower than the maximum, some particles may enter the tube while it is dead. Thus a correction is always needed for accurate work.

Let m be the number of measured counts in time T and let n be the correct number of particles which entered the counter during the same time. Then mt is the total insensitive time during T sec and n/T is the average number of particles which entered the tube per sec ($=$ true count rate). Thus $(n/T)(mt)$ represents the average number of particles which in the time interval T entered the tube during its insensitive time and were not counted, i.e., n-$m = nmt/T$. These are sometimes referred to as "coincidence losses." It is assumed that the particles are not entering so fast that more than one passes through the tube during any one dead time. Solving for n gives

$$n = m\left(1 - \frac{mt}{T}\right)^{-1}. \tag{2-11}$$

When the term in parentheses is expanded by means of the binomial theorem and higher order terms are dropped, the approximate equation suitable for those cases where mt/T is small is found to be

$$n \approx m\left(1 + \frac{mt}{T}\right). \tag{2-12}$$

Dividing by T gives the rate of counting (counts per second)—r the correct rate, and r_m the measured rate. Then

$$r = \frac{r_m}{1 - r_m t}. \tag{2-13}$$

One of the best means of determining the resolving time t, is *the double-source method*. For this, two radioactive sources are counted separately, then together; then the background is counted—all with the same geometry. Let r_1, r_2, r_{12} and r_b be the respective counting rates. Then, since $r_1 + r_2$ includes the background twice, while r_{12} contains r_b but once, $r_1 + r_2 - 2r_b = r_{12} - r_b$, or

$$r_1 + r_2 = r_{12} + r_b. \tag{2-14}$$

Substituting values of r from Equation 2-13 leads to

$$\frac{r_{m1}}{1 - r_{m1}t} + \frac{r_{m2}}{1 - r_{m2}t} = \frac{r_{m12}}{1 - r_{m12}t} + \frac{r_b}{1 - r_b t}, \tag{2-15}$$

which expresses the resolving time t in terms of the measured rates r_m and the background rate r_b. The solution for t is

$$t = t_1\left[1 + \frac{t_1}{4}\left(r_{m12} - r_b\right)\right], \tag{2-16}$$

in which
$$t_1 = \frac{r_{m1} + r_{m2} - r_{m12} - r_b}{2(r_{m1} - r_b)(r_{m2} - r_b)}. \tag{2-17}$$

Since t is small, the term in brackets in Equation 2-16 is nearly equal to unity and $t = t_1$. Equation 2-17 has been found to give the resolving time with adequate accuracy for most work.

EXPERIMENT 2-2

A DEMONSTRATION OF NUCLEAR RADIATION COUNTERS AND CIRCUITS

By G. S. PAWLICKI, Instrument and Control Dept., International School of Nuclear Science and Engineering

The object of this demonstration by the instructor is to assemble the radiation-detection counter and then operate it in conjunction with the necessary electronic equipment. The demonstration is intended to show the nuclear and electrical properties of the counter as well as the operation of the electronic equipment. The demonstration is divided into five phases:

A. Demonstration of a Triggered-Sweep Cathode-Ray Oscillograph. (Tektronix type 530 with 53A plug-in unit or equivalent.)

1. Explain the controls on the oscillograph panel.

2. Display a square wave with slow and fast sweep and indicate the rise time of the calibration square-wave signal included in this particular oscillograph.

3. Display the differentiated square wave with a 5-microsec time constant.

4. Display the integration of the square wave with a 5000-microsec time constant.

5. Display clipping of the differentiated pulses using a crystal diode.

B. Demonstration of Amplifier and Preamplifier. (Commercial version of A1 amplifier and A1A preamplifier.)

1. Apply a square-wave voltage to the input of the preamplifier and observe the output on the oscillograph. Show that the output pulse height is proportional to the input voltage for small signals (2 millivolts or less) and that amplifier saturation occurs for larger signals.

2. Show that the pulse rise time and fall time on the three bandwidth settings agrees with the bandwidth and differentiating time constants specified for the amplifier. Measure the overall gain of the preamplifier and amplifier with the gain control at its maximum setting when the bandwidth is set at 0.1 megacycle sec. With no input signal, measure the output noise of the amplifier and infer the noise level at the preamplifier input. Show that the gain calculated by taking the reciprocal of the feedback ratio is consistent with the measured gain.

C. Assembly of a Parallel-Plate Ionization Chamber

1. Assemble the parallel-plate ionization chamber of Fig. 2-8, installing a 5-mg electroplated sample of fully enriched uranium-235. The sample should have an area of about 10 cm^2.

2. Evacuate the chamber with a mechanical vacuum pump and flush with

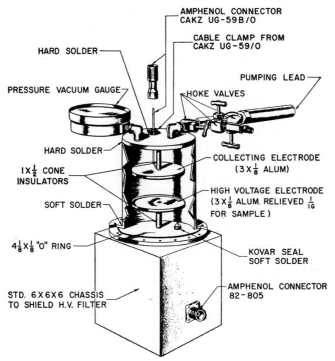

Fig. 2-8.   Parallel-plate demonstration chamber.

dry nitrogen (oil-pumped nitrogen is preferable). Evacuate the chamber and then fill to about 15 psi gauge pressure.

3. Connect the preamplifier to the upper plate of the ionization chamber and connect a negative high-voltage supply to the lower-chamber electrode on which the uranium sample has been placed.

4. With full amplifier gain on the 0.1-megacycle bandwidth setting, increase the output of the high-voltage supply and, using the oscillograph, observe the change in amplifier pulse height output as the voltage is increased. With an electrode spacing of 5 cm in the chamber and 15 psi gauge pressure, the ion-chamber region begins at about 1000 volts. Any further increase of high voltage has only a slight effect on the pulse-height output. A more quantitative demonstration can be performed by observing the counting rate from the amplifier pulse-height selector output terminal, using a scaling circuit. To do this counting, the pulse-height selector is set at some low value slightly above the noise level of the amplifier and the counting rate is observed for various values of the high-voltage setting.

5. Reduce the amplifier gain by at least a factor of 8 so that the amplifier output pulses due to alpha particles from the uranium sample no longer trigger

the oscillograph. Surround the chamber with a paraffin collar into which a neutron source can be placed. The neutron source should have an emission rate of the order of 10^5 neutrons/sec or greater. To minimize the radiation hazard, the neutron source should be either plutonium-beryllium or polonium-beryllium, both of which present no gamma-ray hazard. Infrequent pulses will now appear on the oscillograph screen due to the fission of the uranium by slow neutrons. By taking the ratio of the height of the largest alpha pulses previously observed and the maximum height of the fission pulses, the energy of the fission fragment can be determined to be about 80 Mev. Assuming two fission fragments of equal energy, one of which is directed into the uranium foil, the total kinetic energy of fission is then approximately 160 Mev.

6. Reduce the pressure in the chamber to about one-half atmosphere absolute. Set the amplifier at full gain, the bandwidth at 2 megacycles, and the high-voltage supply at about 1000 volts. On the oscillograph, measure the time duration of the longest-duration fission pulses. The plate spacing of the chamber divided by this time gives the drift velocity of electrons in nitrogen (approximately 5×10^5 cm/sec). Increase the high-voltage supply to 4000 volts and repeat the measurement of time duration of the pulses. The time duration will be seen to be only approximately one-half that of the duration with the lower collecting voltage, so the drift velocity is approximately 10^6 cm/sec.

7. Return the apparatus to the conditions used in Paragraph 4 of Section C, above, and check to see that alpha pulses are visible on the oscillograph. Shut off the high-voltage supply and pump out the chamber. Then admit air at atmospheric pressure and restore the high voltage. No alpha pulses will appear on the oscillograph. The loss of signal is due to the formation of slow-moving negative ions by electron attachment in the counter gas. These slow-moving negative ions produce signal pulses which have too long a rise time for the rather high lower-frequency response of the amplifier. Without changing any settings of the apparatus, apply the paraffin collar and neutron source. Some very small pulses will appear. It then becomes apparent that atmospheric air has a much poorer performance as a fast-pulse-counter gas than dry nitrogen.

D. Concentric Cylindrical Counter

1. Assemble the concentric-cylinder demonstration chamber shown in Fig. 2-9, using a 0.005-in.-diameter center electrode. A small alpha sample should be cemented to the inner surface of the outer counter electrode. The counter is flushed and filled with Matheson P10 gas having the composition 90 per cent argon, 10 per cent methane, to a pressure of 10 psi gauge. Nitrogen filling and different pressures can be used, but the results of this demonstration will be quoted for the P10 filling. In order to save time, it may be assembled prior to the demonstration. The counter may then be dismantled at the end of the demonstration to show the details of its internal construction.

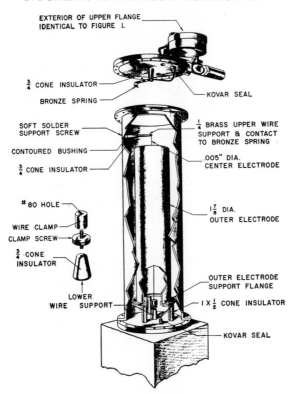

EXTERIOR OF UPPER FLANGE
IDENTICAL TO FIGURE I.

$\frac{3}{4}$ CONE INSULATOR

BRONZE SPRING

KOVAR SEAL

SOFT SOLDER
SUPPORT SCREW

CONTOURED BUSHING

$\frac{3}{4}$ CONE INSULATOR

$\frac{1}{4}$ BRASS UPPER WIRE
SUPPORT & CONTACT
TO BRONZE SPRING

.005" DIA.
CENTER ELECTRODE

#80 HOLE

WIRE CLAMP

CLAMP SCREW

$\frac{3}{4}$ CONE
INSULATOR

$1\frac{7}{8}$ DIA.
OUTER ELECTRODE

OUTER ELECTRODE
SUPPORT FLANGE

LOWER
WIRE SUPPORT

$1 \times \frac{1}{2}$ CONE INSULATOR

KOVAR SEAL

FIG. 2-9.　Concentric-cylinder counter.

2. Using the A1A preamplifier and the A1 amplifier at full gain on the 0.5-megacycle bandwidth, gradually increase the high voltage to the counter in steps of about 50 volts. Pulses will appear on the oscillograph increasing in size with the applied voltage. The pulse size will increase appreciably up to about 700 volts and then very slowly in the interval from 700 to 1200 volts. It may be necessary to reduce the gain of the amplifier before the voltage plateau is reached so as not to overdrive the final stages of the A1 amplifier. As the voltage on the counter is increased above 1200 volts, the pulse-height output of the counter increases rather rapidly with the collecting voltage and the amplification must be greatly reduced so as not to overdrive the amplifier. A factor of 32 reduction will be necessary when the voltage is raised to 2400 volts.

3. The foregoing procedure can be repeated using the pulse-height selector output of the A1 amplifier and a scaler to measure the maximum-output pulse height as a function of the counter voltage. The data to be recorded is the amplifier gain in arbitrary units, the maximum pulse-height voltage as read on the pulse-height selector dial, and the value of the high voltage. When the

pulse-height data are normalized to the same amplifier gain and then renormalized to a multiple of the pulse height obtained in the ion-chamber plateau region, the gas multiplication can be plotted as a function of the collecting voltage for this particular counter. The results are plotted in Fig. 2-10.

E. Operation of a Binary Scaler. The square-wave generator is connected into the scaler input. Using the oscillograph, the signal is followed through the

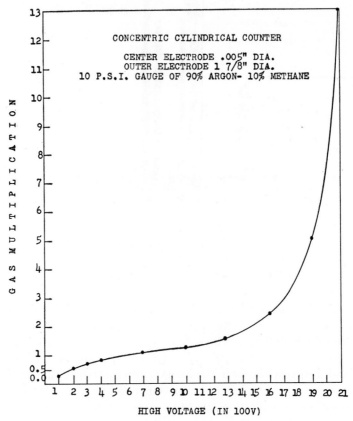

FIG. 2-10.   Gas multiplication demonstration.

pulse-shaping circuit preceding the scaler. The periodicity of the input pulses is noted. The oscillograph is then connected to one of the anodes of the first scaling pair and a square-wave form of twice the input period is observed. Moving to a corresponding point in the second scaling pair, the period is again doubled. However, the waveform has a step on its positive excursion due to the diode coupling system employed in the Higginbotham-type scaling circuit.

F. Dismantle the Concentric Cylinder Chamber.

MODIFICATIONS OF THE DEMONSTRATION

Many extensions to the scope of this demonstration are possible, as well as variations in the procedure, and a few of these should be mentioned. The gas filling of the concentric-cylinder system can be done at lower pressure with argon-ethyl alcohol vapor, and the demonstration can be carried from the ion-chamber region through the proportional region and finally to the Geiger region. To carry out this wide-range demonstration with concentric cylinders, it is necessary to have an amplifier gain control which operates over a range of about 10,000. Demonstration of the same counter used in different regions of gas amplification does seem worthwhile. It may be possible to use a thin-mica end-window counter for this type of demonstration, provided the window is transparent to alpha particles.

Rather than use a small alpha sample in the concentric cylinder counter, it is possible to have several interchangeable outer cylinders with coatings of boron or natural uranium. The large area of coatings should permit demonstration of boron-coated neutron counters and fission counters without requiring isotopically pure boron-10 or uranium-235.

If the procedure of actually assembling the counter is not considered to be important, the demonstration can be made by using some commercial neutron counters. A commercial BF_3 proportional counter filled to an absolute pressure of about one-half atmosphere should be quite satisfactory.

Similar demonstrations with scintillation counters, using different gamma sources and different scintillating compounds, can be made, but the demonstrations of pulse-height distribution with a single-channel analyzer are rather time-consuming.

EXPERIMENT 2-3

MICROPIPETTING AND RELATIVE ALPHA-PARTICLE COUNTING

By RICHARD F. FIRESTONE, Chemistry Department, International School of Nuclear Science and Engineering

I. INTRODUCTION

This experiment will, if carefully performed, serve three purposes. It should:

1. Permit the experimenter to determine the degrees of precision attainable by measurement of small volumes of liquid with several sizes of micropipets.

2. Acquaint him with the techniques required for the operation of a gas-flow proportional radiation counter for the measurement of alpha-particle emission rates from solid samples.

3. Permit him to evaluate experimentally the relative importance of statis-

tical counting uncertainties and errors committed in the preparation of counting samples of various activities.

Briefly, the experiment consists in the preparation of a number of alpha counting plates by delivering uniformly to the surface of each plate a known volume of solution of an alpha-particle-emitting material, evaporation of the solution to absolute dryness, and measurement of the counting rate in a proportional radiation counter. The importance of mastering each of the simple steps for the preparation and use of a radiochemical assay plate cannot be overestimated. This will be apparent when the student realizes that the performance of these steps is often preceded in a radiochemistry laboratory by a series of laborious and time-consuming chemical operations and that the value of a day's laboratory work is therefore often determined by the accuracy of these final measurements.

The student will realize that counting rates measured in an experiment such as this one do not represent the total disintegration rates of the radioactive material on the sample plates. The rates observed are relative counting rates, which are, of course, meaningful only when referred to other counting rates measured under identical conditions with samples prepared in the same manner from radiochemically equivalent solutions. Fortunately, the radiochemist's needs are frequently served by measurement of relative counting rates. Thus, for example, the fraction of the total number of atoms of a particular radioactive species which is separated from other species in a series of chemical reactions can be determined by preparing identical counting samples of the gross material before and after separation and by sampling the separated material. Relative counting rates are therefore usually sufficient for evaluating the efficiency of radiochemical separations. The critical factors in the measurement of useful relative counting rates are those which affect achievement of reproducible counting conditions and accurate preparation of uniform counting samples.

II. Measurement of Liquid Samples for Microanalysis: Micropipetting

Laboratory work with alpha-particle-emitting materials is frequently carried out with microgram quantities. The choice of such small samples is usually dictated by the availability of only small amounts of material and the necessity for minimizing health hazards to the experimenter and his laboratory partners. Both factors are especially important in planning experiments involving transuranium elements. The absence of stable nuclides in this group of elements makes it necessary to deal with solutions of very high specific activity unless microgram quantities can be conveniently and precisely manipulated by chemical and physical means. It should be realized that serious potential health hazards are present even on the micro scale, since the lethal ingested quantity of plutonium-239, for example, is of the order of only one (1) microgram. The maximum permissible amount of this nuclide in the total human body is only 0.1 microgram! Prohibitive experimental difficulties can be encountered with macro quantities of high specific activity even when health hazards are avoided by remote-control operations. Radiation-induced decomposition of a very active solution may, for example, make it desirable to work with more dilute solutions of rather low specific activity.

A convenient unit of volume on the micro scale is the lambda (λ). One lambda is equivalent to 0.001 ml or 0.000,001 liter. Measurement of lambda quantities of liquids can be performed with amazing accuracy with micropipets. Micropipets are not merely tiny models of the milliliter variety commonly used in a standard analytical laboratory. They differ from the larger variety in several significant respects in addition to the great difference in capacity. Micro-pipets are usually constructed from heavy-wall glass capillary tubing with an internal diameter of 0.5 mm. The smallness of the bore minimizes volume errors caused by slight errors in adjustment of the liquid meniscus to the calibration mark. This feature of the capillary pipet is a definite advantage. The narrow-bore pipet cannot be calibrated, like a macropipet, to deliver precise volumes by drainage because the surface tension of most liquids will cause the retention of much of the sample in the capillary. Hence, it is necessary to calibrate micro-pipets to contain known volumes; and the contained volume must be forced out with air pressure from a tuberculin syringe or similar device. The last traces of sample must be recovered with a rinse solution. This means, of course, that the micropipet must be cleaned and dried after each measurement to avoid dilution and contamination of succeeding samples.

Fig. 2-11 shows the characteristic features of a micropipet which must be filled by means of a tuberculin syringe.* The narrow end serves as both the

Fig. 2-11.   A micropipet.

entrance and exit for measured liquids, and the syringe is attached to the thick, blunter end. An etched calibration mark is made on the outside of the tube at the point where the liquid level corresponds to the desired volume of solution. The two bulbs shown in the tubing serve as reservoirs for a major portion of the liquid in the pipet. The bulb nearer the syringe end is a safety reservoir designed to make it difficult to draw solution accidentally into the syringe.

Micropipets can be obtained from a number of scientific supply houses at the present time. Sizes ranging from about 1 lambda to 750 lambdas are usually supplied with a calibration mark and the measured capacity etched on the

---

* Cf. P. L. Kirk, "Quantitative Ultramicroanalysis," John Wiley & Sons, Inc., New York (1950) for discussion of other varieties of micropipets and of the calibration and use of micropipets.

barrel. The pipets are usually calibrated by the manufacturer by weighing delivered volumes of mercury or by introducing predetermined volumes of mercury in order to fix the position of the calibration mark. For careful work it is worthwhile to check the manufacturer's calibration by weighing the volumes of a number of samples of mercury delivered at the temperature of the solution to be measured. A source of error encountered in calibration with mercury is the difference in the shapes of mercury and water meniscuses. Since the water meniscus is convex downward and the mercury meniscus is convex upward, one can correct approximately for the volume difference by adding to the calibrated volume the difference in volume between a sphere and a cylinder both with diameter and height equal to the capillary bore (see Fig. 2-12). This method assumes that the meniscuses are hemispherical. Thus, the volume between meniscuses is taken to be equal to twice the volume bounded by a hemispherical meniscus, by the horizontal plane tangent to it, and by the capillary walls. In a 40-lambda pipet constructed of 0.5-mm tubing the correction amounts to about 0.1 per cent. This correction may be considered minor and generally unnecessary with pipets greater than 25 lambdas, except in extremely careful work. Of course, with smaller pipets this correction becomes more significant and should, at least, be considered relative to errors of performance in use of the pipet.

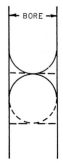

Fig. 2-12. Meniscus correction in a micropipet.

Operation of a Micropipet. Since the surface-to-volume ratio is high in a micropipet, it is important that the pipet be very clean and dry before each use. For this experiment it is sufficient to clean the pipet with concentrated nitric acid, followed by several rinses with distilled water. This is conveniently done by placing the pipet in a glass funnel (4 mm i.d. stem) mounted in the neck of an ordinary chemical filter flask attached to an aspirator or other suction apparatus. The acid is added dropwise to the upper end (thin end) of the pipet and drawn through it by suction. The water rinses follow in the same flask. The pipet can be dried by rinsing it with acetone in a separate filter flask assembly and allowing air to pass through it for a minute or two.

After the pipet is cleaned, it is attached to a 1-ml tuberculin syringe with a short length of rubber tubing or a #00 one-hole rubber stopper. The piston of the syringe should be lightly greased with petroleum jelly to ensure a tight fit in the barrel. The pipet tip is then inserted beneath the surface of the solution to be sampled, and liquid is drawn carefully to a point 1 mm or less above the calibration mark. Most precise control of the syringe is usually achieved by holding the piston handle between the index finger and the thumb, with the barrel of the syringe securely wrapped in the remaining three fingers of the same hand. Withdrawal of the piston can then be accompanied by slow rotation of the piston handle between the thumb and index finger. This permits the operator to apply considerable force to the piston in a manner which removes the piston very gradually and therefore affords better control than can be had by pulling directly on it.

After the pipet is filled to a point 1 mm or less above the calibration mark, the syringe (with pipet attached) should be transferred to the left hand (if the operator is right-handed) and its exterior wiped with a piece of cleansing tissue. (Discard the tissue in the appropriate waste container if the solution is radioactive!) The meniscus can then be adjusted to coincidence with the calibration mark by tapping the open end of the pipet with a small firm wad of cleansing tissue held in the right hand. Capillary action will draw a small amount of liquid from the pipet into the tissue with each tap. Quick gentle taps provide the best control. The liquid sample is then ready to be delivered to any desired surface or solution.

III. Preparation of Sample Plates

Counting of alpha particles is carried out whenever possible under conditions which minimize absorption of the particles by the sample itself. It is also desirable to employ a technique for mounting the emitting material which yields reproducible counting samples. These requirements are not necessarily equivalent because infinitely thick samples of equal surface area can satisfy the second and not the first condition. With carrier-free radioactive compounds, however, an infinitely thick layer will in most cases contain more active material than one cares to handle in one sample. This is particularly true of the transuranium elements. Furthermore, it is relatively easy to prepare reproducible, thin, solid counting samples from carrier-free solutions by the evaporation technique.* This simple method is much more reliable than an attempt to obtain reproducible samples of thick solid slurries and is used in preference to the latter method whenever the sample material can be adapted to the evaporation method. The evaporation method consists simply of delivering a known volume of active solution to a metal plate which is chemically inert to the solution and evaporating the solution to dryness. If nitric acid solutions are to be assayed, stainless-steel plates are suitable. With hydrochloric acid solutions, it is advisable to use glass or platinum plates because hydrochloric acid reacts with stainless steel and defeats the attempt to prepare a thin, essentially weightless sample. In any case, it is desirable to spread the sample liquid in the manner which provides the most uniform and thinnest distribution of resulting solid on the plate. This can be accomplished by use of an organic spreading agent, e.g., tetraethylene glycol (TEG), which by lowering the surface tension causes evaporation to occur from a film of solution rather than from a droplet.

---

* Cf. A. H. Jaffey, National Nuclear Energy Series, IV-14A, McGraw-Hill Book Co., Inc., New York (1951), Chapter 16, for a discussion of other sample-mounting techniques.

Spreading agents therefore promote uniform distribution of a solid on the plate surface. After evaporation, the spreading agent can be volatilized from the plate by ignition in a flame. Spreading agents have been used with particular success in plating uranium and with some success with other heavier elements. The lowered surface tension of a sample diluted with a spreading agent tends, however, to allow liquid to run off the plate edge unless the plate is heated from the rim inwards. A simpler technique, which is quite satisfactory with dilute carrier-free solutions free of large amounts of foreign nonvolatile matter, consists merely in depositing the liquid on the plate in many small droplets. The

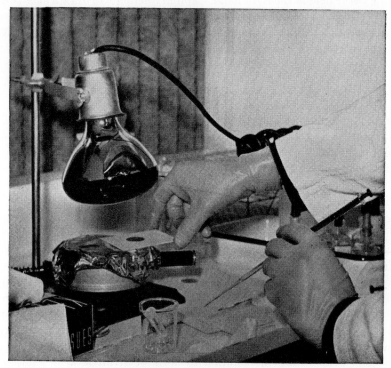

Fig. 2-13. Drying a sample plate.

sample plate is then dried slowly under an infrared heat lamp as in Fig. 2-13, and ignited in a small burner flame to remove the last traces of volatile material. Dilute plutonium solutions in nitric acid can be mounted very successfully in this way on stainless-steel plates. Ignition of the plate fixes the plutonium firmly to the steel surface, and the plate can be handled with slight risk of contaminating the counting chamber or laboratory. The surface of the prepared plate should not, of course, be touched except at the edge, and then only with forceps. As a general rule, the plate should be handled with forceps even before the sample is mounted, to avoid soiling it. Grease from the fingers would make it impossible for small droplets to retain their integrity on the plate surface. When the sample is mounted and dried, it can be carried to the counter in a Petri dish or "cardboard sandwich." The latter is constructed by stapling a cardboard (approximately 2 × 3 in.) with a hole in its center (approximately ½ in. larger than the sample plate) to a solid cardboard of the same size. A third solid piece serves as a lid for the "sandwich" with a piece of adhesive tape at one end as a hinge. The lid is also a convenient space for recording counting data for the sample.

IV. Counting Chambers for Alpha Particles

Among the many types of instruments useful for alpha-particle detection,* the gas-containing chambers have been found to be most adaptable for dependable and convenient routine use. Gas-containing chambers of practical significance are of three types; ionization chambers, proportional chambers, and Geiger-Müller (G-M) chambers. In each type, gas exposed to radiation is contained between two electrodes at high potential with respect to each other. Ions formed in the counting gas are swept apart by the electric field and collected on their respective electrodes, and the resulting charge is measured. In ionization chambers, only the ions directly formed by the alpha particles are collected. In the proportional and G-M chambers, the electric field is maintained at a level high enough to cause secondary ions to be formed by electrons accelerated to high energy in their passage to the anode. Thus, the number of ions collected in the G-M and proportional chambers can be made many times greater than the initial number formed by the incident alpha particles (10^5 to 10^6 is a common "gas" amplification factor for alpha particles in G-M chambers). Hence, these chambers are much more sensitive to alpha particles than are ionization chambers. On the other hand, since the charge collected per event in an ion chamber is proportional to the energy of the ionizing particle, ion chambers are particularly useful for absolute disintegration-rate determinations. Their design also makes them very convenient for counting gaseous samples. Ion chambers are frequently employed in such a way that the charge leakage rate is equal to the rate of arrival of ions at the collecting electrode, and the current through the chamber is the quantity measured.

G-M and proportional counters are most frequently employed as voltage-pulse measuring devices, and high voltages are used to collect the pulses as rapidly as possible. Even at rather high counting rates these instruments are able to resolve pulses from separate primary ionizing events. Coincidence losses in both types increase with increasing counting rate, but become significant at considerably lower rates in G-M counters. For example, one series of measurements† of G-M coincidence losses in alpha counting showed a 20 per cent loss

---

* Cf. A. H. Jaffey, *loc cit.*, for a survey of methods of alpha-particle detection.
† T. P. Kohman, "A General Method for Determining Coincidence Corrections of Counting Instruments," MDDC-905.

at a counting rate of 10,000 counts per minute (cpm). The per cent loss was roughly a linear function of the counting rate above 8000 cpm, increasing approximately 3 per cent per 1000 cpm increase in counting rate. Below 8000 cpm the relation is nonlinear, and it is necessary for careful work with G-M counters to establish experimentally the exact relationship between coincidence loss and counting rate. Coincidence losses with proportional counters are not ordinarily significant below 10^4 to 10^5 cpm.

Proportional counters can be operated with considerably higher counting-gas pressures than is convenient with G-M counters, and can for this reason be used with windows as thin as 0.5 mg/cm² at atmospheric pressure. This affords the proportional counter much greater sensitivity for counting external samples and is an important advantage when short-range particles must be detected with high efficiency. Externally mounted alpha emitters can be counted satisfactorily with thin-window proportional counters. G-M counters are usually filled to about 10 cm pressure and require much stronger windows. The strongest usable mica windows are seldom thinner than about 3 mg/cm² and are fragile and difficult to replace. Most G-M tubes have much thicker windows or walls and are useless for counting external alpha samples. (The range of the Pu^{239} alpha particles is about 3.7 cm in air). Greater gas densities in proportional chambers provide greater sensitivity for detecting highly penetrating radiation, as well as permitting relatively efficient counting of external alpha sources. Thus, proportional chambers are generally superior to G-M chambers because of lower coincidence losses and greater sensitivity. In addition, proportional chambers are, as the name implies, able to respond with voltage pulses proportional to the original charge formed by an incoming particle. With an appropriate electronic discriminator circuit, a proportional counting assembly can be adjusted to respond to pulses above any desired value. This proportional characteristic is useful in discriminating against beta particles from a mixed alpha-beta sample. Since the ion density in a beta-particle track is much less than that in the track of an alpha particle, the pulses of beta particles are weak and can be easily excluded.

Proportional chambers can be used to even greater advantage if they are constructed to permit replenishment of the counting gas. Flow-type counting chambers accomplish this by continuous purging of the chamber with fresh counting gas. The lifetime of a good commercial argon-filled G-M chamber (approximately 10 cm pressure) containing a small amount of "quenching gas" (methanol, for example) is only 10^8 to 10^9 total counts because of decomposition of the "quenching gas." The lifetime of a flow-type proportional chamber is indefinitely long. Since the flow chamber is open to the atmosphere via gas passages, it is possible to provide another opening for introducing counting samples directly to the interior of the chamber. This constitutes an enormous advantage for counting alpha particles and weak beta particles, because every particle leaving the sample surface (in the proper direction) will be counted. A

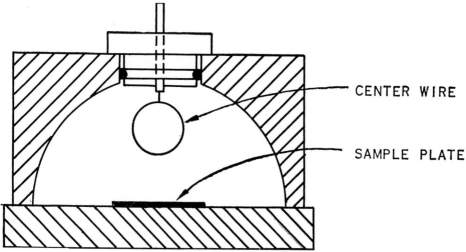

FIG. 2-14.   Cross-sectional view of a hemispherical chamber (schematic).

schematic diagram (approximately actual size) of an internal proportional chamber for use with solid samples is shown in Fig. 2-14. The center wire acts as the electron collector, while the positive ions move to the oppositely charged walls of the chamber. A popular model of a commercial proportional converter is shown in Fig. 2-15 (Nuclear Measurements Corporation Model PCC-14). This instrument is designed to adapt standard beta-gamma types of scaling circuits to proportional counting. The chamber itself is designed so that the

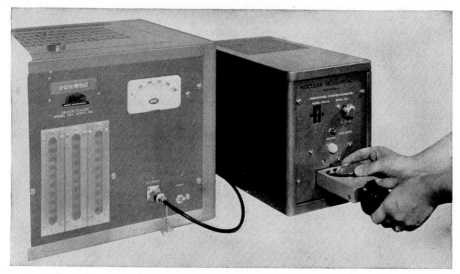

FIG. 2-15.   A proportional-counter converter.

majority of multiplicative ionizations take place within a millimeter or so of the center wire, thus making the chamber practically equally sensitive to primary events in all increments of the gas volume. Access to the chamber is provided by a removable sample-plate mount equipped with a rubber O-ring which makes an air-tight seal with the base of the upper hemisphere in the operating position. The sample-plate mount can be elevated or lowered with respect to the hemisphere by rotation of the control knob in Fig. 2-15, and will slide toward the operator in the lowered position. This brings the mount clear of the housing and permits introduction or removal of sample plates. The rate of gas flow can be determined by reference to the bubbler on the face of the chamber panel. It is adjusted by means of a valve on the tank of the counting gas or elsewhere. A convenient counting gas, consisting of 10 per cent methane and 90 per cent argon, is commercially available at the present time (Matheson Company, Type P-10 Counting Gas). Operation of the chamber can be described in four steps, as follows:

1. Center the sample plate on the mount, slide the mount to its extreme inward position, and seal the chamber by rotating the control knob in a clockwise direction until the indicator arrow is vertical.
2. Turn the counting gas on and flush the chamber for about 30 sec to 1 min at a lively flow rate.
3. Readjust the flow rate to a point where a bubble forms in the bubbler about once per second, in order to conserve gas.
4. Commence counting, with the proper voltage on the chamber as indicated by a voltmeter on the scaler panel.

The proper setting of the chamber voltage should be determined after considering the following. Since secondary ionizations occur in the counting chamber, the electric charge reaching the electrodes will be greater than the original charge created by the ionizing particle. The amount of this increase at a given voltage is proportional to the amplification factor A. A is a function of applied voltage and must be adjusted beyond the point where pulses from a given type of particle (alpha or beta, for example) will be great enough to pass the discriminator and register as counts on the scaler. All samples will emit particles of various energies into the counter-gas volume, if only because of partial loss of energy from some particles by scattering in the sample, or from the sample backing. This is true even of monoenergetic alpha-particle-emitting samples. Of course, it is obviously true for samples which emit particles in different energy groups (alphas) or with a continuous energy spectrum (betas). Thus, a plot of counts per minute (cpm) vs. voltage for a given alpha-beta sample will look something like Fig. 2-16. In order to obtain reproducible counting rates which are essentially insensitive to fluctuations in the applied voltage, it is necessary to operate the counter on one or the other of the "plateaus" of such a curve—on the alpha plateau if one wishes to discriminate against beta and

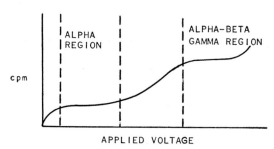

FIG. 2-16. Determining the proper chamber voltage: the curve with plateaus.

gamma rays. Incidentally, one can prevent alpha particles from counting in the presence of beta and gamma rays by employing a sample covering thicker than the range of the alpha particles.

V. Experimental Procedure

1. Obtain a supply of clean (greaseless!) stainless-steel plates ($1\frac{5}{16}$ in. diameter, 0.005 in. thick) and prepare a number of "cardboard sandwiches" for carrying active sample plates.

2. Grease the piston of a 1-ml tuberculin syringe *lightly* with petroleum jelly, taking care not to put any grease on the piston tip. Force a #00 one-hole rubber stopper over the tip of the syringe barrel to serve as a holder for the micropipet.

3. Prepare several 25-lambda counting plates in accordance with the instructions in Section II, above, *using distilled water,* until adequate proficiency is attained. Remember to distribute the liquid about the plate surface in small droplets. *Save space on the plate for a rinse solution of equal volume!* Retain the last droplet in the pipet and draw a pipet-load of $3N$ HNO_3 into the pipet as a rinse solution. The rinse solution can be placed on the free space of the plate with a reagent dropper, drawn into the pipet, and expelled in one drop on the same spot, if space permits. If not, the rinse can be drawn from a piece of waxed paper or Parafilm and delivered to the plate in small droplets.

4. Using forceps (tweezers), carefully place the sample plate on a small glass stool (e.g., a 15-mm glass rod 1 cm high) beneath an infrared heat lamp. Allow the sample to dry slowly under the lamp until no moisture is visible on the plate surface.

5. Again using forceps, hold the plate in the flame of a semimicro Bunsen burner until it emits a dull red glow. Allow the plate to cool and place it carefully in a "cardboard sandwich." The sample plate is now ready to be counted.

6. Using a dilute nitric acid solution ($3N$) of Pu^{239} containing about 4×10^5 alpha disintegrations per minute, prepare three 25-lambda plates. Clean and dry the pipet before each use. *All work with the radioactive solution must be*

performed in a hood! Rubber gloves should be worn to prevent contamination of the hands.

7. Place one of the 25-lambda plates in the proportional counting chamber and flush the chamber with counting gas in accordance with the procedure outlined in Section IV above. Determine the range of the alpha plateau of the counter by preparing a plot of cpm vs. applied voltage. Select as your counting voltage a setting approximately one-third of the distance from the left side of the plateau. Measure the background counting rate of the chamber. If it is higher than 4 or 5 cpm, ask the instructor to show you how to clean the chamber.

8. After calculating the total number of counts which must be taken to give a standard deviation of 0.5 per cent in the counting rate, count each of the 25-lambda plates.

9. If the counting rates of the 25-lambda plates agree within 1 or 2 per cent, prepare three 10-lambda plates from the same solution. Count each of these for the time necessary to give a standard deviation of 0.5 per cent. What precision can you expect among the 10-lambda plates relative to that obtainable in preparing the 25-lambda plates?

VI. PROBLEMS

1. Assuming that exactly one-half of the alpha particles emitted by the plutonium samples were detected, calculate the concentration of Pu^{239} atoms in the active solution in units of gram-atoms/liter; in units of grams/liter.

2. In a smoothly spread, homogeneous sample, the fraction of alpha particles lost by self-absorption is given approximately by

$$F = 1/2(t/R), \qquad (2\text{-}18)$$

where t/R is the ratio of sample thickness (mg/cm^2) to the range of the alpha particles (mg/cm^2). Calculate the value of F for the 25-lambda samples. Assume $R = 17$ mg/cm^2 for Pu^{239} alpha particles absorbed in plutonium metal. Assume the samples were spread over the entire area of the counting plates.

3. How thick must a Pu^{239} sample be in order to lose 1 per cent of the alpha particles by self-absorption? Suppose a sample of plutonium is spread uniformly over 1 cm^2 as part of a solid precipitate of LaF_3 weighing 1 mg. Calculate the fraction of particles lost in this solid by self-absorption. Assume the range of the alpha particles is proportional to the square root of the atomic number of the absorbing material and that the range in air is 3.7 cm. The density of air at 25°C is 1.2 mg/cm^3.

EXPERIMENT 2-4

BETA AND GAMMA MEASUREMENTS

By GEORGE W. REED, Chemistry Division, Argonne National Laboratory

I. INTRODUCTION

Beta and gamma radiations are almost universally measured by instruments which detect and record each individual event; these instruments are called counters. Charge-accumulation devices such as electroscopes have been largely displaced by counters.

Counters are principally of two types, those which respond to ionization produced in a gas, i.e., Geiger or proportional counters; and those which respond to light emitted from an atom or molecule which has been excited by incident radiation, i.e., scintillation counters. We shall not consider scintillation counting here or the counting of a radioactive gas introduced with the counting gas into a Geiger or proportional counter–gas counter.

End-window Geiger and proportional counters are the most widely used. These are usually mounted above a shelf arrangement inside a lead or iron shield (see Fig. 2-17). Samples prepared for routine analysis generally weigh

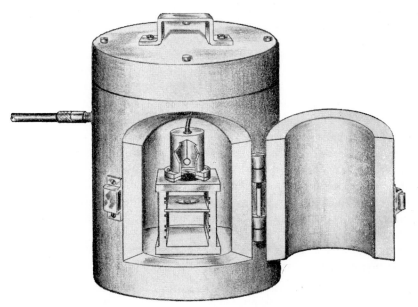

Pb OR Fe SHIELD, SHELF ARRANGEMENT AND END-WINDOW COUNTER

FIG. 2-17. Apparatus for beta and gamma counting.

from 5 to 40 mg and are mounted on Al or cardboard backs. Very good precision may be obtained when samples of the same radionuclide, having approximately the same weight and mounting, are compared in a given counting setup.

A beta assay technique that is very useful when large samples (several hundred mg) are to be measured makes use of a cylindrical counter, as shown in Fig. 2-18. Low activity or unavoidable large amounts of nonradioactive mate-

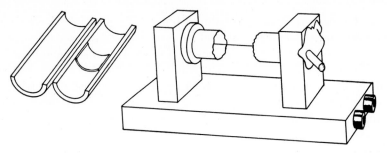

FIG. 2-18.   Thin-walled cylindrical flow counter.

rial may make large samples necessary. The samples are spread on half cylinders of plastic such as Bakelite and these are assembled—"wrapped"—around the counter.

Neither of these methods is an absolute measuring technique. The most direct absolute assay method is 4π counting.* In the counting arrangements described here, only a fraction of the radiations initially leave the sample at such an angle as to enter the counter. This, however, is not the only factor affecting the counting rate. The efficiency of the counter for detecting radiations; the scattering of radiation by the backing, sample, air, and shield; the absorption of radiation by the sample, sample cover, air, and counter window must all be considered. Throughout the following discussion it will be assumed that the corrections for counting losses and background have been made.

Gamma radiation may be measured with end-window counters; however, the detection efficiency is quite low, of the order of 1 per cent. Scintillation counters using organic or inorganic phosphors are much more efficient (10 to 100 per cent) for detecting gamma rays and they also have the advantage of giving a pulse proportional to the photon energy and hence may be used as spectrometers.

The discussion that follows will be confined to measurements made with end-window counters. However, in view of the potentialities of the cylindrical

---

* B. D. Pate and L. Yaffe, "Disintegration-Rate Determination by 4π-Counting," Can. J. Chem., **33**, 929 (1955); H. H. Seliger and L. Cavallo, "The Absolute Standardization of Radioisotopes by 4π Counting," J. of Res., NBS, **47**, 41 (1951); "Conference on Absolute Beta Counting," Div. of Math. and Phys. Sciences, Nat'l Research Council, Prel. Report No. 8, Nuclear Science Series (1950).

counter, some of its features will be briefy described. Sugihara et al., Suttle and Libby, and Libby have discussed the techniques of counting with cylindrical counters.* The above investigators have shown that nuclides decaying by a transition from a single excited state to the ground state all show exponential absorption in a close cylindrical geometry. Therefore, the disintegration rate of thick samples can be measured "to within 5 per cent" by applying only an absorption and geometry correction.

The disintegration rate per mg (r dis/min/mg) of a sample of finite thick-

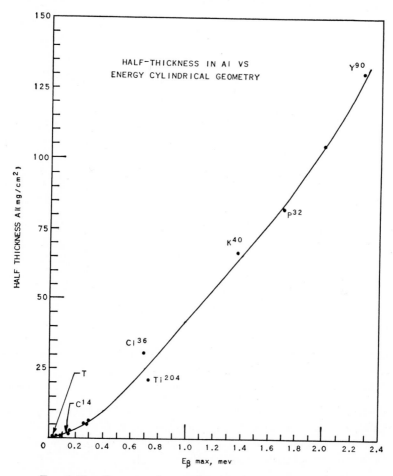

Fig. 2-19. Curve used to make the absorption correction.

* T. Sugihara, R. Wolfgang, and W. F. Libby, "Large Thin-Wall Geiger Counters," Rev. Sci. Instr., 24, 511 (1953); A. D. Suttle, Jr., and W. F. Libby, "Absolute Assay of Beta Radioactivity in Thick Solids," Anal. Chem., 27, 921 (1955); W. F. Libby, "Relation Between Energy and Half-thicknesses for Absorption of Beta Radiation," Phys. Rev., 103, 1900 (1956).

ness x, counting rate R cpm, area A cm², with a reciprocal mean absorption thickness $\lambda(\text{mg/cm}^2)^{-1}$, and counted with a cylindrical counter having a geometry G, is given by the equation

$$r = RG/A\lambda\,[1 - \exp(-x/\lambda)]. \qquad (2\text{-}19)$$

The window is considered negligibly thin. The absorption correction can be made using data given by Libby, Fig. 2-19 (this curve is very similar to that

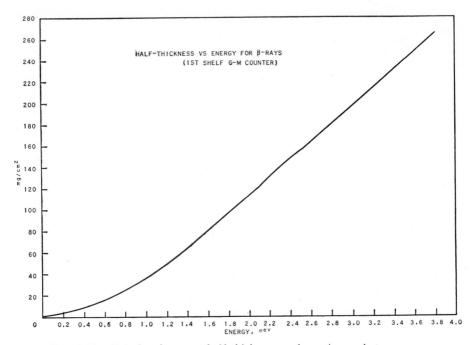

FIG. 2-20. Relation between half-thickness and maximum beta energy.

for samples counted on the first shelf of Geiger counters) or from an empirical relation (Fig. 2-20) of half-thickness, $x_{1/2}$, vs. the $E_{\beta,\max}$:

$$x_{1/2},\ (\text{mg/cm}^2) = 38\,(E_{\max})^{3/2}. \qquad (2\text{-}20)$$

The geometry is determined by measuring a standard (K^{40} betas from a KCl sample whose specific activity in dis/min/gram for K is well known).

Since counters can be made quite small, the background, which usually limits the sensitivity, can be significantly reduced.

II. EXPERIMENTAL SETUP AND EQUIPMENT

A. Counter. A typical end-window counter is bell-shaped, having a center electrode of about 0.002-in. tungsten wire and a window of mica (in Geiger counters) or thin plastic such as rubber hydrochloride, RHCl (in proportional counters). The windows are made conducting to prevent accumulation of charge. The wall of the counter acts as the cathode. Geiger counters are filled to less than atmospheric pressure with counting gas (A-CO_2 mixture, for example); whereas proportional counters are usually of the flow type and operate at atmospheric pressure. The electronic equipment used for proportional counters is more elaborate than that for a Geiger counter; a stable 1- to 5-kilovolt high-voltage supply and a preamplifier are required in addition to the usual scaler-amplifier.

B. Shield and Shelf Arrangement. The counter is placed on a Lucite or aluminum shelf inside a shield. A typical shelf setup is shown in Figs. 2-17 and 2-28. The shield may be lead or iron and serves to reduce the background due to cosmic rays or to nearby radioactive sources. The inside of the shield is lined with a low-Z material to minimize the scattering of radiation into the counter.

C. Sample Preparation. Samples for beta-activity measurements are usually prepared by filtering 5 to 40 mg of precipitate through a filter chimney onto a small disc of filter paper. The sample is well defined on an area of 1 to 2 cm². The sample and filter paper are dried and placed on a cardboard or an Al card, and covered with a thin, ~0.5- to 3-mg/cm² plastic film. The purpose of this cover is to prevent loss of the sample and contamination of the equipment.

On occasion, an isotopic tracer may be used to measure the chemical yield—the fraction of the desired isotope recovered from decontamination steps—instead of weighable amounts of carrier. For example, Np^{237} is used as tracer for Np^{239}, or vice versa. Should either the tracer or the sought-after isotope be an alpha emitter, the sample must be made as nearly weightless as possible. Some of the techniques for doing this are electrodeposition onto Pt or stainless-steel discs, evaporation of an organic or aqueous phase containing the activity, or stippling a small precipitate over a given area of a disc followed by drying and (usually) ignition.* The samples on the discs may then be beta- and alpha-counted. Proportional counters of the end-window type may be used for both measurements since the windows can be made thin enough to permit counting alpha particles.

III. Counting Corrections

For many radioactive measurements no special corrections are necessary. However, when the number of radioactive atoms in a source is to be measured, or when radioactive nuclides of differing decay energies are to be compared, corrections must be made to obtain accurate results.†

* See D. L. Hufford and B. F. Scott, "Techniques for the Preparation of Thin Films of Radioactive Material," MDDC-1515.

† "Conference on Absolute Beta Counting," cited above; "Radiochemical Studies: The Fission Products," National Nuclear Energy Series, Vol. 9, Div. IV, Part I; G. W. Reed, "Absolute Beta Assay with End-Window Geiger-Mueller Counters," ANL-5608. See also G. W. Reed and A. Turkevich Phys. Rev., 92, 1473 (1953).

Corrections in beta assay work fall into three major classifications:

1. *Scattering,* which increases the amount of radiation reaching the counter.
2. *Absorption,* which tends to decrease the amount of radiation reaching the counter.
3. The actual physical *geometry* of the counting setup; i.e., the solid angle subtended by the sensitive volume of the counter.

A. Scattering Corrections. The backing, sample, sample cover, sample holder, air, and shield are sources of scattered radiation. Scattering not only affects the counting of a sample, it also makes identification of the activity under measurement difficult. As will be seen, absorption curves serve as one of the principal means for identification of a radioactive species. Since scattered radiations are degraded in energy, the shapes of the absorption curves are affected.

Backscattering from the sample mount may lead to an increase in the counting rate of from 10 to 80 per cent, depending upon the thickness and atomic number of the backing, the distance between the sample and the counter, and to some extent on the energy of the beta rays. As the thickness of the backing increases, the amount of backscattering approaches saturation.

The part of the scattering caused by the sample cannot be readily separated from the absorption by the sample; therefore, *self-scattering* and *self-absorption* are considered together. The self-scattering effect becomes saturated at fairly low sample thicknesses, about 5 mg/cm^2 for 1-Mev betas and much less for softer radiations. As the amount of material increases, absorption will eventually predominate and cancel the self-scattering effect. The increase in the counting rate may range from 10 to 30 per cent for samples mounted 4 mm from the window of a Geiger counter. The probability of detecting self-scattered radiations decreases as the distance from the window increases.

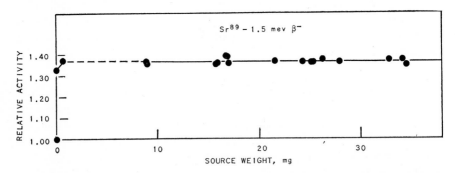

Sr^{89} SCATTERING AND SELF-ABSORPTION CURVE. SOURCE AREA ~1.5 cm^2. SOURCE BACKING—ALUMINUM. SOURCE TO WINDOW ~0.4 cm. G.M. COUNTER WITH 1.9 mg cm^{-2} WINDOW

FIG. 2-21. A curve for correction for self-scattering, self-absorption and backscattering, for Sr^{89}.

mounted as a weightless, backless source.* The counting rate corrected for absorption (absorber is added to remove RaF alphas) is compared with the disintegration rate of the sample. The latter is determined by counting the RaF alphas. Other standards of known disintegration rates may also be used.

D. Other Corrections. It is beyond the scope of this discussion to do more than alert the reader to some of the other factors that may affect beta-activity measurements. Some of these are the reproducibility of the sample position, the distribution of the active material, the nonlinearity of absorption curves.

E. Summary. For the most accurate activity measurements, ~5 per cent, the sample-counting rate is corrected for "coincidence losses" (see Dead Time and Resolving Time earlier in this Chapter) and contaminating radiations γ, β^-, etc.; scattering by the sample and backing, f_s; absorption by the air, window, and added absorber, f_a; and the geometry, G. If D is the true disintegration rate, then $D \times G = \text{cpm} \times f_s \times f_a$.

When it is only necessary to compare samples, f_s and G may be assumed constant and the absorption correction is approximately given by $f_s = e^{-\lambda x}$ where $\lambda = 0.693/x_{1/2}$ and x is mg/cm^2 of added absorber, effective sample thickness, air, and window.

When the sample disintegration rate is desired, the sample-counting rate is corrected to that of a weightless, backless source using scattering–self-absorption curves (Figs. 2-23 and 2-24). Then, only the geometry correction and a small correction for absorption by the air and window are necessary.

IV. GAMMA COUNTING

When gamma radiation is measured on an end-window counter, absorption and scattering corrections are usually negligible. The most important correction is for the detection efficiency of the counter. This varies with the energy of the photon, and the counting gas. The higher the Z and the pressure of the gas, the greater the counting efficiency. Fig. 2-25, based on unpublished work of D. Engelkemeir of Argonne National Laboratory, illustrates the dependence of counting efficiency on photon energy for a counter filled with 9 cm of argon.

V. SAMPLE PURITY AND IDENTIFICATION

A. Beta Emitters. The identification and purity of the radionuclide must be established. This is done by following the decay to determine the half-life, by taking an absorption curve to determine the energy of the radiations, and by repeated specific activity measurements (cpm/mg) on a sample by subjecting it to further decontamination steps.

---

* T. B. Novey, "RaDEF Standard Sources for Beta Disintegration Rate Determinations," Rev. Sci. Instru., **21**, 280 (1950); G. W. Reed, *op. cit.;* Reed and Turkevich, *loc. cit.*

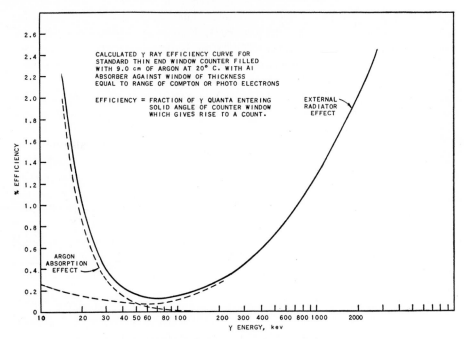

FIG. 2-25.   Counting efficiency vs. energy of the gamma rays.

The energy may be determined by measuring the absorption half-thickness (see page 58 and Figs. 2-19 and 2-20), the end point, or by a "Feather analysis." The end point is difficult to measure and is seldom used.* A better measure of the energy of beta particles, using an absorption curve, is made with a "Feather analysis." † The method consists of comparing a very accurate absorption curve of an activity having a well-known energy with that of the unknown. A "Feather analyzer" is constructed from the known absorption curve by marking off on a cardboard strip the fraction of the activity corresponding to a certain fraction of the range in mg/cm² of absorber. The "analyzer" is placed opposite the unknown absorption curve (taken under identical conditions and corrected for background and tail). It is assumed that equal fractions of activity are absorbed for equal fractions of range. A graphical determination of the apparent range vs. the fraction of range is made and the range determined by extrapolation.

To obtain the most accurate information for sample identification it is often necessary to correct for a longer-lived isotope or for contaminating radiations. Correction for the former is made by using the decay curve. The correction for

* L. E. Glendenin, "Determination of the Energy of Beta Particles and Photons by Absorption," Nucleonics **2**, 12 (1948).

† *Ibid.*; and G. Friedlander and J. W. Kennedy, "Introduction to Radiochemistry" John Wiley & Sons, Inc., New York (1955), pp. 200-201.

the long-lived component is made by subtracting, i.e., "peeling off," its contribution. Contaminating gamma radiation may usually be corrected for by
"peeling off" the tail of an absorption curve.

B. Gamma Emitters. The energy and purity of gamma radiation may be

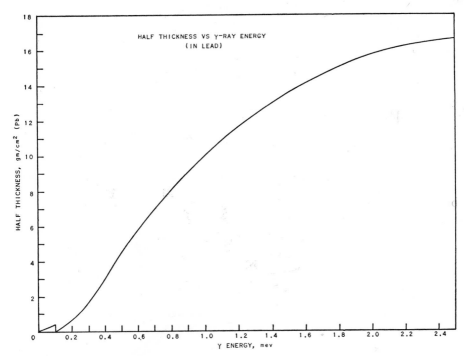

FIG. 2-26. Half-thickness of lead for gamma rays of various energies.

determined by an absorption curve using high-Z absorbers such as Pb. Absorption is exponential and the energy can be determined from the half-thickness.
Fig. 2-26 can be used for this purpose. (The data for this figure was compiled
by A. H. Jaffey, Argonne National Laboratory.)

VI. Experiments: Procedures

The experiments are designed to illustrate some of the techniques involved
in beta and gamma assay and also to indicate the considerations necessary for
making accurate determinations.

A. Counting Standard and Geometry Determination. Since most reliable
radioactive measurements span a period of time, a means for monitoring the
counter behavior is required. A counting standard having a long half-life compared with the time of measurement is used for this purpose. Daily fluctuations
in the response of the counting system may be checked and counters inter-

calibrated if a counting standard is available. A counter background is also taken daily, since all counts must be corrected for this quantity.

Procedure. Obtain a solution of Na^{22}. The solution should contain approximately 10^5 dis/min/100 λ (0.1 ml). CAUTION: *The extreme care that must be exercised in handling radioactive substances cannot be overemphasized.*

1. Pipet *exactly* 100 λ solution onto an aluminum card, on rubber hydrochloride (RHCl) stretched over an Al ring and into four 40-ml conical centrifuge tubes. Smear a thin ring of Lubriseal grease on the card just outside the sample area (~1.5 cm²) before pipetting. To define the sample area on the RHCl film, wet an area of 1.5 cm² with insulin solution, using a small paint brush or pipestem cleaner.

Evaporate the solution on the card under a heat lamp, and that on the RHCl in a vacuum desiccator. Cover the sample area of the card with RHCl

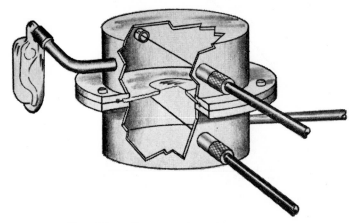

Fig. 2-27. Cutaway view of a 4π counter

film (~0.5 mg/cm²) and count on the top shelf (see Paragraph 1 of Section C below). Now cover this area with an Al foil (~10 mg/cm²) and seal the foil to the card with Duco cement. Count again and retain this source as a counting standard.

2. *Demonstration.* Mount the RHCl source on the ring used in the 4π counter (see Fig. 2-27 for the details of a 4π counter). Paint the surfaces of contact with Aquadag or silver paint. Place in the 4π counter and count to at least 1 per cent standard error. This is the true disintegration rate of the sample.

3. Mount the RHCl ring on an Al card with an annular ring milled out; see Fig. 2-28.

    a. Count on each shelf of the proportional counter.

    b. Take an absorption curve (see Section B below) on shelves 1 and 3.

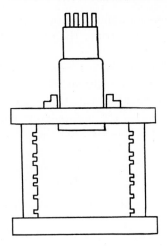

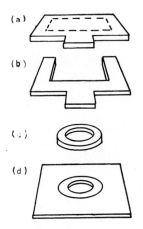

(a)

(b)

(c)

(d)

STANDARD COUNTING SET-UP

(a) ABSORBER, (b) SPACER TO RAISE ABSORBER TO COUNTER FLANGE
(c) SOURCE MOUNTING RING WITH RUBBER HYDROCHLORIDE FILM
ATTACHED. (d) SOURCE IN PLACE ON SHELF

Fig. 2-28.   Details of standard counting setups.

c. Correct the counting rate to zero total absorber (no air, window; air
(mg/cm^2) = 1.3 × distance (cm) from sample to counter, window ≈0.5
mg/cm^2).

d. Calculate the geometry, $G = A°/D$, where $A°$ is the activity of the
sample corrected for absorption and D is the 4π disintegration rate of
the sample.

B. Absorption Curves. The shape of an absorption curve depends on many things, such as the beta energy and spectrum, the distance from the counter, sample backing, and sample thickness.

1. Place the RHCl source on shelf 1. Use a spacer to raise absorbers to the counter window (see Fig. 2-28) and count. Repeat with heavier absorbers until there is little or no change in the counting rate. Since the initial part of an absorption curve should be well defined for extrapolation purposes, the points should be closely spaced. Increase the spacing after the counting rate has been lowered by one-half.

2. Plot the cpm as ordinate vs. absorber thickness as abscissa on semilog graph paper.

   a. Compare (on the same paper) absorption curves taken with the RHCl source on shelves 1 and 3.

   b. Compare the weightless sample absorption with that of the standard (sample on Al card).

   c. "Peel off" the tail by drawing a straight line back to zero absorber and then plotting the differences between the total and the tail counting rate.

   d. Extrapolate the initial part of this curve to zero total absorber (no air or window). This gives the absorption correction, f_a.

C. Scattering and Self-Absorption: Chemical Procedure. Add 2, 5, 10, 20 mg of Na from a standardized carrier solution to the centrifuge cones.

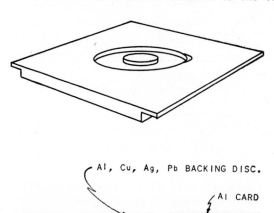

FIG. 2-29.   Details of a backing disc mount.

Evaporate the solutions to dryness. Suspend in 10 ml propyl alcohol, then add 2 ml propyl alcohol saturated with HCl, filter, wash with alcohol, dry 10 min at 110°C, weigh and mount.

1. Compare the first-shelf counting rate of these samples corrected to 100

per cent chemical yield, and also the counting rate of the standard on the Al card with that of the weightless sample on RHCl. The fractional change in the counting rate is the scattering-self absorption factor, f_s.

2. Repeat on shelf 3. Plot on the same paper.

3. Place the RHCl sample over Al, Cu, Ag, and Pb backings and count. These backings are aluminum cards with $\frac{1}{16}$-in.-high disc of the backing material cemented on (see Fig. 2-29). The ring to which the RHCl is attached is slipped over the disc. Plot counting rate vs. Z of backing, using the counting rate on RHCl as a reference.

D. Gamma Energy Measurements. Obtain a Na^{22} source from the instructor ($\sim 10^6$ β c/m). Place an Al card on shelf 1 and the sample on shelf 2. Measure the activity as Pb absorbers are added on top of the sample. Make a semilog plot of the data and determine the energy of the gamma rays, using Fig. 2-26.

Chapter 3

MODERATOR ASSEMBLIES

INTRODUCTION

A moderator assembly consists of a rather large volume—say, 5 to 15 ft on a side—of moderator material such as graphite (carbon) or water (light or heavy) inside which there is a neutron source; together with neutron detectors and counting equipment. When used to establish known neutron fluxes, and for the standardization of foils for absolute neutron density measurement, it is called a *standard pile*. When used for cross section measurements it is called a *sigma pile*. It can also be used to measure the diffusion and slowing down lengths of neutrons.

EXPERIMENT 3-1

ABSOLUTE NEUTRON FLUX MEASUREMENT

By W. H. McCORKLE, Director, Reactor Operations Division, ANL

DISCUSSION

Neutron Flux. The term neutron flux, expressed as $\phi = nv$, is taken to mean the product of the number of neutrons per unit volume n, and their speed v. This would imply that all the neutrons under consideration have the same speed. Of course, this is not true in general. However, it is proper to speak of a flux of 1 Mev neutrons, etc., where the energy range is very small. Generally, though, neutron fluxes are referred to as the thermal neutron flux (0.025 ev), the resonance neutron flux (roughly 1 to 1000 ev), and the fast neutron flux (above 0.1 Mev). It is also quite common to speak of the slow neutron flux and the fast neutron flux as related to the neutron speeds or energies below and above those at which the absorption by cadmium undergoes a very great change of magnitude (about 0.4 ev). Hence, the neutron flux would represent the sum of the products of the neutrons per unit volume and their respective speeds over whatever range of energy is being considered.

To measure neutron fluxes, one may make use of a number of properties of materials which are influenced by the actions of neutrons. In general, when neutrons are captured, the capturing atoms become radioactive, with characteristic half-lives for the decay of their radioactivities. The molecular arrangements in crystals and other forms of matter are also influenced by the recoils of particles and by other effects which may occur as the result of neutron bombardment. Thus, changes in electrical conductivity, in density, etc., may be observed for materials which have been irradiated with neutrons. The ionization of gases, by the alpha particles from boron or by energetic particles produced by fission of uranium, has been widely used to detect neutrons and to give relative indications of neutron flux. Analytical determinations of fission product yields from small measured amounts of uranium-bearing materials, and of the yield of helium from boron, as a result of its bombardment by neutrons, provide additional methods of indicating neutron fluxes.

Standard Neutron Source. By establishing an absolute procedure for measuring neutron flux, it becomes possible to calibrate or standardize the methods of determining neutron fluxes. Just as in the measurement of other quantities, it is essential that standards should be established. Thus, a standard source of neutrons should be provided and an arrangement developed to supply standard neutron fluxes. The standard neutron source should be one which remains essentially constant over long periods of time and for which the small corrections with time are well known. Then, carefully prepared and preserved arrangements for using a standard neutron source to provide standard neutron fluxes should be established.

Determinations of the emission rates of neutrons from a number of neutron sources have been made by various groups of scientists and standard neutron sources have been established for several nations. Intercalibration or comparison of some of these sources has been accomplished* to effect a degree of international uniformity in establishing neutron-flux values.

The Argonne National Laboratory, formerly known as the Metallurgical Laboratory, was among the very earliest to secure standard neutron sources for which the emission rate of neutrons was determined by the production of helium from the (n, α) reaction of neutrons captured by boron in a water bath surrounding the source.† A method of intercalibrating neutron sources by use of a subcritical multiplying lattice pile has also been developed ‡ so that other standard neutron sources may be calibrated by less tedious procedures.

Standard Neutron Flux. A Standard Pile. With standard neutron sources established, it next becomes essential to develop some arrangement for employing a standard source to provide standard or known values of neutron fluxes. A device known as a standard pile was developed early in the study of

* D. J. Hughes, Nucleonics, **12**, No. 12, 26 (1954).
† S. P. Harris, and F. G. P. Seidl, CP-2661 (Jan. 1945).
‡ A. Wattenberg and C. Eggler, AECD-3002 (1950).

nuclear or atomic energy. The first standard pile assembled at the Palos Park, Argonne Laboratory site, to which the original nuclear reactor CP-1 was moved in February 1943 and rebuilt as CP-2, was in the form of a parallelopiped of graphite 5ft × 5ft × 9ft, with recesses for holding one or more standard neutron sources at known positions relative to its 9-ft vertical axis and other recesses into which thin metal foils could be accurately positioned to be activated by known fluxes of neutrons from a standard source. Calibration* of this standard pile provided a means of determining absolute values of neutron fluxes in other locations such as the various regions of the CP-2 and other reactors. The standard pile now used at the Argonne National Laboratory is 7ft × 7ft × 10ft. It was built to take the place of the smaller one and has been calibrated † and compared with the former standard pile. After several years of use at the Palos Park location, this standard pile was moved to its present location in the Physics Building at the DuPage site of the Laboratory.

Standard Foils. When metal foils are prepared from materials which are uniformly pure and of very uniform thickness, they may be cut accurately by a punch and die so that each foil is very closely identical with every other foil. A small correction may be made to the observed activity of each foil by weighing individual foils and calculating the number of active atoms each would have possessed at saturation, if it had contained a standard mass when it was placed in a neutron flux. Foils prepared in this manner may be called standard foils. By using standard foils, it is only necessary to select a few of them from a rather large supply and to calibrate or standardize the foils by subjecting them to known neutron fluxes in the standard pile. This procedure would then establish the radioactivity which a standard foil would have at saturation in a known flux supplied by the standard pile.

Foil Counting. The process of determining the radioactivity of the standard foils is referred to as foil counting. The technique of foil counting may be used to measure either relative or absolute values of neutron fluxes. For measurement of the absolute values of neutron fluxes, the individual standard foils, exposed in known neutron fluxes as provided by the standard pile, are placed in a shielded container (called a "counter shield" or "pig") where they occupy a definite and accurately reproducible position or geometry relative to a Geiger counter tube, a scintillation counter, or some other suitable counter. The counts obtained per unit time, corrected to that for a standard foil of unit mass at saturation activity in the standard pile location, serve to standardize the counting equipment for a specified operating condition of the voltage applied to the counter tube and the particular geometry of the standard dimension foils and counter tube. To provide day-to-day or hour-to-hour checks on the condition of the counting equipment, other extremely long-lived radioactivities are employed, such as those of radium or normal uranium. For

---

* L. Seren, CP-704 (June 1943).
† C. Redman, CP-3432 (Feb. 1946).

this purpose, a small foil or plate of the radioactive material is imbedded in a fixed position in a holder arranged to position it accurately in a reproducible geometry relative to the counter tube. This test standard is applied to the counter immediately before and after the standardization of the counter by the calibrating standard foil. The counting rate for standard operating conditions of the counter is recorded and referred to at subsequent checks of the counter by the test standard. As long as the counting rate for the test standard agrees with the recorded value, no further standardization of the counter is required. When a counting tube ceases to be reliable, it is replaced by another and the entire standardization procedure is repeated for the new counting setup.

Wide Range of Fluxes. The fluxes which are obtainable in a standard pile are necessarily many decades lower than those encountered in operating high-power nuclear reactors. Thus, techniques have been developed* for accurately extending the range of the foil counters to cover activations in low and in very high neutron fluxes. To accomplish this extension to high flux measurements, an arrangement is provided to supply two or more accurately reproducible geometries for the foils relative to the counter tube, along with calibrated absorbers accurately positioned between the foils and the counter tube to give adequate increases in the range of foil activations which may be counted.

Choice of Foils. Since the conditions will vary widely under which measurements of neutron fluxes may be required, it is likely that sometimes materials with relatively short-lived neutron-induced radioactivities will be desirable for use as counting foils, while at other times long-lived activations may be more suitable. Also, on some occasions it may be desirable to have a foil material which has a relatively large activation cross section or perhaps has pronounced resonances for neutrons above the thermal energy range, which is usually considered to be approximately 0.025 ev. On other occasions, materials with relatively small activation cross sections may be preferable. Hence, for some fast-neutron measurements, foils or, more properly, films or layers of phosphorus or neptunium or other materials may be deposited on a supporting base such as styrene or Lucite, to provide a means of measuring fast-neutron fluxes.

Alternative Methods. For a number of materials, significant reactions may occur with neutrons of energies extending above thermal to beyond the 1-Mev range. Hence, it is possible to use films or foils of these materials for measuring fast-neutron fluxes. In some cases, chemical separations followed by radioactivity counting or other chemical analyses may be used to determine the magnitude of the neutron flux producing the observed reaction. Certain other materials which may have too short-lived neutron-induced radioactivities to be successfully counted, or for which the activation cross section is less useful than some other property for measuring neutron flux, may, as previously mentioned, still be employed for that purpose. Crystalline carbon in the form of small graphite rods or small diamond chips has been used for this purpose by

* By A. Wattenburg and D. Sachs.

measuring changes in the electrical resistivity or the density of the calibrated measuring element.* The counting of fission-product activities in such materials as normal uranium foils or in aliquots of solutions formed by dissolving small portions of specially prepared nuclear fuel materials has also been employed† as a means of making neutron flux measurements. The methods mentioned, as well as others, may be specialized for certain applications, and in general will yield only relative values of neutron fluxes unless they have been calibrated by absolute measurements such as those associated with standard neutron sources and standard piles.

In this study we shall limit our attention to one set of absolute flux measurements.

Procedure for Making an Absolute Determination of a High Neutron Flux by Foil Activation

In preparation for making a measurement of a high neutron flux by foil activations, a 1-cm-square standard gold foil was weighed and at a recorded time placed in a known flux region of the Argonne standard pile. During the

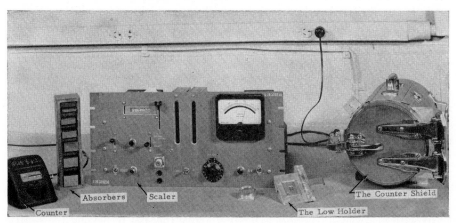

Fig. 3-1. Equipment for standard foil counting, showing the "low holder," the various absorbers, and the counter shield.

period of several weeks required to effectually saturate the 93.6-hr mean life of the neutron-induced radioactivity in gold, the counting equipment shown in Figs. 3-1 and 3-2 was selected and tested.

A counting-rate-vs.-voltage plateau, and a dead-time determination‡ were made for the counting tube, see Figs. 2-5 and 3-3 and Table 3-1. The counting

---

* W. L. Primak, L. H. Fuchs, and P. P. Day, Phys. Rev., **92**, 1064 (1953).

† J. H. Kittel, Nucleonics, **13**, No. 3, 70 (1955).

‡ D. H. Wilkinson, "Ionization Chambers and Counters," Cambridge University Press, London (1950), Chapter 8.

FIG. 3-2. Closeup view of the foil-counting tube and shield, with the "high holder" in position.

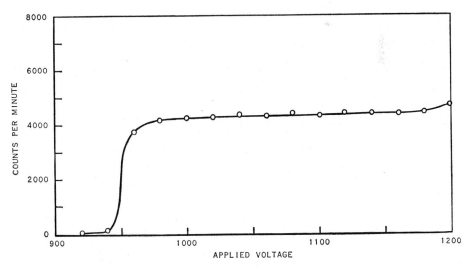

FIG. 3-3. Voltage calibration of a G-M counter tube.

rate produced by the long-lived test standard was observed and recorded. Background readings were taken without and with the foil holders and absorbers positioned below the counting tube in the lead shield to be sure that the holders and absorbers were not contaminated. Any detected contamination was carefully cleaned away with acetone and toilet tissues or a soft cloth.

TABLE 3-1. DEAD-TIME DETERMINATION (YELLOW COUNTER[a])

| | SOURCE IN COUNTER | | | | |
	A	(A + B)	B	Background	Dead Time (min)
Counting time (min)	3	3	3	5	$\left[\dfrac{A + B - (A + B)}{2\,AB}\right]$
Counts	36737	85656	51864	215	
Counts/min	12246	28552	17288	43	
Corrected counts/min	12203	28509	17245		2.23×10^{-6}
Counting time (min)	5	5	5	5	
Counts	82928	162742	86316	215	
Counts/min	16586	32548	17263	43	
Corrected counts/min	16543	32505	17220		2.28×10^{-6}
Counting time (min)	5	5	5	5	
Counts	45139	138626	97571	195	
Counts/min	9028	27725	19514	39	
Corrected counts/min	8989	27686	19475		2.22×10^{-6}
Average dead time					2.24×10^{-6} min

[a] The color is merely a local identification scheme and has no physical significance.

After the several weeks of irradiation in the standard pile, the standard foil was removed at a recorded time and brought to the counting laboratory to use in standardizing the counting equipment. The test standard was again used with the counter to verify its proper performance. Then, at a recorded time, the standard foil was placed in the "High" holder and positioned under the counting tube in the lead shield. A series of observations of counting rates were made for the standard foil, as shown by Tables 3-2 and 3-3.

After standardizing the counter, the High and Low holders, the aluminum absorbers used with the Low holder and the remaining absorbers were interrelated by using a series of other standard foils which had been activated to varying degrees by exposures in high neutron fluxes. For this procedure, the counting rates with a highly active foil were obtained for the thickest absorber, the next thickest, and the third thickest absorber. Special care was taken to remove the foil and the covering absorber from beneath the counting tube between absorber changes, and also to avoid using an absorber so thin that

TABLE 3-2. STANDARD FOIL ACTIVATION IN STANDARD PILE

Standard foil (1 cm^2 × ~0.001-in. thick and weight = wt = 0.0495 gram)

nv = 6611: Time in: 0855, 3-8-55
              Time out: 1400, 4-18-55
              Total irradiation time: 41.212 days = T

Half-life of gold activity = 2.7 days (λ = 0.693/2.7 days^{-1})

Per cent of saturation = $100(1 - e^{-\lambda T})$ = 99.9975 per cent

Expected counting rate of foil (100 per cent geometry and 100 per cent counter efficiency) at removal from standard pile = $(CPM)_{std}$

$(CPM)_{std}$ = $(nv)60\sigma_{act}$ (wt/at wt)(6.02×10^{23}) (rel. sat.)

$(CPM)_{std}$ = (6611) (60) (95×10^{-24}) $(0.0495/197.2)$ (6.02×10^{23}) (99.997)

$(CPM)_{std}$ = 5693

the counter came anywhere near jamming. In a stepwise fashion, less and less active standard foils were used to obtain overlapping counting-rate data on all absorbers from the thickest to the uncovered foil in the High holder. In this way, as shown by Tables 3-4 and 3-5, the counting rate with the thickest absorber for a foil exposed in a very high flux may be related to the counting rate which would be found if the counting equipment could accommodate the uncovered foil in the High holder without jamming the counter. Then, by means of the standardization from the foil irradiated in the standard pile, it becomes possible to calculate the absolute value of the very high flux.

In a similar manner, other sets of counting equipment may be standardized and their absorbers intercalibrated. It is also possible to intercalibrate one set of counting equipment with another set which has been standardized. This was done for a second counting set, with the results given in Table 3-5.

After the counters were standardized and the absorbers intercalibrated, a weighed standard foil was exposed in a high-flux region of a CP-5 vertical thimble for known insertion and removal times. The foil was then stored in a shielded container for about two days. Just prior to using the foil in the counter, it was swished through a dish of acetone to remove radioactive dirt which might have contaminated the foil. It was then placed in the Low holder and the 2.5-cm Pb absorber placed over it. The shielded foil was then moved into position under the counting tube and the data, shown by Table 3-6, taken to calculate the magnitude of the neutron flux in the CP-5 thimble.

TABLE 3-3. STANDARDIZATION OF FOIL COUNTERS USING HIGH HIGH HOLDER WITH NO ABSORBER

λ for gold activity $= 0.693/2.7$ per day $= 0.693/3888$ per min $= 0.0001782$ per min

Dead times: Yellow counter $= 2.24(10)^{-6}$ min/count

Dead-time correction $=$ Dead time $\times$ (CPM)^2

YELLOW COUNTER

Counting Time				Counts (obs.)	(CPM) (obs.)	Corrections		CPM	CPM at $t = 0$	$\dfrac{(\text{CPM})_{\text{std}}}{\text{CPM}}$	Average Calibration Factor
In (min)	Out	t	$e^{-\lambda t}$			Dead Time	Background CPM				
192.0	194.0	193.0	0.9662	1304	652	1	20	633	655.1	8.69	
140.0	142.0	141.0	0.9752	1331	666	1	29	638	654.2	8.70	
117.0	119.0	118.0	0.9792	1296	648	1	20	629	642.4	8.86	
1370.0	1372.0	1371.0	0.7833	1034	517	1	16	502	640.8	8.88	
1384.0	1386.0	1385.0	0.7813	1046	523	1	16	508	650.2	8.76	
1409.0	1411.0	1410.0	0.7778	1080	540	1	18	523	672.4	8.47	8.73

TABLE 3-4. ILLUSTRATIVE DATA AND CALCULATIONS FOR CALIBRATION OF COUNTERS

(NOTE: $t = t_1 + 1390$, where 1390 is the number of minutes after removal from the pile to the start of counting. Dead-time correction $= A^2$ (dead time); A^2 $(2.24 \times 10^{-6}) = $ D.T.C. for yellow counter.)

Absorber (Holder)	t_1 min	t_1 Av.	t min	Counts	A Counts/min (CPM)	B Back-ground (CPM)	C D.T.C. (CPM)	$A+C-B$ (CPM)	D $e^{-\lambda t}$	E $(A+C-B)/D$ $(t=0)$ (CPM)	Foil No.	M Foil Mass (g)	E/M (CPM)/g
None (Low)	90.00 92.00	91.00	1481	0 19600	9800	26	215	9989	.7680	13007	137	.0491	264908
None (Low)	93.00 95.00	94.00	1484	19866	9933	26	221	10128	.7676	13194	137	.0491	268717
None (High)	96.00 98.00	97.00	1487	57188	28594	20	1831	30405	.7672	39631	137	.0491	807149
None (High)	99.00 101.00	100.00	1490	57056	28528	20	1823	30331	.7668	39555	137	.0491	805601
None (High)	104.00 106.00	105.00	1495	32496	16248	20	591	16819	.7660	21957	156	.0491	447189
None (High)	107.00 109.00	108.00	1498	32453	16227	20	590	16797	.7657	21937	156	.0491	446782
None (Low)	110.00 112.00	111.00	1501	10558	5279	19	62	5322	.7653	6954	156	.0491	141629
None (Low)	113.00 115.00	114.00	1504	10463	5232	19	61	5274	.7649	6895	156	.0491	140428

TABLE 3-5. INTERSTANDARDIZATION OF COUNTERS

YELLOW COUNTER

Absorber (Holder)	Absorbers and Holders Compared	Ratio Average (CPM)/g	Calibration Factor
None High (H)	$\frac{\text{H(CPM)}_{\text{std}}}{\text{H(CPM)}}$ (Table 3-3)	—	8.73
None Low (L)	H/L	3.09	26.97
0.010 in. Al (L)	L/0.010	2.98	80.40
0.020 in. Al (L)	0.010"/0.020"	4.48	360.1
0.030 in. Al (L)	0.020"/0.030"	3.65	1.31×10^3
0.040 in. Al (L)	0.030"/0.040"	3.38	4.44×10^3
0.5 cm Pb (L)	0.040"/0.5 cm	3.00	13.33×10^3
1.0 cm Pb (L)	0.5/1.0	3.36	44.77×10^3
1.5 cm Pb (L)	1.0/1.5	2.83	12.68×10^4
2.0 cm Pb (L)	1.5/2.0	2.46	31.17×10^4
2.2 cm Pb (L)	2.0/2.2	1.30	40.53×10^4
2.5 cm Pb (L)	2.2/2.5	1.43	57.95×10^4

RED COUNTER

Absorber (Holder)	Absorbers and Holders Compared	Ratio Average (CPM)/g	Calibration Factor
None High (H)			11.01
None Low (L)	H/L	2.95	32.48
0.010" Al (L)	L/0.010"	3.83	124.4
0.020" Al (L)	0.010"/0.020"	3.83	476.4
0.030" Al (L)	0.020"/0.030"	4.57	2.18×10^3
0.040" Al (L)	0.030"/0.040"	2.47	5.38×10^3
0.5 cm Pb (L)	0.040"/0.5 cm	2.79	15.00×10^3
1.0 cm Pb (L)	0.5/1.0	3.32	49.81×10^3
1.5 cm Pb (L)	1.0/1.5	2.76	13.75×10^4
2.0 cm Pb (L)	1.5/2.0	2.29	31.48×10^4
2.2 cm Pb (L)	2.0/2.2	1.27	39.98×10^4
2.5 cm Pb (L)	2.2/2.5	1.44	57.58×10^4

TABLE 3-6. FLUX DETERMINATION

Gold foil No. 35, in Al

Mass of foil = 0.0479 gram
Position of foil: 48 in. from bottom of vertical thimble No. 24 in CP-5 reactor
t_1 = time of irradiation = 20 min
t_2 = time elapsed from removal to counting = 4758 min
Absorber: 2.5 cm Pb
Calibration factor = 57.95 × 10⁴

$$\phi = \frac{(A + C - B)}{\text{wt } (e^{-\lambda t_2})(1 - e^{-\lambda t_1})} \cdot \frac{(\text{At. wt.}) (\text{Absorber factor})}{N \sigma (60)} \text{ neutrons/(cm}^2)(\text{sec})$$

$(A + C - B)$ = observed counting rate + dead time correction − background
wt = mass of foil in grams
(At. wt.) = atomic wt. of gold
N = Avogadro's number = 6.02 × 10²³
σ = activation cross section of gold = 96 × 10⁻²⁴ cm²
λ for gold = 0.0001782/min
A = 18664 counts/min
B = 36 counts/min
$C = A^2(2.24 \times 10^{-6}) = (18664)^2 \times (2.24)^2 \times 10^{-6} = 780$ counts/min
$A + C - B = 19408$ counts/min
$1 - e^{-\lambda t_1} = 0.003558$
$e^{-\lambda t_2} = 0.42823$

$$\phi = \frac{19408}{0.0479 \times 0.42823 \times 0.003558} \cdot \frac{197.2 \times 57.95 \times 10^4}{6.023 \times 10^{23} \times 96 \times 10^{-24} \times 60}$$

$$= 8.7 \times 10^{12} \text{ neutrons/(cm}^2)(\text{sec})$$

EXPERIMENT 3-2

THERMAL DIFFUSION LENGTHS

By J. B. Hoag, ANL, International School of Nuclear Science and Engineering

INTRODUCTION

The purpose of this experiment is to measure the diffusion length of thermal neutrons in a medium.

The thermal diffusion length L is the square root of one-sixth of the "crow-flight" or mean-square distance $\overline{r^2}$ from the place where a neutron first becomes thermal to the place where it is absorbed, as in Fig. 3-4.

APPARATUS

The **source of neutrons** may be provided for in a number of ways. For example, they may come from an operating reactor, or from a material bombarded by particles from a Van de Graaff or other accelerating machine. Electrons of

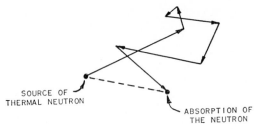

Fɪɢ. 3-4. The actual path of one thermal neutron. The diffusion length, $L = \sqrt{\bar{r^2}}/\sqrt{6}$, is $1/\sqrt{6}$ of an "average" of the crow-flight distances of many neutrons.

2-Mev energy, striking gold, produce gamma rays which may be used to irradiate beryllium, with resultant emission of neutrons. Fifty microamperes of 2-Mev deuterons on beryllium will give approximately 5×10^{10} neutrons/sec.

A satisfactory source of neutrons is one made of antimony and beryllium, as shown in Fig. 3-5. Antimony-123 (Sb^{123}) is bombarded with neutrons to become Sb^{124}. The gamma rays emitted by this radioisotope are used to bombard beryllium. The result of this reaction, Be^9 (γ,n) Be^8, is the emission of neutrons of 30- to 40-kev energy. With 50 c of Sb^{124}, a source of approximately 10^8 neutrons/sec is available. The yield is approximately 2×10^5 neutrons/sec from

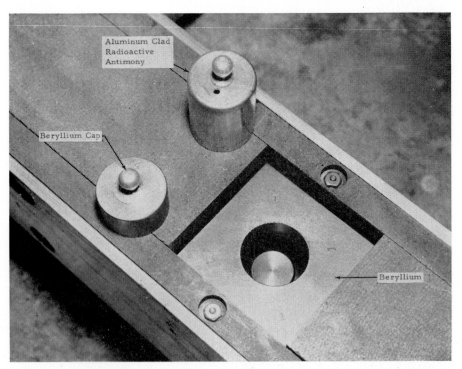

Fɪɢ. 3-5. Source and stringer. Antimony is shown removed from beryllium block.

a standard source, i.e., 1 c at a distance of 1 cm from a target of 1 gram. The half-life of Sb^{124} is 60 days, so that it must be reactivated every four months or so. As a rule of thumb, one may expect 1 per cent decay each day.

Other neutron sources may be used, such as a radium-alpha–beryllium (½ gram emitting 5×10^6 neutrons/sec) with a maximum neutron energy of 13 Mev, a minimum of 1 or less Mev, and a most probable value of 5 Mev; polonium-beryllium (5 c giving 10^7 neutrons/sec); or plutonium-beryllium, a 10-gram source (about 0.7-c emitting 9×10^5 neutrons/sec). These are relatively stable but are more costly. Also they emit neutrons of considerably higher energy, which is a disadvantage in this experiment.

The neutrons from the source are slowed down to thermal energy (0.025 ev) and diffused over a large plane before entering the base of the moderator. For

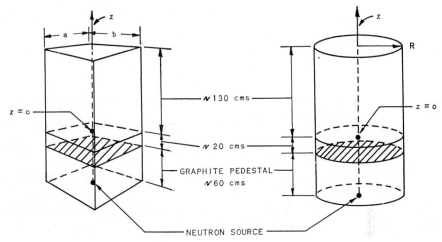

Fig. 3-6. A solid block of graphite moderator or a tank of D_2O is used in this experiment.

these purposes, the source is placed at the bottom center of a **pedestal** of graphite, two feet tall, upon which the moderating material rests as in Fig. 3-6 (see also Figs. 4-1, 4-13 and 4-14).

Since the neutron intensity is low, heavy shielding is not needed around the moderator under study; sheets of cadmium 20 mils thick, mechanically protected between aluminum sheets, suffice to capture the neutrons which leak out of the sides and top. They also prevent the perturbing flux due to re-entry of neutrons backscattered from apparatus, walls, etc., external to the assembly. Since the neutron intensity is low, complex safety controls are not needed.

However, **shielding** is required around the pedestal to protect from the gamma rays emitted by the source. Six inches of lead and a layer or two of ordinary concrete blocks are sufficient for a 50-c antimony-beryllium source.

The container for shipping the active source and the details of installation in the assembly are given in Chapter 4. Installation should be done by the instructor. The student should have on his person during this experiment the prescribed radiation detectors such as a dosimeter and/or a film badge.

In order to measure the neutron flux, a small boron detector can be located at various places in a central vertical hole in the moderator. More accurate but more time-consuming flux measurements can be made by inserting indium foils mounted on an aluminum strip, as in Experiment 4-1, in a central vertical hole or slot. The saturated activities (see Chapter 1) are proportional to the fluxes.

THEORY

The flux ϕ in the z direction, of the thermal neutrons diffusing from a plane source into an infinitely long rectangular parallelopiped of nonmultiplying, nonabsorptive moderating material, is given by the diffusion theory,* at distances not too close to the plane source or to the top of the assembly, by the equation

$$\phi = \phi_0 \, e^{-\gamma z}, \tag{3-1}$$

where z is measured from a plane where the neutrons are thermalized (see Fig. 3-6) and γ is contained in the expression

$$\frac{1}{L^2} = \gamma^2 - \frac{\pi^2}{a^2} - \frac{\pi^2}{b^2}. \tag{3-2}$$

Here L is the desired quantity and a and b are the extrapolated dimensions of the moderator in the x and y directions.

The saturated activities I_∞ of the foils are proportional to the fluxes. Then, taking logarithms of both sides of Equation 3-1,

$$\ln I_\infty = \ln k - \gamma z, \tag{3-3}$$

where k is a constant. Hence a plot of $\ln I_x$ vs. z gives a straight line whose negative slope is γ.

Each dimension, a or b in Equation 3-2, is the actual dimension of the assembly plus twice the linear extrapolated distance d. The latter is given by $d = 0.71 \, \lambda_{tr}$, where λ_{tr} is the transport mean-free-path. For graphite $d = 2.71$ cm and for D_2O, $d = 2.4$ cm. Note that if a and b in Equation 3-2 were made increasingly large, to such an extent that there is no leakage of neutrons from the sides of the pile, $1/L^2$ would then approach γ^2. Hence, the last two terms of the equation represent leakage of neutrons from the sides.

In the case of a right cylinder, the same exponential equation (Equation 3-1) for the decrease of flux in the z direction holds true under the same limitations.†

---

* Glasstone and Edlund, "The Elements of Nuclear Reactor Theory," D. Van Nostrand Co., Princeton, N. J. (1952), p. 124.

† *Ibid.*, p. 285.

Again, γ is determined from the slope of a semilog plot of the saturated activities of indium foils vs. z. However, the equation to be used to compute the thermal diffusion length L is

$$\frac{1}{L^2} = \gamma^2 - \left(\frac{2.405}{R}\right)^2, \tag{3-4}$$

where R is the extrapolated radius, i.e., the radius of the moderator plus 0.71 λ_{tr}.

In order to determine whether the neutrons are thermalized or not, indium foils (5 mils thick) may be inserted at a succession of points on the z axis, from close to the pedestal and upward. The saturated activities are determined. Then the foils are each completely covered with cadmium approximately 30 mils (0.030 in.) thick and the experiment repeated. The neutrons are thermalized if the cadmium ratio—the ratio of activity without the cadmium to that with this covering—remains constant as z is increased.

The diffusion coefficient D of the moderating material may be computed from the equation $L = \sqrt{D/\Sigma_a}$, in which the macroscopic absorption coefficient of the moderator is taken from known values. Or if D is known, one may calculate Σ_a from the same equation. Also, one may compute the transport mean-free-path $\lambda_{tr} = 3D$, and the macroscopic transport cross section $\Sigma_{tr} = 1/\lambda_{tr}$ of the moderator.

PROCEDURE AND CALCULATIONS

1. Locate 5 to 10 indium foils equally spaced on the z axis, from 60 cm to 120 cm above the top of the pedestal, and irradiate them for a known time— say overnight. Record their positions in the pile, the "wait time," and the counting time. The "wait time" between removal from the assembly and the counting should be approximately 1 hr in order to allow the short-lived indium isotope to disappear. If necessary, make correction for the dead time of the counter circuits. Then subtract the background counting rate. If more than one counter is used, an intercalibration must be made between them as described in Experiment 3-1.

2. If necessary, calculate the saturated activity I_∞ of each of the bare foils as described in Chapter 1. This will be necessary only if a short irradiation time is used. Six hours' irradiation will give 98 per cent of the saturated activity and is probably long enough.

3. Plot $\ln I_\infty$ vs. z on semilog paper and, from the slope of the straight line, determine γ.

4. Calculate L from Equation 3-2 or Equation 3-4 and compare the result with published values. The published value of L for graphite assumes its density to be 1.600 grams/cm³. What would you expect L to be if the density of the graphite in your pile were greater?

5. From the known value of Σ_a compute the diffusion coefficient D and also λ_{tr} and Σ_{tr}.

EXPERIMENT 3-3

FERMI AGE AND SLOWING-DOWN LENGTH

By J. B. Hoag, ANL, International School of Nuclear Science and Engineering

INTRODUCTION AND THEORY

The neutron or Fermi age τ is one-sixth of the "crow-flight" or mean-square distance $\overline{r^2}$ that neutrons travel from their origin at energy E_o to a place where they have a lesser energy E. Thus $\tau = \overline{r^2}/6$ and has the dimensions of an area. It was named "age" by analogy with the time derivative which appears in a differential equation used in heat-conduction theory. However, it is *not* a time or a time squared.

The slowing-down length is the square root of the Fermi age.

THEORY

The Fermi-age theory assumes that neutrons slow down in a moderating material, losing energy in a *continuous*, exponential manner rather than, as actually happens, in a succession of sharp energy drops, one at each elastic collision of a neutron with an atomic nucleus. In the case of the heavier moderators such as graphite, there are relatively many small energy drops, so that the elementary theory may be used.

This theory gives, for the slowing-down density q—the number of neutrons/(cm³)(sec) slowed down past a given energy—from a point source in an infinitely large volume of moderating material,*

$$q = \frac{Qe^{-r^2/4\tau}}{(4\pi\tau)^{3/2}},$$
(3-5)

where r is the distance from the neutron source, Q is the strength of the source, i.e., neutrons/(cm³)(sec), and τ is the Fermi age.

An alternative interpretation can be given to the Fermi age. Basically, τ is defined by

$$\tau \equiv \int_E^{E_o} \frac{\lambda_{tr}\lambda_s}{3\xi} \frac{dE}{E},$$
(3-6)

where ξ is the average logarithmic energy decrement per collision, λ_{tr} is the transport mean-free-path and λ_s is the scattering mean-free-path of the moderating material. The corresponding macroscopic cross sections are the reciprocals of these mean-free-paths. For a given moderator and source energy E_o, τ

* D. J. Hughes, "Pile Neutron Research," Addison-Wesley Publishing Co., Inc., Boston (1953), p. 29.

depends only on the energy E to which the neutrons are slowed down. When the neutrons have been slowed down only a little from E_o, their "age" is small, i.e., they are still close to the source. When they have been slowed down to a low energy, their "age" is greater, i.e., they are farther from the source. A plot of q vs. r, as seen from Equation 3-5, is of the form of a Gaussian curve whose shape is determined by τ. When τ is small, this curve is sharp; the neutrons are fast and grouped closely around the source. When τ is large, the curve is broader; the neutrons are slow and are more widely spread out.

THE EXPERIMENT (3-3)

A neutron source is placed inside a pile of graphite. For the source one may use a polonium-beryllium mixture* emitting approximately 10^5 neutrons/(cm³) (sec). These neutrons have a probable energy of 3 Mev, a maximum of approximately 10.8 Mev, and a minimum of 1 Mev. The subcritical assembly described in Chapter 4 may be used by replacing the uranium rods with graphite rods. In one of the horizontal holes, approximately one-half way from the bottom of the pedestal to the top of the pile, a half-length rod of graphite is inserted. Then the source, supported in a graphite ring, is inserted to the center of the pile and the remainder of the hole filled with a second, half-length graphite rod.

Approximately ten indium foils, each 5 mils thick, are placed in cadmium boxes (wall thickness 30 mils) so as to exclude thermal neutrons. These are mounted with masking tape in recesses in an aluminum strip and lowered into a central vertical slot in the graphite so as to be activated over the region from about 20 to about 50 cm from the source. An overnight exposure will bring them essentially to saturation; 3½ hr will give 93 per cent of full saturation. Remove the foils to the counting room and determine their saturation activity I_∞ (see Chapter I).

Because of the strong resonance of indium at 1.46 ev, the I_x values are proportional to the slowing-down density q at this energy. Equation 3-5 can therefore be written

$$I_\infty = Ke^{-r^2/4\tau}, \tag{3-7}$$

where K is a constant. Taking logarithms gives

$$\ln I_\infty = \ln K + \left(-\frac{1}{4\tau}\right)r^2. \tag{3-8}$$

A plot of $\ln I_x$ vs. r^2 then gives a straight line whose negative slope is $\frac{1}{4}\tau$. Thus the Fermi age and the slowing-down length $\sqrt{\tau}$ can be determined.

For *small* values of r, the experimental values on the semilog plot lie above

---

* They may be purchased on the market. The source is sometimes contained in an aluminum capsule approximately 1 cm o.d. and 2 cm long.

a straight line. This is because the indium foils absorb an appreciable number of the fast neutrons, above the 1.46-ev value. At *large* values of r, the points on the curve will also lie above the straight line. This results from an assumption made in the derivation of Equation 3-5 that the neutrons are scattered with spherical symmetry in the laboratory frame of reference. A more exact theory introduces another factor in the equation which could be used with the larger values of r. In this experiment, however, only the comparatively straight portion of the curve is to be used, together with the elementary theory given above.

Chapter 4

SUBCRITICAL ASSEMBLIES

INTRODUCTION

By J. B. HOAG, ANL, International School of Nuclear Science and Engineering

A subcritical assembly, sometimes called a subcritical reactor, is a portion of the core of a nuclear reactor. It consists of an arrangement of nuclear fuel, moderator and coolant small enough in volume, usually 5 to 30 per cent that of an operating reactor, so that it cannot sustain a chain reaction without the aid of an external source of neutrons. With an external source, it is possible to offset the losses due to leakage from the sides, and a constant neutron flux level can be maintained in the assembly.

The name **exponential pile** is given to those subcritical assemblies in which the neutron flux decreases exponentially along a line directed away from the external neutron source.

Subcritical assemblies have been used to determine the optimum arrangement, spacing, and proportions of the fuel, moderator, and other parts of proposed full-sized operating reactors. This method of optimizing a reactor can be carried through relatively quickly, cheaply, and safely. No heavy shielding is necessary, since the neutron intensity is low and the complex safety controls of a full critical experiment are unnecessary. The assemblies can be used to measure the flux distribution and its buckling, the effects of both heterogeneous and homogeneous poisons or absorbers, and the effects of control rods and reflectors. In addition, they can be used to determine fundamental properties of the interaction of neutrons with matter such as Fermi age, diffusion lengths, migration areas, disadvantage and thermal utilization factors by interlattice cell studies, and fast fission fractions, some of which were described in Chapter 3.

Both natural and enriched uranium have been used as the fuel. The moderator may be any material of low atomic number and small absorption cross section for neutrons, such as carbon (graphite), light or heavy water, paraffin, and beryllium. Coolants that have been used are air and heavy and light water. The external or primary neutron sources that have been used were described in Chapter 3. The neutron detectors most commonly used are indium and gold foils, boron and fission chambers.

A basic experiment with a subcritical assembly is the measurement of the neutron flux distribution in various directions throughout the assembly. From these measurements it is possible to determine the buckling of the flux for the particular arrangement at hand. From the buckling it is often possible to compute the mass of fuel and moderator and the volume of the full-sized reactor which could sustain a chain reaction by itself, without the aid of an external neutron source.

The buckling, symbolized by B^2, is a measure of the spatial rate of change of the curvature of the neutron flux at a given point per unit flux. In one direction only, in Cartesian coordinates, it is given by $(d^2\phi/dx^2)/\phi$, where ϕ is the flux at the given point. In general, the buckling is defined by

$$B^2 \equiv \frac{\nabla^2\phi(r)}{\phi(r)}, \text{ at } r. \tag{4-1}$$

where ∇^2 is the Laplace operator.

There are two kinds of buckling—the geometric buckling, B_g^2, involving the size and shape of the reactor; and the material buckling, B_m^2, which depends only upon the material and composition of the multiplying medium. For a subcritical reactor, B_g^2 is greater than B_m^2, while for a critical or near critical reactor, $B_g^2 = B_m^2$, and the effective multiplication factor k is equal to unity.

As described in detail below, the material buckling is determined by measurements on a subcritical or exponential assembly. This value is then substituted in the equation for the geometric buckling and the dimensions of the critical reactor computed.

In the case of a *rectangular parallelopiped*, the flux distribution in the x, y, and z directions is given by the diffusion theory* as

$$\phi = \phi_0 \cos \frac{\pi x}{a} \cos \frac{\pi y}{b} e^{-\gamma z}, \tag{4-2}$$

where the coordinates are shown in Fig. 3-6, a and b are the "extrapolated" dimensions of the assembly, and γ is the reciprocal of the relaxation length. From measurements of ϕ in the z direction, keeping x and y constant, a value of γ is determined from Equation 4-2. Quantities proportional to the fluxes are measured either from the activity induced in foils inserted along the central z axis or from the output of boron or fission chambers. Then

$$\phi = \phi'_0 e^{-\gamma z}. \tag{4-3}$$

* D. J. Hughes, "Pile Neutron Research," Addison-Wesley Publishing Co., Cambridge, Mass., (1953); H. Soodak and E. C. Campbell, "Elementary Pile Theory," John Wiley & Sons, New York (1950); Glasstone and Edlund "The Elements of Nuclear Reactor Theory," D. Van Nostrand Co., Inc., Princeton, N. J. (1952); S. Glasstone, "Principles of Nuclear Reactor Engineering," D. Van Nostrand Co., Inc., Princeton, N. J. (1955) B. T. Feld, "Experimental Nuclear Physics," E. Segre, Vol. II; A. Weinberg, AECD-3471; D. J. Littler and J. F. Raffle, "An Introduction to Reactor Physics," McGraw-Hill Book Co., Inc., New York (1955).

Hence, a plot of log ϕ vs. z gives a straight line whose negative slope is equal to γ. In practice, the line is not straight near the source, where harmonic flux terms cause distortions, nor near the outer boundary of the assembly, where the neutrons leak out. The value of γ, as obtained above, is then substituted in the following equation to obtain $B_m{}^2$.

$$B_m{}^2 = \left(\frac{\pi}{a}\right)^2 + \left(\frac{\pi}{b}\right)^2 - \gamma^2. \tag{4-4}$$

Since for a critical reactor, $B_g{}^2 = B_m{}^2$, this value of $B_m{}^2$ may be used in place of $B_g{}^2$ in the following equation to compute the dimensions a', b', c' (extrapolated) of a critical reactor:

$$B_g{}^2 = \left(\frac{\pi}{a'}\right)^2 + \left(\frac{\pi}{b'}\right)^2 + \left(\frac{\pi}{c'}\right)^2. \tag{4-5}$$

It is understood that two of the three quantities, a', b' and c', are chosen and the third is computed from Equation 4-5. The minimum volume, V_m, of a bare critical reactor of cubical shape, and with the same internal structure as that of the subcritical assembly is given by

$$V_m = \frac{161}{B_g{}^3}. \tag{4-6}$$

Note that V_m is inversely proportional to the cube of the buckling.

The "extrapolated" dimension of a rectangular reactor is the actual dimension a_0 plus twice the linear extrapolated distance d. Thus

$$a = a_0 + 2d. \tag{4-7}$$

It may be determined by running a flux traverse across the assembly—say, in the x direction. A straight line tangent to the flux plot near the edge of the assembly cuts the axis outside the core at a distance d from that edge. According to transport theory, for flat surfaces

$$d = 0.71 \lambda_{tr}, \tag{4-8}$$

where λ_{tr} is the transport mean-free-path of the neutrons, which is equal to 2.71 cm for carbon and 2.4 cm for heavy water.

For an assembly whose shape is a *right cylinder*, the diffusion theory gives,

$$\phi = \phi_0 J_0\left(\frac{2.405r}{R}\right) e^{-\gamma z}, \tag{4-9}$$

where r is a radius vector, J_0 is the zero-order Bessel function and R is the extrapolated radius, equal to

$$R = R_0 + d \tag{4-10}$$

where R_0 is the actual radius of the assembly and d is the linear extrapolated distance as obtained from a flux traverse along r. Also, for the lowest eigenvalue, the theory gives

$$B_m{}^2 = \left(\frac{2.405}{R}\right)^2 - \gamma^2. \tag{4-11}$$

The flux is measured in the vertical direction, away from the source and along the central line where $r = 0$. A semilog plot of ϕ vs. z yields a straight line over a region not too close to the source or too near the top boundary. The negative slope of the straight line is equal to γ, which may be substituted in Equation 4-11 to give the material buckling $B_m{}^2$.

The radius R' or the height H' (extrapolated values) of a critical reactor is then chosen and the other is computed from

$$B_g{}^2 = \left(\frac{2.405}{R'}\right)^2 + \left(\frac{\pi}{H'}\right)^2, \tag{4-12}$$

where the value of $B_m{}^2$ from Equation 4-11 is set equal to $B_g{}^2$. The minimum volume of the cylindrical, critical reactor with the same internal structure as that of the subcritical assembly is then given by

$$V_m = \frac{148}{B_g{}^3}. \tag{4-13}$$

EXPONENTIAL ASSEMBLIES

By A. B. Smith, E. W. Rylander and V. H. Shoemaker, ANL, International School
of Nuclear Science and Engineering

The Argonne National Laboratory has three subcritical assemblies available for student use. Two of the assemblies have a moderator of graphite, the third has a moderator of heavy water; each utilizes natural uranium as the fuel and an antimony-beryllium neutron source.

A Graphite Exponential Assembly*

The graphite exponential assembly consists of graphite bars,† each approximately 4 × 4 in. in cross section, placed horizontally to form a rectangular parallelopiped approximately 5 × 5 ft in cross section and approximately 8 ft in height. This pile of graphite is divided into two components—the pedestal and the multiplying lattice.

The pedestal consists of solid graphite bars stacked 2 ft high, as shown in Fig. 4-1. The trench at the back is for the neutron source stringer shown in Fig. 4-2, together with the lead bricks to protect from the gamma rays of the

* See also W. H. McCorkle, "Using Intermediate Experiments for Reactor Nuclear Design," Nucleonics, Vol. **14**, No. 3, p. 54, Mar. (1956).

† The graphite used in this assembly is of the AGOT type, reactor grade. Graphite of sufficient purity is commercially available. Graphite can be machined with ordinary woodworking tools.

Fig. 4-1. Installing the graphite pedestal.

source. The pedestal serves as a thermalizing medium for the neutrons emitted by the source and provides essentially a plane source of thermal neutrons at the interface of the pedestal and lattice. Approximately 3 tons of graphite are incorporated in the pedestal. The vertical surfaces of the pedestal are covered with a 0.020-in.-thick cadmium sheet laminated between 0.060-in.-thick aluminum sheeting to provide structural strength. The cadmium sheet is essentially "black" to thermal neutrons. It is surrounded with a layer of lead bricks and a layer of concrete blocks for protection from gamma rays, as can be seen at the bottom of Fig. 4-10.

The lattice consists of an arrangement of natural uranium fuel, graphite moderator, and air coolant. The graphite consists of 19 layers, with 17 blocks to the layer, stacked to a height of approximately 6 ft above the pedestal. Fig. 4-3 shows the lattice when partially constructed. Alternate blocks in this array have through-holes* 1¾ in. in diameter to accommodate fuel rods or graphite plugs. A total of 162 such holes are provided. These give the assembly considerable versatility as a training tool, since they permit the selection of

* An alternative and less expensive method is to chamfer the corners of four adjacent blocks to form a diamond-shaped fuel port.

FIG. 4-2. Source stringer and lead shield.

various fuel-to-moderator ratios. Those voids not used to contain the fuel can be converted to moderating material by the insertion of graphite plugs such as are shown at the bottom of Fig. 4-3. With plugs inserted, the lattice contains approximately 9 tons of graphite.

Through slots, $1\frac{1}{4}$ in. wide and $\frac{5}{16}$ in. deep are machined in the graphite bars to allow entrance into the assembly of foil-bearing stringers in the x, y, and z directions. An example of these slots is shown in Fig. 4-4. In addition, $1\frac{1}{8}$-in.-diameter aluminum tubes are installed vertically, as seen in Figs. 4-3 and 4-4, and horizontally, to permit neutron density measurements by means of ion chambers.

The top and sides of the lattice are covered like the pedestal with aluminum-clad cadmium sheets to absorb all thermal neutrons leaking out, thus providing the boundary conditions necessary for the calculations. These absorbing sheets also remove room perturbations and eliminate possible radiation hazards. As may be seen in Figs. 4-5 and 4-10, the sheets may be slid aside for the insertion of fuel rods and graphite plugs. The holes and slits where the neutron detectors are to be inserted are covered with discs of the aluminum-cadmium sheeting.

The fuel: For routine laboratory experiments, the exponential assembly contains 90 natural-uranium rods (1418 kg of U) to form square lattice cells 7.62 in. on a side. As shown in Figs. 4-6 and 4-7, each fuel rod consists of 8

Fig. 4-3. The graphite of a partially constructed exponential assembly.

natural-uranium cylinders, each 1 in. in diameter and 8 in. long, contained in a 61-ST aluminum tube of 0.040-in. wall thickness. An aluminum cap is welded on one end and a rubber bottle-stopper is used to seal the other end. Three graphite bushings, one in the center, the others near the ends, are used to center the rod in the 1¾-in. holes in the graphite. The air channels between the rods and the graphite simulate **the coolant** ducts of the reactor.

The assembly, as just described, represents 6 to 8 per cent of the volume of a bare, critical reactor.

The source of neutrons is shown in Fig. 3-5, where the beryllium block is shown mounted in the graphite stringer near the base of the pedestal. This block is $2\frac{3}{4} \times 2\frac{3}{4} \times 3\frac{1}{8}$ in., and is machined to contain the $1 \times 1\frac{1}{2}$ in. radioactive antimony cylinder. Once placed in the stringer, the beryllium block is not removed. The irradiation of the antimony in a reactor is described in detail at the end of Chapter 1. Equation 1-20 applies to this photo-neutron source. Fig. 4-8 shows the special lead container used to transport the gamma-ray source

FIG. 4-4. A view of the graphite exponential pile under construction, showing the slots and aluminum holder used for the irradiation of foils in the completed pile.

FIG. 4-5. A graphite exponential assembly nearing completion. Uranium rods and graphite plugs have been installed and aluminum-cadmium sheets are being placed.

Fig. 4-6.   Fuel rod and components.

(Sb) and the method of lowering it through a hole in the lead-brick shield into the beryllium cup by use of a flexible gripping device. With 50 c of gamma activity, the source emits approximately 10^8 neutrons/sec. Since antimony-124 has a half-life of 60 days, it is desirable to re-irradiate the Sb at 4- to 5-month intervals. The gamma radiation of the source necessitates lead and concrete shielding around the base of the assembly. Other sources that might be used are mentioned under Apparatus in Experiment 3-2.

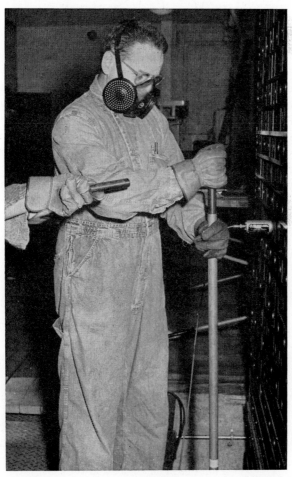

Fig. 4-7.   Loading uranium cylinders into aluminum tubes for use in exponential piles.

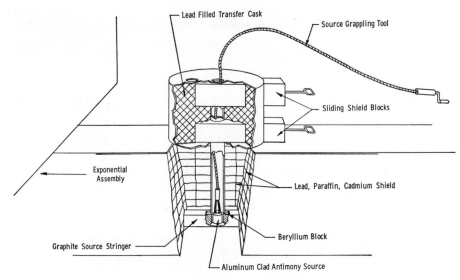

FIG. 4-8. Source transfer system.

The neutron detectors: Indium-metal foils $1\frac{1}{8}$ in. in diameter, weighing approximately 0.5 gram, and 0.005 in. in thickness are used to measure the neutron distribution within the assembly. Indium 115, which is 95 per cent abundant in natural indium, has a large capture cross section for thermal neutrons, as shown in Fig. 1-7. This capture produces the radioactive isotope indium-116, which emits a negative beta particle of 0.7-Mev energy, followed by gamma rays of 1.2- and 2.4-Mev energy, to become tin-116, which is stable.

FIG. 4-9. Foil holder and foils.

Thus standard beta and gamma counting techniques may be used. Furthermore, the half-life of 54 min is long enough for good counting yet short enough for rapid activation. It is assumed in this experiment that there is no epithermal component of the neutron flux under examination. Thus we can neglect the effect of the large indium resonance capture at 1.44 ev.

FIG. 4-10.   The completed graphite exponential assembly.

To provide durability, the fragile indium foil is backed by a thin disc of 2S aluminum, as shown in Fig. 4-9. Identifying numbers are marked on the aluminum backing. Aluminum does not noticeably depress the flux nor does it activate appreciably.

The foils are placed in the assembly by the use of an aluminum foilholder, a thin strip of metal in which recesses have been machined at regular intervals,

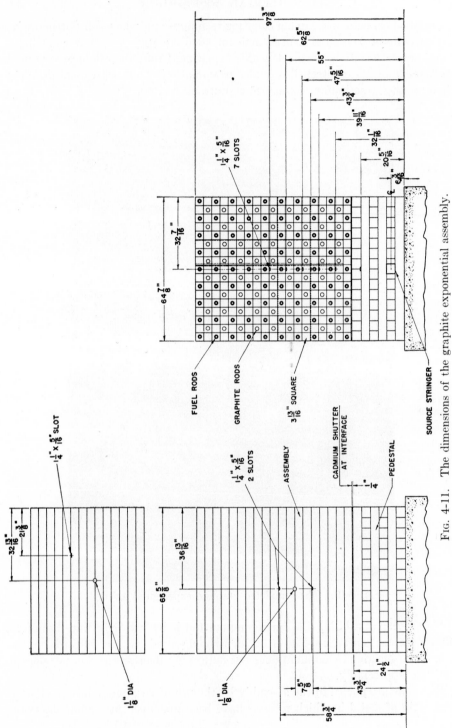

Fig. 4-11. The dimensions of the graphite exponential assembly.

corresponding to whole-number multiples of the lattice spacing. Thus every foil has the same relative radiation with respect to the lattice. The foils are held in place with masking or Scotch Tape. They are usually irradiated in the assembly overnight to allow the 54-min half-life indium-116 to reach saturation activity.

The activities of the foils after removal from the assembly are measured in a separate counting room, with an end-window proportional counter or with a 3π scintillation counter, using MPC (multipurpose counter) scaling circuits.

The complete assembly is shown in Fig. 4-10 and its dimensions are given in Fig. 4-11. A monitor traversing mechanism is shown in Fig. 4-10, installed at the top.

EXPERIMENT 4-1

FLUX DISTRIBUTION AND BUCKLING IN A GRAPHITE EXPONENTIAL

PROCEDURE

All personnel are to wear the prescribed radiation detectors, such as a dosimeter and/or film badge. The cadmium sheeting is to be in place all around the exponential assembly. The weight of each foil has been determined and recorded on its container, together with the foil's identification number as marked on the back of its planchette. Foils are taped in the recesses of an aluminum stringer and their positions recorded on their containers so that their location in the assembly will be known. The instructor carefully shoves the neutron source (in its stringer) from its lead cave to its operating position under the center of the pedestal.

The stringer with foils is inserted in the uppermost horizontal slot of the assembly, where it is left for not less than 6 hr, perhaps overnight, to allow indium-116 to reach saturation. After withdrawal, the foils are returned to their respective containers and taken to the counting room.

"Count the foils," i.e., determine their activity, as follows:

(1) Place a foil at various distances from an end-window Geiger-Müller counter tube in a shield such as is shown in Fig. 2-17. Select the geometry (position) that gives approximately 10,000 counts/min.

(2) Determine the gross counting rate, starting at time T, which is t min after removal from the pile ($=T_0$). If a binary scaler is used, multiply the register reading, taken over (say) 1 min, by the scaling factor (say, 64) and add the interpolation reading. An example is given in Data Sheet 4-1.

(3) Correct for the dead time of the counter, using Equation 2-12.

(4) Subtract the background counting rate. This is to be determined periodically during the foil counting and the average value used. Note that this correction is made *after* the dead-time correction.

DATA SHEET 4-1

Exponential assembly [carbon].   Date _____

Traverse: [horizontal, x or y, or vertical z; and distance from side or base].

G-M counter No. _____ , Resolving Time, $\tau = 175 \times 10^{-6}$ sec $= 2.91 \times 10^{-6}$ min.

Background counting rate $=$ Bkg $=$ _____ , _____ , _____ , Aver. [51]/min.

Detector foils [indium], at [x or y or z] cm inside pile.

Decay factor $= e^{\lambda t}$, where $\lambda =$ _____ , $t = (T - T_0)$. $T_0 =$ _____ .

$\epsilon =$ relative foil sensitivity.

Foil			Time			Measured Counting Rate		
No.	ϵ	$x, y,$ or $z,$ cm.	T	$\Delta T,$ min	$t,$ min	Register. Scale of (64)	Interp. Lights	$r_m =$ counts/min
Exple	1.03	10	9:55	1		100	32	6432

Counting Rate Corrections					Final Activity (After Foil Weight Correction)
Dead Time		Backgr'd	Decay		
$(1 + r_m\tau)$	$r_n = r_m(1 + r_m\tau)$	$(r_n - \text{Bkg.})$	$e^{\lambda t}$	I_0	I_0/ϵ
1.0186	6551	6500	1.40	9100	8830

(5) Since the foils cannot all be counted at one time, it is necessary to project the activities backward to a common time—say, the time (T_0) when they have just been removed from the exponential assembly. This is accomplished by solving Equation 1-7 for I_0. For indium-116, $\lambda = 0.693/54.3 = 0.01276$ min^{-1}. In Equation 1-7, t may be taken as the time from removal from the assembly to the start of the counting.

(6) Finally, correction is made for the differences in weights (hence differences in number of atoms) of the various foils. The relative foil sensitivity ϵ is the weight of a given foil divided by that of the "standard" foil (say the one in the center of the stringer). The counting rate from (5) above, is divided by ϵ to obtain the final corrected activity of the foil.

Repeat the measurements, using successive horizontal slots closer and closer to the source. Also repeat the measurements along the vertical or z direction. Finally, determine the cadmium ratio, using Equation 1-40, at the center of each horizontal slot.

INTERPRETATION AND RESULTS

Plot the corrected activities of the foils in the uppermost horizontal slot against the location of the foils across the assembly. The resultant curve represents the horizontal flux distribution and should have the shape of a cosine curve, Equation 4-2, with a maximum at the origin in the center of the assembly. In the upper slot the foils are separated from the source by 56.5 in. of graphite and the neutron flux is essentially thermal.

Plot the curves for the horizontal flux distributions made in the lower slots on the same graph as for the upper slot. Do these curves still resemble a cosine function? Explain. At what level above the pedestal do the cadmium ratio values become constant? What does this mean?

Extrapolate the upper horizontal flux distribution curve to zero activity. This x intercept gives the linear extrapolated distance, d. Compare with Equation 4-8 and subsequent data. If the horizontal data are fitted to a cosine curve $(\phi = \phi'_0 \cos \pi x / a)$, by substitution of numerical values, a value of the extrapolated dimension a of the assembly can be obtained. Then, using Equation 4-7, a more accurate value of d can be computed.

Plot the logarithms of the corrected activities of the foils in the central vertical slot against their distance above the pedestal, on semilogarithmic paper (3-cycle paper will probably be required). Notice the deviation from linearity at the upper end of the assembly, where the curve drops rapidly. This "end or boundary effect" is not considered in the simplified Equation 4-3. Explain it. From the slope of the straight part of your curve, compute γ. The value of γ may also be evaluated between any pair of measured points on the same range. Select four or five "good" points and calculate from all possible combinations of these measurements. How does your calculated γ agree with the graphical estimate?

Compute the material buckling $B_m{}^2$ using Equation 4-4 $(a = b = a_0 + 2d)$. Assume values for the a' and b' dimensions of a full-sized reactor and compute the third dimension c', using Equation 4-5. Also from this equation, compute the dimensions of an operating reactor of cubical shape. Compute the minimum volume of this reactor, using Equation 4-6, and the mass and volume of the uranium and graphite needed. Give the ratio of the volume of the subcritical to that of the critical reactor.

The photo-neutron source is located near the base of the pedestal and along the central vertical axis of the assembly. What effect would be expected on the horizontal flux distribution if the source were retracted to a point equidistant from the central axis and the side face of the assembly? Would the slope of the vertical distribution change? What effect, if any, would be expected if the temperature of the assembly were raised? If it were lowered?

Assume reasonable values for the constants in the critical equation and calculate the multiplication constant k for the lattice used.

Additional experiments can be made in the manner described above, but with different ratios of moderator to fuel. With several repetitions, a plot of the buckling vs. lattice space can be made and the condition of optimum spacing determined.

Additionally, it is of interest to study the harmonics in the neutron flux near the pedestal, and the end correction at the top of the muliplying medium.

EXPERIMENT 4-2

A REFLECTOR STUDY WITH THE GRAPHITE EXPONENTIAL

The graphite subcritical reactor can be used in an interesting reflector study. Remove the cadmium from one side of the reactor and stack a graphite reflector, say, 8 in. thick, over this face. The addition of one layer of 8 in. ordinary concrete blocks must be added outside the reflector for personnel protection.

As in Experiment 4-1, measure the flux throughout the assembly in a horizontal line. Repeat at various levels above the pedestal. It will be found that the normal cosine distribution is altered, the flux decreasing from the center more slowly, then dropping rapidly, and ending at the same extrapolated distance (which is now in the reflector) as with the unreflected assembly. The observed *flattening* of the flux due to the reflector is very important in reactor design. What is meant by *reflector savings?* What is the effect of various thicknesses of reflector?

EXPERIMENT 4-3

A CONTROL ROD STUDY WITH THE GRAPHITE EXPONENTIAL*

The graphite subcritical assembly has an aluminum tube installed vertically near the central axis, as seen in Figs. 4-3 and 4-4. This hole can be used for the insertion of a control rod.

The control rod can be made by wrapping 0.020-in. cadmium sheet around an aluminum tube of smaller diameter than that of the vertical hole, or it may be made by filling an aluminum tube of 0.912-in. o.d. with cadmium pellets and sealing both ends. Another form would consist of a boron steel rod, with o.d. of 0.912 in. and i.d. of $1\frac{7}{32}$ in. All of these should be at least 6 ft long.

Determine the flux distribution in the upper horizontal slot, as in Experiment 4-1, both with and without the control rod fully inserted in the vertical hole. Plot both on the same graph. A large dip, perhaps 20 per cent, may be expected in the flux near the center. How far out horizontally, in terms of diffusion

* The assistance of Rudi Yu Tung Yang is gratefully acknowledged.

lengths, do you find that the control rod lowers the flux below the cosine distribution?

ABSORPTION CROSS SECTION MEASUREMENT WITH A GRAPHITE EXPONENTIAL

The Argonne National Laboratory has a graphite exponential assembly in which a vertical aluminum tube of large diameter (4⅝ in. o.d.) has been installed near the center. This can be used for the insertion of a neutron detector and of various samples whose absorption cross section is to be measured.

FIG. 4-12. This subcritical reactor is constructed of graphite and uranium metal used by Enrico Fermi and his associates in the development and construction of the world's first nuclear reactor.

Fig. 4-12 shows the assembly during construction. The graphite pedestal and external source are similar to those previously described in this chapter. The lattice is an 8-ft cube and is surrounded on the sides and top with a cadmium sheet. Every other layer of graphite has holes in a square array with 8¼-in. sides in which chunks of natural uranium are located. Thus the assembly is a portion of the original CP-1 reactor, where power production by the chain reaction of nuclear fissions was first accomplished on December 2, 1942, under the leadership of Dr. Enrico Fermi.

Remove the graphite plug from the 4-in. aluminum tube and lower an *annular* neutron detector such as a boron chamber into the region of greatest thermal neutron flux. Replace the graphite plug. This has a hole which permits the insertion of a 1-in.-diameter sample can into the inside of the annular chamber. The neutron flux is measured with and without an absorber in the sample can. The flux depression which results from the presence of the sample —say, boron—is a measure of the absorption cross section. The determinations may be standardized by use of a sample such as gold for which the cross section has been established by other methods.

HEAVY-WATER EXPONENTIAL ASSEMBLY*

The equipment consists of an exponential assembly in an aluminum tank 5 ft in diameter and 6 ft tall, containing a natural-uranium lattice in D_2O, resting on a graphite pedestal with an external source of neutrons in its base,

Fig. 4-13.   Graphite pedestal, drip pan, and heavy-water storage tank.

all covered with cadmium sheeting; a D_2O storage tank with pumping equipment; and neutron flux measuring and recording devices.

Figs. 4-13 and 4-14 show the pedestal from opposite directions. It consists of a 3-ft column of reactor-grade graphite blocks, with an antimony-beryllium photo-neutron source planted under its center by means of the stringer of Fig.

* A. H. Barnes, et al., "The Exponential Experiments at the Argonne National Laboratory," TID-72, "Reactor Science and Technology," Vol. I, No. 2 (Aug. 1951); A. B. Smith, "Subcritical Reactor Is Useful for Research and Training," Nucleonics, 14, No. 11, 81 (Nov. 1956).

4-14. The arrangement is essentially the same as that described in detail in this chapter in connection with the graphite exponential.

If one is to avoid the production of source neutrons in an unknown manner directly in the multiplying medium, care must be taken in the selection of the gamma emitter. The photo-neutron threshold of D_2O lies at 2.18 Mev.* Antimony-124 has a gamma emission above the 1.66-Mev threshold of beryllium but below the 2.18-Mev threshold of heavy water. Hence it is eminently

FIG. 4-14. The source stringer in its "cave" before adding lead bricks.

suited, in conjunction with beryllium, to be the neutron source for heavy-water exponential piles.

The pedestal is sheathed with 0.020-in. cadmium sheeting, clad on each side with 0.060-in. aluminum, and is surrounded with lead bricks and concrete blocks, as shown in Fig. 4-15, to protect personnel from the radiations from the Sb-Be neutron source.

* See, for example, J. Blatt and V. Weisskopf, "Theoretical Nuclear Physics."

FIG. 4-15. Lead and concrete blocks are being placed to provide shielding from the neutron source in the pedestal.

FIG. 4-16. The heavy-water transfer pump and valve system.

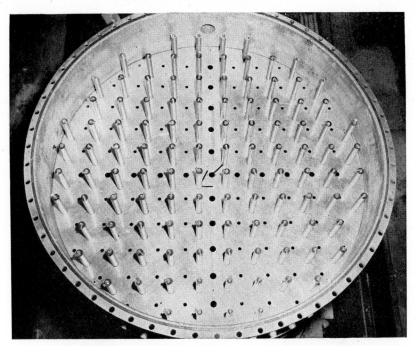

FIG. 4-17. A view looking down at the fuel rods in the heavy-water exponential assembly.

FIG. 4-18. The cover of the D_2O exponential before the vertical monitor has been installed.

A large amount—approximately 3000 kg—of heavy water is used as the moderator. When not in use, this remains in the storage tank shown in the foreground of Fig. 4-13. It is moved by the pumping equipment of Fig. 4-16, to and from the assembly by the instructor only. The care which must be used with the heavy water is justified not only because it is expensive but also because its contamination by only a fraction of 1 per cent of light water, absorbed from the moisture of the air, can alter the numerical results of the

FIG. 4-19. Completed exponential with horizontal and vertical probe drive in place.

experiment, i.e., the prediction of the size of a full-scale operating reactor, drastically. An aluminum catch basin to contain an accidental spill is provided, as in Figs. 4-13 and 4-14. The entire system is closed to prevent loss of D_2O by evaporation or contamination from H_2O of the atmosphere.

For routine instruction, 112 uranium rods are used. These are identical with those of the graphite exponential previously described in this chapter. They are placed vertically in the tank to form a square array 4.9 in. on a side, as shown in Fig. 4-17. Students have found that this loading approaches 33 per

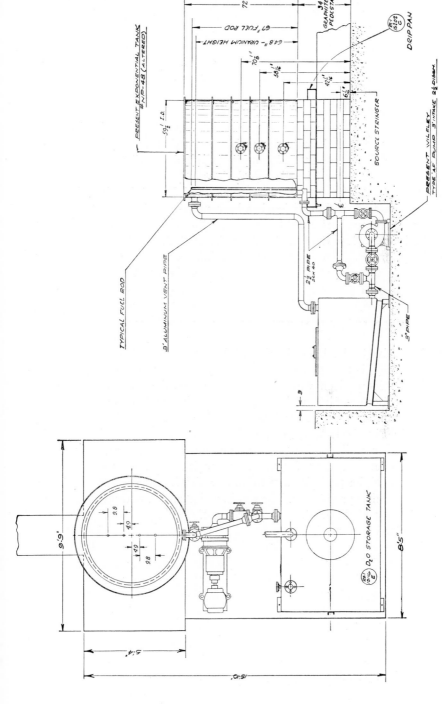

FIG. 4-20. Details of the heavy-water exponential assembly.

cent of criticality. Each rod is held in its vertical position by means of aluminum grid plates which determine the geometry and moderator-to-fuel ratio of the particular lattice chosen for study. These factors can be varied in many ways—with uniform spacing between fuel elements, for example, or with clustered arrangements. After insertion of the fuel elements, a cover, as in Fig. 4-18, is bolted on. This has several sealed ports which may be opened for exploration of the neutron flux at various positions; also a window and a micrometer for measurement of the level of the D_2O.

As with the graphite exponential previously described in this chapter, perturbations from thermal neutrons outside the tank are excluded by a heavy cadmium wrapping around the aluminum tank. This provides the "black body" boundary conditions used in the calculations.

Fig. 4-19 shows the completed assembly and Fig. 4-20 gives its detailed dimensions. Notice that provision has been made for the measurement of the neutron flux in three horizontal traverses in "through-tubes," which are welded to the tank and isolate the detector from the D_2O. A selection of similar tubes is available for vertical measurements. In using these tubes, care must be taken that they are not distorted, because of the possibility of their fracture, with attendant loss of D_2O.

THE USE OF NEUTRON COUNTING CHAMBERS

An alternative to the determination of the neutron flux distribution by means of foil activation is to use small, neutron-sensitive chambers directly inside the assembly. In comparison with the foil technique, these are in general much quicker, but more costly and less accurate. Either of two types of miniature ionization counters may be used. The details of a boron-10 current chamber are given in Fig. 4-21. When bombarded by neutrons, the thin boron lining of the chamber walls undergoes the reaction B^{10} (n,α) $Li^7 + 2.7$ Mev. The large thermal cross section for this event makes the instrument exceedingly sensitive. The alpha particles and lithium nuclei from this reaction ionize the gas of the chamber prolifically. The resultant ionization current is proportional to the intensity of the neutron bombardment.

A second type of miniature neutron detector is the U^{235} fission chamber shown in Fig. 4-22. This instrument is loaded with approximately 0.1 gram of fissile material and filled to a high pressure with argon gas. Low-energy neutrons cause fissions of the U^{235} nuclei, creating high-energy, heavily ionized fission fragments which produce large ionization of the gas in the chamber. Unlike the B^{10} current chamber described above, this detector is operated as a pulse counter, i.e., individual events are recorded on a conventional scaler.

At the bottom left of Fig. 4-19 can be seen an automatic traveling mechanism used to move the neutron detector at a uniform speed through one of the horizontal through-tubes of the D_2O exponential assembly. A motor operates a

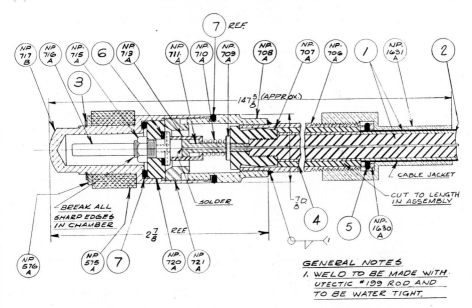

Fig. 4-21.　Construction of a B^{10} current chamber.

cogwheel along the horizontal rack (6 to 7 ft long) to drive the detector back and forth. Microswitches are used to prohibit overdriving the mechanism in either direction. The preamplifier of the detector can be seen above the motor in Fig. 4-19. This feeds the amplifier and a chart recorder whose horizontal motion is driven in phase with the chamber as it moves through the assembly, to give a permanent record of the flux distribution in a matter of minutes.

The following method of data recording with the B^{10} chamber is recommended. Turn on the power for the drive units, current amplifier, and chart mechanism. Move the detector to one extremity of its travel, just outside the assembly. With the chart recorder just started, mark the chart and start the chamber in its slow movement through the assembly. The pen of the recorder

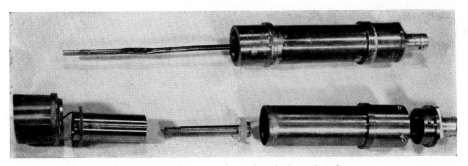

Fig. 4-22.　Construction of a fission chamber.

will show the increase, then the decrease of the neutron flux as the detector progresses through the assembly. Watch carefully as the detector approaches the opposite extremity of its travel. Mark the chart when the drive unit stops. You now have a ready-made plot of the horizontal neutron distribution in the assembly.

The fission chamber may be connected to the same drive mechanism and positioned with identical controls. However, this is a pulse counter. Hence, individual measurements must be made at selected points.

Both chambers provide a sensitive, direct response which is proportional to the neutron flux and thus avoid the long irradiation and counting times required with foils. But the results are not as accurate and the equipment is more costly.

EXPERIMENT 4-5

FLUX DISTRIBUTION AND BUCKLING IN A D₂O EXPONENTIAL

The normal precautions for protection of personnel around radioactive materials, such as wearing a dosimeter and/or film badge, are to be followed. In addition, there should be no smoking, since D gas may be present and is explosive.

With the cylindrical geometry of this assembly, Equations 4-9 through 4-13 and their physical implications are applicable.

Measure, by means of indium foils as in Experiment 4-1 or by means of the automatic plot with a boron chamber or by means of the fission chamber, the flux distributions in the radial and axial (vertical) directions. From the radial measurements, determine the linear extrapolation distance d, Equation 4-10, and compare with the value computed from the transport mean-free-path.

From the vertical flux distribution, using a semilog plot of ϕ vs. z, determine γ and hence the buckling of the flux, using Equation 4-11. From the buckling so determined, compute the dimensions, masses, and volumes of a critical reactor of the same structure as your subcritical assembly, using Equations 4-12 and 4-13.

EXPERIMENT 4-6

EXPERIMENTS WITH NATURAL WATER EXPONENTIALS *

The equipment of the heavy-water exponential assembly previously described in this chapter may be used with light rather than heavy water. Since impurities can alter the results markedly, it is advisable to use distilled water. For simplicity, the axial and radial flux distributions can be measured with

* These notes are contributed by J. B. Hoag.

indium foils as in Experiment 4-1. A tetragonal lattice may be used * with a volume ratio of 1.5 of water to uranium. The diameter of the lattice would then be approximately 25 in. Then in Equations 4-10 and 4-11, $R_0 = r\sqrt{N}$, where πr^2 is the area of a single lattice cell, N is the number of uranium rods, and d is the reflector savings (6 to 12 cm for light water).

The migration area M^2 can be measured by dissolving boric acid (B_2O_3) in the moderator water and repeating the measurements of the buckling for various concentrations of this neutron "poison." † In the summary paper just referred to, further details are given of the measurements of buckling, reflector savings, relaxation lengths, migration area, the fast effect, and neutron temperature, using slightly enriched uranium rods in ordinary water.

EXPERIMENT 4-7

ARGONAUT SUBCRITICAL MULTIPLICATION AND CONTROL ROD WORTH

By D. H. LENNOX and H. BRYANT, ANL, Reactor Engineering Division

INTRODUCTION ‡

The purpose of this experiment is to determine the critical and the control properties of a subcritical "zero" power "reactor."

When a primary source of neutrons is placed in a pile of material such as graphite, there will result a steady-state neutron density which will depend upon the strength of the source, the absorption of neutrons inside, and the leakage of neutrons from the sides of the pile. When a fissile material is added inside the pile, there will be an increase in the neutron density, which at a given point depends upon the kind and amount of fissile material and upon the geometric arrangement of all the materials in the pile.

The multiplication m is defined as the ratio between thermal neutron flux due to both the primary source and fission, and that due to the primary source alone. A neutron detector located in the pile will have a count rate proportional to the flux. Thus, with the primary source present, the multiplication is given by:

$$m = \frac{\text{cpm with fuel}}{\text{cpm without fuel}} = \frac{I}{I_0}. \tag{4-14}$$

If k is the number of neutrons at the end of one generation or cycle for each

* L. B. Borst, "Subcritical Reactor in a Pickle Barrel—NYU's Training Tool," Nucleonics, **14**, No. 8, p. 66 (Aug. 1956).

† H. Kouts et al., "Exponential Experiments with Slightly Enriched Uranium Rods in Ordinary Water," Proceedings of the International Conference on the Peaceful Uses of Atomic Energy, Vol. **5**, p. 183, United Nations, New York (1956) (A/Conf. 8/P/600).

‡ This introduction is contributed by J. B. Hoag.

neutron present at the start of that generation, there will be $(1 + k)$ neutrons at the end of one cycle, $(1 + k + k^2)$ after the next generation, etc. For a sub-critical assembly, where k is less than unity, this series may be written $1/(1 - k)$. Using a source which emits not one but α neutrons per unit time, and a detector whose efficiency is K, the number of counts observed each unit of time will be $I = K\alpha/(1 - k)$. In the absence of fissile material, the counting rate would be $I_0 = K\alpha$ because k is equal to zero. Hence, the multiplication constant is given by $[K\alpha/(1 - k)]/K\alpha$, or

$$m = \frac{I}{I_0} = \frac{1}{1 - k}. \tag{4-15}$$

The value of the multiplication is to be measured as more and more fissile material is added to the pile. A plot is made of $1/m$ vs. the mass of fuel as in Fig. 4-23. For criticality, i.e., for $k = 1$, $m = \infty$ and $1/m = 0$, as can be seen from Equation 4-15. Hence, extrapolation of the curve to the x axis gives a

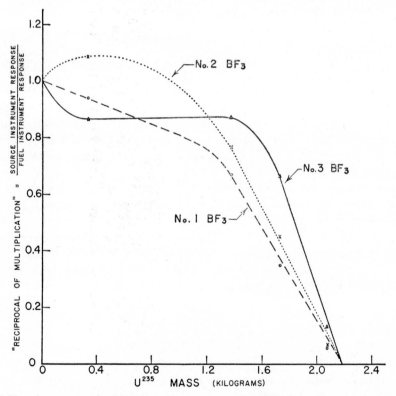

Fig. 4-23. Argonaut subcritical experiment: Determination of critical mass (2.18 kg of U^{235}) of a "slab" lattice arrangement (Lennox and Bryant) No. 1 BF$_2$ detector located at top of center hole; No. 2, outside the reflector on the fuel side; and No. 3, about 4 ft over the center hole.

prediction of the fuel loading needed to make the assembly just critical. Note in Fig. 4-23 that with the BF_3 neutron detectors in different locations in the assembly, different curves are obtained, but that they all extrapolate to the same value of the mass of fuel required for criticality.

Great care is needed in this experiment not to approach criticality too abruptly or it may be overreached, making k greater than unity, when the reactor flux might rise out of control.

APPARATUS*

The Argonaut multiplication assembly is basically a cube of graphite 5 × 5 × 4 ft high, containing a centrally located water annulus 2 ft i.d. × 3 ft o.d. × 4 ft high, formed by two concentric aluminum tanks. A schematic drawing is

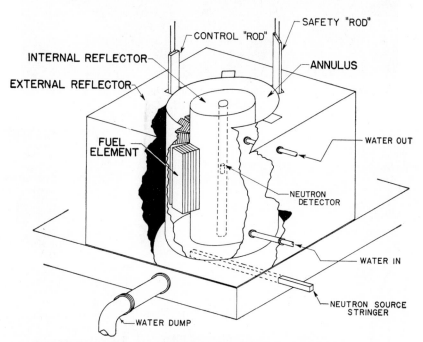

FIG. 4-24. Cut-away view of the Argonaut multiplication assembly.

shown in Fig. 4-24. Additional details are shown in Figs. 4-25 through 4-28, and in Chapter 7. The Argonaut contains an annular space 6 in. wide between graphite internal and external reflectors. Fuel elements and graphite interfuel

* When operated as a critical reactor, the subcritical assembly, as described below, becomes the Argonaut (see Chapter 7). This "subcritical reactor" serves as a training facility intermediate between exponential piles and an operating, critical reactor such as the Argonaut.

FIG. 4-25. Argonaut reactor tank before graphite has been stacked and the source shield installed.

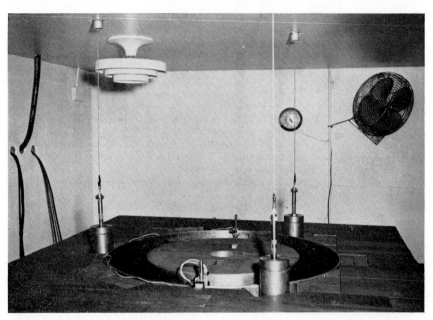

FIG. 4-26. Argonaut multiplication experiment ready for the loading of fuel. The control panel is on the opposite side of the thick concrete wall on the left. A "shadow shield" of this nature must be used and can be made of 2-ft thickness of heavy concrete or 5 ft of light concrete.

elements can be inserted in the annular space. Light water, as a moderator and coolant, can flow upward between the plates in the fuel elements and be dumped quickly through a large pipe in the bottom for safety. Control and safety rods are inserted in vertical slots around the outside perimeter of the annular space. There are numerous holes in the reflectors and in the interfuel spaces for the location of neutron detectors and experimental equipment. A neutron source, located in a graphite stringer, can be inserted under the assembly.

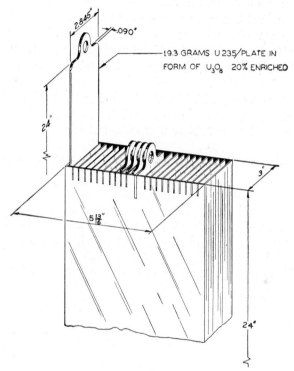

Fig. 4-27. A suggested fuel element.

The Reflectors. The graphite should be of reactor grade, i.e., very pure, such as AGOT. For the inner reflector, or as it is sometimes called, the internal thermal column, the graphite fills a circular aluminum (type 6061-T4) tank, 2 ft in diameter, with $\frac{3}{16}$-in. wall, and 4 ft high. There is a central vertical hole and four radially located vertical holes for detectors and experiments.

If used between fuel boxes or plates, graphite blocks and wedges are hung in the annulus on aluminum mounting brackets from the edge of the outer tank. The graphite is milled to shape and coated with Krylon aluminum paint to resist crumbling in the water environment. The rectangular blocks are of the same shape and size and are interchangeable with the fuel elements or boxes. The wedges fill the remaining space in the annulus.

The outer tank is of the same type of aluminum (6061-T4), 3 ft in diameter, with $\frac{1}{4}$-in. wall, and 4 ft high. Graphite is fitted around the outside of this tank, except for the control and safety rod spaces, to an over-all dimension of 5 ft square and 4 ft high. One standard graphite block size is $15\frac{1}{2} \times 4 \times 4$ in.

The Fuel. An assembly of fuel plates in a fuel box is indicated in Fig. 4-27. Each plate contains as the "meat," 35 weight per cent of U_3O_8 in aluminum, the uranium being 20 per cent enriched in U^{235}, and is aluminum clad. They are 2.8×24 in. long and 0.096 in. thick and each contains approximately 19 grams of U^{235}. A typical fuel box is made of aluminum, is approximately $3 \times 6 \times 24$ in., is slotted for plate insertion and removal, and contains 17 plates. For this experiment, six fuel assemblies should be available, with a total of approximately 2 kg of U^{235}. They may be supported at mid-height in the annulus by graphite wedges from below.

The Moderator-Coolant. Light water is used as the moderator and coolant. It is introduced through a 3-liter mixed-bed ion-exchange column. Further details are given in Chapter 7. Note that there is 1 ft of water above and below the core.

The Primary Neutron Source. An antimony-beryllium source of the type used with the exponential assemblies previously described in this chapter can be used. It should emit 10^7 to 10^8 neutrons/sec, being sufficiently active so that the trip circuit detectors can see a thermal flux of approximately 10^5 neutrons/(cm)(sec) at a multiplication of 100. Additional shielding against the gamma rays of this source must be provided around the base of the assembly. The region around the shield should be monitored with especial care to make certain that the activity is sufficiently low. Also, the gamma background around the entire assembly should be monitored. This can be done first without the beryllium in the source and with dummy aluminum plates in the fuel boxes, and with the water in the annulus.

The Detectors. Multiplication measurements are made and audible monitoring of the neutron density in carried out using BF_3 proportional counters. For visual observation of small changes in multiplication, a recorder with a bucking voltage may be used with one of the d-c amplifiers.

The Control and Safety Features. The control and safety rods are ZPR-I type, gravity-actuated, 24×4-in. cadmium shutdown blades, as shown in Fig. 4-28. They have a magnetic clutch release and a time of insertion of 0.3 sec or less. The cover is placed on top so that no large mass of material can be dropped in while the fuel is in the annulus and the water is up. In addition there is a 6-in. pipe at the bottom of the annulus, closed by a counterweighted flap valve, for rapid dumping of the water moderator. The valve is held closed with a magnetic clutch; the dump time is about 7 sec.

Shutdown is automatically initiated by any one of three independent multiplication trip channels. Two are made up of d-c amplifiers fed by a parallel-plate, boron-coated ionization chamber giving 10^{-13} amp/nv (see Figs. 7-3

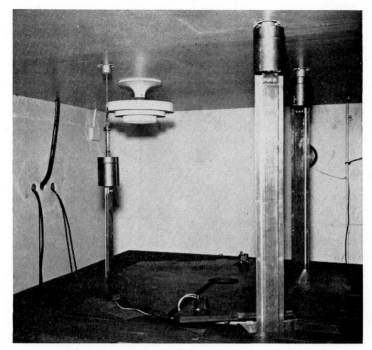

Fɪɢ. 4-28. The Argonaut as used for the measurement of multiplication. The control rod at the left is partially withdrawn. The two cocked safety rods are at the right.

and 7-4). The other is a count-rate meter with a BF_3 proportional chamber. One chamber is located in the internal reflector (= internal thermal column) and the remainder in the external reflector.

The trip conditions and resultant actions are as follows: (1) automatic safety-rod drop when there is (a) too high a multiplication, (b) a power failure, (c) a trip instrument failure; (2) automatic water dump when there is (a) too high a multiplication, (b) a power failure, (c) a trip instrument failure, (d) top cover open, (e) safety rods not cocked, (f) neutron source level too low.

In addition to the above-mentioned automatic controls, the water and safety rods can be dropped at the discretion of the operator by means of a manually operated scram button. After an instrument or manual scram, a manual reset is necessary to re-energize the safety-rod and dump-valve clutches.

Circuits are shown in Figs. 7-22 and 7-24. A signal from any safety circuit will initiate a shutdown.

Interlocks are arranged so that fuel addition, rearrangement, and the introduction of voids can take place only when the annulus is drained. The interlocks are wired so that the following sequence of operations must be satisfied before water can be added to the system. (1) To close the dump valve: (a) trip instruments on, (b) top cover closed, (c) source level satisfied, (d) two safety rods raised and cocked; (2) to start the water pump: (a) all conditions under (1) satisfied and (b) control rod fully inserted. Appropriately located microswitches are used in tripping the cover, the control and the safety rods. An ionization chamber and amplifier circuit is used as a source detector so that the interlocks can be energized only if an active source has been inserted under the assembly.

If too much fuel were to be added to the system, perhaps by mistaken book-keeping as the plates are added, the assembly could go critical while the water was being pumped into the annulus, or when, subsequently, the control rod was being withdrawn. To prevent criticality under these conditions, the pump-ing rate and the rod withdrawal rate are both limited mechanically. It must be arranged that the reactivity cannot be added fast enough to outstrip the response of the trip system. Circumvention of this drive speed limitation, by manual removal of a safety rod, is possible only when the annulus is drained.

An integral part of this experiment is training in the proper safety attitude. To avoid grossly unsafe practices, the experimenter must carry out his oper-ations in a prudent manner, just as, when working with an exothermic chemical experiment involving a potentially explosive reaction, he uses a safety glass.

It is reassuring, however, that in the Argonaut type of reactor, excessive reactivity will boil the water away and shut the unit down in a few minutes even though all automatic safety features have failed to operate.

EXPERIMENTAL PROCEDURE

*To be performed only under the direct supervision of the instructor.**

The control rod is to be withdrawn only by the instructor. Prior monitoring of the area around the assembly is to have been made beforehand and any necessary precautions posted.

The annulus is preloaded by the instructor with six dummy aluminum fuel elements and graphite interfuel blocks. The safety precautions and the startup

---

* The instructor must have an understanding of and familiarity with the following as-pects of the facility: (1) general design and operating characteristics, (2) the control and safety mechanisms, (3) the control instrumentation, (4) standard operating procedure, and (5) emergency shutdown system and procedure. He should be well aware (6) that an approach to criticality experiment is potentially hazardous, (7) that the experimenters must work slowly and must know the status of the reactor at all times, (8) that high multiplication values are to be avoided, (9) of the need for close supervision of the stu-dents, (10) of the necessity of avoiding a complacent attitude with the assumption of a known value of the critical mass, (11) of the need to maintain strict indoctrination of each new group of students in the necessary precautions, even though he has repeated this program to one hundred previous teams, (12) of the need for strict security of the fuel when the reactor is not in operation, to avoid a foolish and dangerous experiment by an enterprising student operating on his own initiative. *The instructor should never have available sufficient fuel to achieve criticality for the particular configuration* (approximately 2 kg of U^{235}).

procedures are explained by the instructor. The students in a given team are assigned individual responsibilities as follows:

Team Assignments

(1) One man at the controls.

(2) One man, as recorder, keeps a log of all operations. Part of the log is a detailed uranium fuel accounting.

(3) One man makes a graphical plot of the relative reciprocal counting rate $(1/m)$.

(4) One man removes and replaces fuel elements from storage. (A standard four-door combination-lock-type filing cabinet near the pile can be used while the experiment is in progress. Each drawer is lined with cadmium sheet. Not over 1 kg of U^{235} is in any one drawer).

(5) and (6) Two men load and unload the reactor.

(7) A liaison man between the construction crew and the control panel. He may also serve between the detector equipment (three detectors) and the recorder. This man is also to determine the actual response of the controls by visual observation of rod action, water level, etc.

These positions are to be rotated during the course of the experiment.

Regular Start-up Procedure

(1) Insert neutron source to obtain reset of the low-level trip.

(2) Check each of the instrument and manual scrams by dropping the safety rods. *The instructor has the responsibility of suspending operations in the event of equipment malfunction.*

(3) Open inlet water valve.

(4) Reset all trips.

(5) Cock both safety rods.

(6) Close the water dump valve. It takes about 15 min to fill the tank.

(7) Pump water to a level slightly over the overflow.

(8) Take several 1-min counts on each of at least three detector channels to obtain the saturation counting rates of the channels.

(9) Instructor slowly withdraws the control rod from the core in steps, while count rates are observed.

(10) Take several 1-min counts on each of three detectors.

(11) Record and plot readings.

(12) Scram the reactor. This drops the safety rods and opens the dump valve.

Loading

(1) Fuel boxes numbered 1 and 2 are assembled and installed in the reactor. The location of each fuel box is shown in Fig. 4-29. The following con-

ditions are to be satisfied during loading: (a) Water down, dump valve open, water pump locked off, with the pump key in the instructor's possession. (b) Control rod fully inserted. (c) Two safety rods cocked. (d) Trip instruments on lowest scale. (e) Scaler on for audible monitoring. Repeat startup procedure. Take data and plot. Shut down the facility.

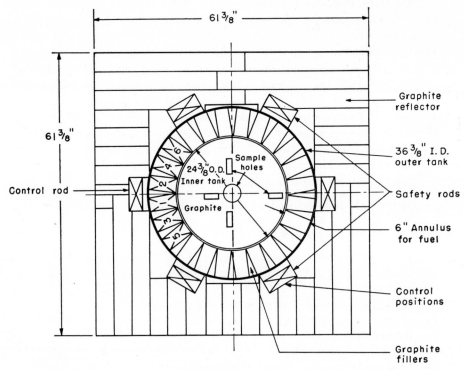

FIG. 4-29. A section through the Argonaut during multiplication experiment.

(2) Assemble fuel boxes Nos. 3 and 4 and install. Take data and plot. Shut down.
(3) Assemble fuel box No. 5, install, repeat startup procedure, take data, plot, shut down.
(4) Extrapolation of the data taken, with the control rod in and out, permits estimation of the rod's worth. This is set as a loading limit and is not to be exceeded. In other words, the total loading (mass of U^{235} in the reactor) is to be less than the value obtained when the rod worth (in, say, kilograms) has been subtracted from the extrapolated or critical mass. Then, the reactor cannot go critical even with the control rod completely removed. Fig. 4-30 shows a plot taken to determine the control rod worth. Estimate the loading limit, decide upon the

number of fuel plates to be used in box No. 6 such that the total load will be *less* than this limit. This number of plates, perhaps five, are loaded in box No. 6, which is then installed in the reactor. Repeat startup procedure. At this point particular attention is given to the counting rate as the instructor withdraws the control rod. If the indi-

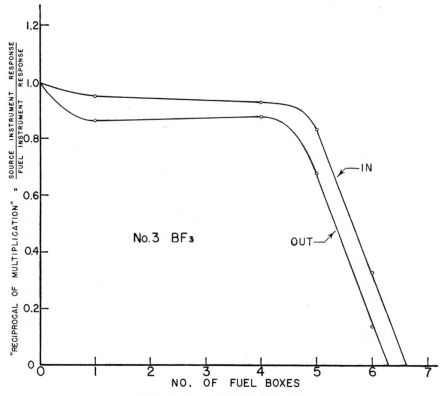

Fig. 4-30.   Control-rod worth.

cations are that the multiplication m will exceed a value of 50 ($1/m = 0.02$) by complete withdrawal of the control rod, shut down the facility and remove sufficient fuel to avoid this condition. If a multiplication of 50 less is certain, even with the control rod completely removed, continue with the experiment; take data, plot, and shut down.

Secure the Equipment

(1) Control and safety rods in.
(2) Water out.
(3) Fuel plates returned to storage and locked.
(4) Neutron source withdrawn to its cave.

(5) Top cover locked.

(6) Pump power switch open and locked.

(7) Main power switch open and locked.

(8) All keys in storage and locked.

RESULTS

(1) A final determination of the critical mass is now made by extrapolation.

(2) The control rod worth is stated in terms of mass equivalent.

ADDITIONAL

(1) Time permitting, or with other teams, repeat the experiment above, with various spacings between the fuel plates in the fuel boxes, such as ⅛, ¼, and ⅜ in. Plot a curve of the critical mass vs. these spacings and state the spacing which requires the least fuel for criticality.

(2) Start with a fuel loading which gives a multiplication close to 50. Study the control properties, in terms of changes in the critical mass, (a) for various voids in the annulus, (b) for various poisons, such as cadmium located at various places in the annulus and in the internal and external reflector, and (c) for various reflectors (reflector worth). The sensitivity of the lattice to various perturbations is thus determined.

(3) Various degrees of enrichment, as well as locations of the fuel, can be tried.

(4) Studies can be made of various approach-to-criticality information as a function of the position of the detector relative to the assembly, and in particular, with respect to that of the fuel.

Chapter 5

CROSS SECTIONS

INTRODUCTION

By J. B. Hoag, ANL, International School of Nuclear Science and Engineering

Consider a parallel beam of neutrons of cross-sectional area of 1 cm², incident normally on the face of some target material of frontal area a, as in Fig. 5-1. Let I be the number of neutrons/(cm²)(sec), and $(-dI)$ the neutrons/(cm)² (sec) captured in the target; the negative sign indicates a decrease in the intensity of the neutron beam as it progresses through the target material.

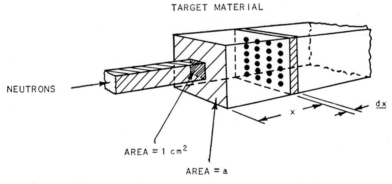

TARGET MATERIAL

NEUTRONS

dx

x

AREA = 1 cm²

AREA = a

FIG. 5-1. The interpretation of cross sections.

Then the probability of capture of the neutrons by the target nuclei can be expressed as $-dI/I$.

Let σ be the area in cm² of capture of a given neutron by one target nucleus. This is called the microscopic cross section and is usually expressed in "barns" ($=10^{-24}$ cm²), but is in cm² in the equations below. It is a measure of the probability of occurrence of the nuclear reaction (capture, in this case) of one neutron by one nucleus.

If a is the frontal area of the target and dx the thickness of a very thin slice of this material, then $a\,dx$ is the volume of the slice. If there are N nuclei (and also N atoms) per cm³, then N $(a\ dx)$ is the number of nuclei in the slice. The thickness dx is chosen so thin that the nuclei do not overlap; all are exposed to the incident neutrons. Then $\sigma(Na\ dx)$ is the total capture area of the slice, as suggested by the dots in Fig. 5-1. The chance or probability of capture = (the total capture area)/(frontal area) = $(\sigma Na\ dx)/a = \sigma N\ dx = \Sigma\ dx$, where $\Sigma \equiv N\sigma$ and is called the macroscopic cross section. It represents the probability of capture of a nuetron by all the target nuclei in 1 cm³.

Equating the two expressions just stated for the probability of capture gives:

$$-dI/I = \Sigma\ dx. \tag{5-1}$$

Upon integration, and by taking the intensity as I_0 for $x = 0$; one finds:

$$\boxed{I = I_0 e^{-\Sigma x}} \tag{5-2}$$

where e is the base of the Naperian logarithm system. This equation may be compared with the law for the absorption of a parallel beam, $I = I_0 e^{-\mu x}$, where μ is the linear-absorption coefficient.

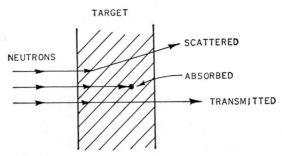

FIG. 5-2.   Neutrons may be scattered, absorbed, or transmitted.

Types of Cross Sections. The previous discussion considered only one type of reaction, that of capture of neutrons. Among other reactions may be mentioned elastic and inelastic scattering collisions and also fission, as indicated in Fig. 5-2. The total cross section would be the sum of the separate values. Thus:

$$\underset{\text{total}}{\sigma_t} = \underset{\text{scattered}}{\sigma_s} + \underset{\text{absorbed}}{\sigma_a} \tag{5-3}$$

$$= \underset{\text{elastic}}{(\sigma_e} + \underset{\text{inelastic}}{\sigma_i)} + \underset{\text{capture}}{(\sigma_c} + \underset{\text{fission}}{\sigma_f)}. \tag{5-4}$$

Similar equations may be written for the macroscopic cross section, Σ.

Elastic collisions are of the billiard-ball type, where both the total kinetic energy and the momentum are conserved, but the kinetic energy of the incident particle is decreased as the target nucleus recoils. In inelastic collisions, the momentum is conserved but the total kinetic energy is decreased, the excess appearing in the form of radiations as the target nucleus settles back from an excited state into its ground state. When a capture occurs, a compound nucleus is formed of the neutron and the nucleus, which shortly emits a radiation. In the "radiative capture" process, a neutron is captured and a gamma ray is radiated. When the compound nucleus itself is radioactive, measurements of this activity give "activation cross sections." Fission cross sections are a measure of the probability that the compound nucleus will cleave or fission into two approximately equal halves.

The various cross sections depend not only upon the target material but also upon the energy of the incident neutrons as is roughly suggested in Fig. 5-3.

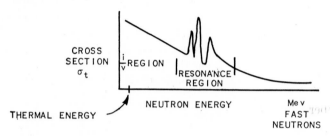

FIG. 5-3. A very rough indication of the variation of total microscopic cross section of a given material for neutrons of various energies.

Values vary from a small fraction of a barn to tens of thousands of barns.*

Obviously, a knowledge of the various cross sections or probabilities of the competing reactions is of the utmost importance in studies of the materials used in a reactor, as well as for an understanding of the nature of the nuclei themselves. Consequently many measurements, by a wide variety of methods, have been made of the various cross sections.†

Transmission Experiments. Total cross sections may be measured by the "transmission method." Successive thicknesses of the material under study are placed in the path of a highly collimated beam of neutrons. A carefully shielded neutron detector measures the number of neutrons per unit time which get through the transmitting material (sometimes called the absorber, depending on the viewpoint). The neutrons may be of a single energy, as from a crystal spectrometer; they may cover a limited range of energies; they may cover all energies above or below a certain value; or they may have a wide range of values from below thermal (0.025 ev) to fast neutrons of many Mev's, as from the core of a thermal reactor. The word "apparent" or "experimental" total cross section can be used in the latter cases.

Taking logarithms, to the natural base, of both sides of Equation 5-2, gives

---

* D. J. Hughes and J. A. Harvey, "Neutron Cross Sections," BNL 325. For sale by the Superintendent of Documents, U. S. Government Printing Office, Washington 25, D. C.

† D. J. Hughes, "Pile Neutron Research," Addison-Wesley Publishing Co., Cambridge, Mass. (1953).

$\ln I = \ln I_0 - \Sigma x$. Hence, if $\ln I$ values are plotted as ordinates and x values as abscissae (usually done on semilog paper) a straight line, $y = b + mx$, should result, whose y intercept is $\ln I_0$ and whose negative slope (m) is Σ, as in Fig. 5-4.

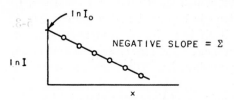

Since $\Sigma = N\sigma$, the microscopic cross section σ can be determined when N has been computed. The number of atoms (and also nuclei) per cm^3 is to the number in 1 mole $(N_0 = \text{Avogadro's number})$ as the mass per cm^3 $(\rho = \text{density, grams/cm}^3)$ is to the mass of 1 mole $(A = \text{atomic weight})$. Thus, for a target made of a single element, $N = N_0\rho/A$. But the density ρ is the mass m (grams) per unit volume. For a uniform foil the latter is equal to the area a times the thickness x of the material. Hence, $N = N_0 m/Aax$. Since

FIG. 5-4. To determine Σ. This is the logarithmic fraction transmitted by unit thickness, $= \ln(I_0/I)/x$.

$$\sigma = \frac{\Sigma}{N} = \frac{\ln I_0/I}{Nx}, \tag{5-5}$$

the measured or apparent cross section σ_m is given by

$$\sigma_m = \frac{\ln (I_0/I)}{(N_0/A)(m/a)}, \tag{5-6}$$

where I_0 is the intensity without transmitter, I is the intensity with a transmitter (absorber) of atomic weight A, mass m (grams) and area a (cm^2) and $N_0 = 0.602 \times 10^{24}$. The values of I_0 and I need not be absolute; proportion values are sufficient since their ratio is used. The denominator of Equation 5-6 is the number of atoms per square centimeter of the transmission sample. For convenience, this is computed in terms of a constant times 10^{24} for all the samples and foils. The calculations from Equation 5-6 then lead directly to the cross sections in barns.

The neutron absorption cross sections of a sample can be obtained by taking the difference between the total cross section (measured, say, by the transmission method) and the scattering cross section (measured, say, with an annular scattering counter). These values have meaning only if the absorption and scattering cross sections differ by a sizable amount.

A Beam Catcher. In order to protect people working around a reactor from the neutron-gamma beam in use in a particular experiment, a beam catcher such as shown in Figs. 5-5 and 5-6 may be used. The paraffin slows down the neutrons, the boron in B_2O_3 captures them (with emission of additional gamma rays), and the lead and outer shield of heavy concrete absorb the gammas. The dimensions are dependent on the intensity and energy of the neutrons and gammas.

FIG. 5-5. Some experiments using Argonne National Laboratory's research reactor CP-5.

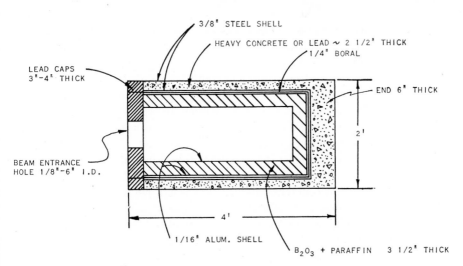

FIG. 5-6. A neutron-gamma beam catcher.

CROSS-SECTION MEASUREMENTS WITH AN ANNULAR SCATTERING COUNTER

By C. T. HIBDON, ANL, Physics Division

INTRODUCTION

A number of methods of measuring various neutron cross sections have been used and a number are currently in use.[*] The methods, in general, have depended on the stage of development of the equipment and neutron sources used at the time the measurements were made and on the type of cross section desired. Among the methods used in the past and those currently in use may be found the following:

1. Activation of thin foils, particularly by self-detection, to determine resonance parameters.[†]

2. The crystal spectrometer has been very useful in obtaining monoenergetic beams with good resolution from 0.1 to 10 ev and at somewhat higher energies with less well defined energies.

3. The annular, scattering, boron trifluoride (BF_3) counter has been used to obtain various cross sections such as scattering, total, and self-detection in the subcadmium and epicadmium regions, i.e., below and above approximately 0.4 ev, respectively.

4. Neutron time-of-flight spectrometers (neutron choppers) of various designs are currently in use at many reactors. These instruments provide very good resolution from the thermal region to about 1000 ev and are useful with poorer resolution at higher energies.

5. The Van de Graaff electrostatic generator is one of the modern tools and is very useful in supplying beams of monoenergetic neutrons for cross-section measurements. It was long used at high energies. In recent years a method for using this type of equipment at lower energies has been devised.[‡] With this equipment cross sections are measurable from 1 kilovolt up.

It is the aim of the present experiment to make some neutron cross-section measurements for illustrative purposes by use of method 3 above, namely, the annular scattering BF_3 counter. This instrument can be used with the reactor as a source of neutrons. It requires a highly collimated beam of neutrons for best results. The advantage of using this equipment is its ease of operation and simplicity of design, and the fact that fundamental measurements can be made directly. Its chief disadvantage lies in energy selection. A few of the many

---

[*] For a thorough discussion of the topic, see D. J. Hughes, *op. cit.*
[†] H. A. Bethe and G. Placzek, Phys. Rev., **51**, 450 (1937), particularly Sec. 5.
[‡] Hibdon, Langsdorf, Jr., and Holland, Phys. Rev., **85**, 595 (1952).

measurements that can be made with this instrument are pointed out later, with some detail. An adequate number of measurements have been planned in the present experiment to provide sufficient data to enable one to calculate a variety of cross sections.

APPARATUS*

A schematic diagram of the equipment is shown in Fig. 5-7, while one form of the equipment is shown in Fig. 5-8. In the diagram, a beam of neutrons and gamma rays from the core of a reactor is highly collimated and then passes through the counting chamber.

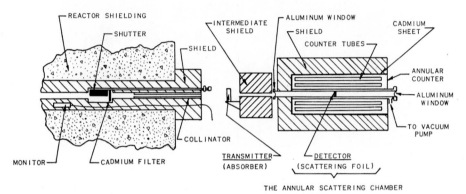

THE ANNULAR SCATTERING CHAMBER

FIG. 5-7.   Schematic diagram of the annular scattering BF_3 proportional counter equipment.

The Annular Scattering BF_3 Proportional Counter. This instrument, called the annular counter for brevity, is an ingenious device for counting neutrons in the presence of other radiations, particularly in the presence of gamma rays. Pulses arising from gamma rays are completely biased out by the associated amplifier. A number of individual BF_3 (enriched in B^{10}) proportional counters of small diameter ($3/4$ or 1 in.) are embedded in a drum of paraffin as shown in Fig. 5-9. Each counter contains $B^{10}F_3$ gas at a pressure of about 40 cm of Hg, and operates at 1600 to 1800 volts, without a preamplifier. The cathodes are each grounded to the metal end plate, while the anodes of each ring of tubes are tied together and operate a separate scaler and register. The sum of the readings of the registers, per unit time, gives the counting rate I. To form the unit, metal tubes of the size of the counter tubes or slightly larger

* For methods used and results obtained see: C. T. Hibdon and C. O. Muehlhause, Phys. Rev., **76**, 100 (1949); C. T. Hibdon, Phys. Rev., **79**, 747 (1950); Hibdon, Muehlhause, Selove, and Woolf, Phys. Rev., **77**, 730 (1950); Hibdon and Muehlhause, Phys. Rev., **79**, 44 (1950); Harris, Hibdon, and Muehlhause, Phys. Rev., **80**, 1014 (1950); Hibdon, Muehlhause, Ringo, and Robillard, Phys. Rev., **82**, 560 (1951).

FIG. 5-8. Equipment installed at the CP-5 reactor.

are assembled in the drum, with approximately ¼-in. spacing between them and the central tube, between rings, and between one another. Molten, white paraffin, containing 2 to 4 per cent carnauba wax to increase the rigidity, is poured around the tubes. After the wax hardens, the tubes are withdrawn. Then the counter tubes are inserted and their lead wires soldered as indicated above. About 20 tubes may be used (12 to 80), the more the better. The drum may consist of a brass tube, say 1½ ft in diameter and 2½ to 3 ft long. The cad-

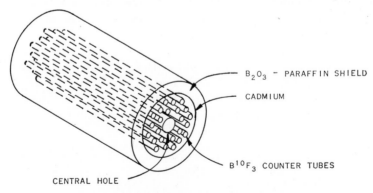

FIG. 5-9. An annular scattering chamber.

mium sheet is 30-40 mils thick. To minimize the background counting rate, the counter-paraffin assembly is encased in a B_2O_3 (boron oxide) shield as indicated in Fig. 5-9. This may contain lead shot and paraffin, but is mostly B_2O_3. This arrangement approximates a 4π neutron counter, i.e., it is nearly a spherical counter.

An alternate BF_3 counter* is shown in Figs. 5-10 and 5-11.

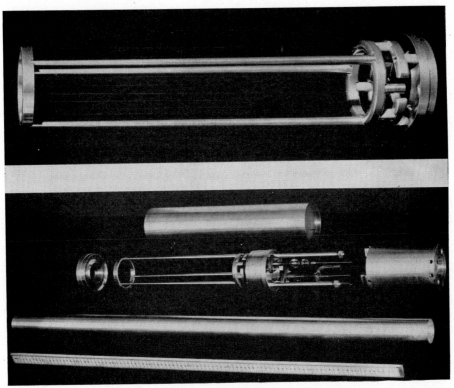

FIG. 5-10. Annular BF_3 counter components.

This BF_3 counting tube consists of a continuous detecting wire wound back and forth thirty times in the annular volume between two concentric cylinders, as is shown enlarged in the upper part of Fig. 5-10, the outer cylinder being $4\frac{1}{2}$ in. in diameter. By this means the counting efficiency is multiplied many fold. The lower part of Fig. 5-10 shows the unassembled component parts of the counting tube. In Fig. 5-11, the parts are shown as well as a nearly assembled counting tube. The tube is filled with $B^{10}F_3$ gas to a pressure of 15 cm of Hg. It is operated at 1800 volts and uses a single amplifier plus a preamplifier, with an over-all voltage amplification of about 6000. It is surrounded on the sides

* Designed by A. Langsdorf, Jr., and assembled by George Thomas and Sigmund Harris.

and front with an inch or so of paraffin and then with several inches of B_2O_3 shielding material.

In Fig. 5-11 the long, central, hollow tube of aluminum (some 4 ft long, with an o.d. of 2 in.) extends beyond the active region of the counter in order to pass completely through the shielding material. When in operation, the central tube is evacuated, since scattering by air is much larger than background

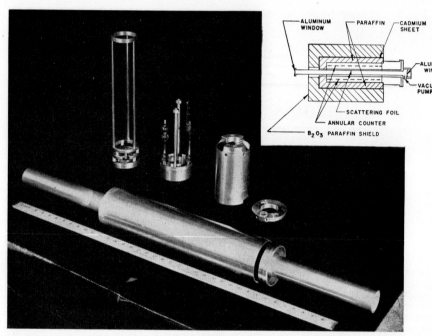

FIG. 5-11. Annular BF_3 counter and components.

effects. It may, in fact, be larger than the scattering due to some detector foils which one may desire to use in making measurements. For evacuation purposes the ends of the tube are sealed by 2-mil aluminum foils. By use of the long, central, evacuated tube, neutrons enter and leave the evacuated region at some distance from the active region of the counter, which reduces that part of the background due to air scattering. The mounting of the end windows is shown in Fig. 5-12. The tube is evacuated with a fore pump; but the pressure need not be measured, since it is not critical.

The Collimator. A plug, Fig. 5-7, is built to fit into one of the horizontal holes of the reactor. It is, say, 6 in. square and 6 ft long and contains a central metal tube of about 1-in. i.d., which is the collimator. At its outer end there is an additional metal tube about 20 in. long and of ½-in. i.d. to give a narrower beam of neutrons. The plug is filled with B_2O_3, paraffin, and lead, similar to the shield around the annular counter. Just inside the 20-in. metal tube, a space

1 ft long is left to accommodate the shutter and cadmium filter. The shutter consists of alternate layers of iron and masonite, $1\frac{1}{2}$ in. in o.d., so arranged with a rack and pinion that it can be raised or lowered into the path of the neutron beam by a knob on the front of the plug. Just in front of the shutter there is a cadmium filter 30 or 40 mils thick which can be swung into or out of the neutron

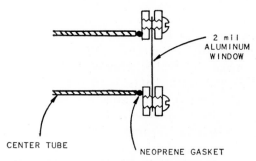

FIG. 5-12.   Mounting for the end windows.

beam by turning a knob on the front of the plug. Also built into the B_2O_3 paraffin shield there is a monitor tube of the fission type whose function will be discussed later.

The Intermediate Shield. Between the collimator plug and annular counter there is a shield about 16 in. thick and 16 in. square or more, with a hole of $\frac{3}{4}$-in. i.d. through its center. This shield may be built of alternate layers of iron and masonite. A ledge on the reactor side is used to support the various transmitter (absorber) materials.

Alignment Procedure. For a rough alignment, a metal rod is poked through the entire apparatus. Final alignment is made by counting, as follows: A quadrant of graphite $\frac{1}{8}$ in. thick is placed at the "detector" position, as indicated in Fig. 5-13. The machine is moved until one gets the same number of counts per unit time with the graphite in each of the four positions indicated. This is checked by repeating the process with the graphite first near one end, then near the other, of the central tube of the annular counter.

The Detector or Scattering Foil. This is positioned for maximum counting rate, usually near the center of the counter, as indicated in Fig. 5-7. It is held in an aluminum ring so that it may be removed easily from the counter. A duplicate ring is used for background measurements and so that the foil need never be touched after it has been fitted in its retainer ring. To perform any and all experiments, it

FIG. 5-13.   The four positions of the graphite alignment quadrant.

is necessary to place the scattering foil in the detector position. The material of which the foil is made and its thickness depend on the type of experiment to be performed. Details are given below. In general, the foil is thin, of the order of a few mils or less in thickness. For some experiments, the thinnest foils obtainable consistent with a desirable counting rate are necessary. Many experiments have been performed with foils 1 mil or less in thickness.

The Monitor. Counts may be obtained for fixed time intervals if the reactor operates at a really steady power. Rather than follow this procedure, a fission monitor is ordinarily used in the neutron flux of the reactor as indicated in Fig. 5-7. Associated with the monitor is a scaling circuit which is so interconnected with the scaling circuit of the BF_3 counter that both may be started together and later stopped simultaneously at the end of a selected number of monitor counts. The time interval is recorded for the purpose of making the dead-time corrections. This method of taking data provides a way of eliminating fluctuations in the observed counting rates due to variations in the reactor power.

The Counters. Although the BF_3 proportional counter itself (see Chapter 2) does not have an appreciable dead time, the circuit does. At high counting rates, above 25,000 cpm for the B-4 unit of the Argonne National Laboratory, it is necessary to make a dead-time counting correction if accurate results are to be obtained. The corrected number of counts N, is given by Equation 2-11, which may be stated as:

$$N = \frac{N_0}{1 - N_0 \frac{\tau}{T}},$$

(5-7)

where T, measured in seconds, is the time required for the observed N_0 counts made during a specified number of monitor counts. The chamber-circuit deadtime τ can be measured as in Chapter 2. For the circuit mentioned above, $\tau = 15 \times 10^{-6}$ secs. The dead-time correction is made on each individual reading and *before* subtracting the background.

Background counting rates are determined for this apparatus in a manner somewhat different from that in most experiments. To obtain the background, the detector foil is removed, the duplicate foil retainer ring is inserted and counts recorded, with all other conditions unchanged from those for which the desired measurement is made. It is necessary to subtract the appropriate background for every reading before calculations are made.

ENERGY DETERMINATIONS

To gain some idea of the energy of the neutrons observed, the beam may be filtered by a cadmium, boron, or other appropriate filter. See Fig. 5-14. Detector foils having scattering resonances at known energies may also be used to define the energy of a band of neutrons for measurements at known energies. This latter method is particularly useful when self-detection measurements of resonances are desired and when the resonance considered is due to scattering of neutrons. The method has also been used extensively to measure transmission cross sections at known energies.

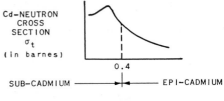

A band of neutrons principally in the thermal energy range may be selected by filtering the beam with a cadmium filter. This is often and more accurately termed the subcadmium beam. To obtain the effect of the subcadmium beam it is necessary to subtract the filtered counting rate from the unfiltered counting rate.

Fig. 5-14. The insertion of a sheet of cadmium about 40 mils thick in the path of the neutrons more or less cuts out neutrons of energy less than about 0.4 ev and transmits those of higher energy.

(NOTE: Do not subtract cross sections to obtain this effect.) Altogether, this cadmium filtering method provides data sufficient to determine three cross sections, viz., reactor cross sections, epicadmium cross sections, and subcadmium cross sections. This method is applicable to all neutron measurements that are discussed in connection with this experiment. The subcadmium cross sections should not be confused with thermal values, since they are an "average" for all energies below about 0.4 ev and are not taken at the single thermal energy of 0.025 ev. Furthermore, hardening of the neutron beam as it passes through thick filters makes it difficult to interpret the meaning of "average." However, values so obtained are useful in the design of reactor components.

SCATTERING CROSS SECTIONS

A standard sample of known scattering cross section σ_2 and known number of atoms per cm², N_2, is placed in the detector position of Fig. 5-7, and the counting rate I_2 measured. No transmission sample is used, but the cadmium filter is or is not in the beam according to the energy range under study. Then an unknown sample is used in place of the known. Using subscripts 1 for the unknown, it can be shown that

$$\sigma_1 = \frac{I_1}{I_2} \frac{N_2}{N_1} \sigma_2. \tag{5-8}$$

As will be shown, this equation is true only for very thin foils, i.e., when $N\sigma \ll 1$. The proof of this follows: Suppose a neutron beam of intensity I_0 neutrons/(cm²)(sec) is incident on the foil. Then the intensity I passing through the scattering foil is $I = I_0 e^{-N_s \sigma}$, where N_s is the number of atoms per cm² and σ is the desired scattering cross section. The intensity of the neutrons scattered will be the incident number, I_0, minus the number passing through, I, i.e., $I_0(1 - e^{-N_s \sigma})$. This is for a monoenergetic beam of neutrons. When the beam contains neutrons of various energies, σ will be an "average" value and the previous expression must be integrated as follows:

$$I_1 = \int K(1 - e^{-N_1\sigma_1})\, dE, \tag{5-9}$$

where dE is an energy interval and K is a constant which includes I_0 and the efficiency of the counter circuit. The integration is taken over the range of neutron energies in the beam. For the standard foil, a similar equation is true, with subscripts 2. From these two equations,

$$\frac{I_1}{I_2} = \frac{\int (1 - e^{-N_1\sigma_1})\, dE}{\int (1 - e^{-N_2\sigma_2})\, dE}. \tag{5-10}$$

"Flat detection" occurs when the scattering sample has no neutron resonances. Then σ_s vs. E is a flat line and the terms in the integrals are constant, so that

$$\frac{I_1}{I_2} = \frac{1 - e^{-N_1\sigma_1}}{1 - e^{-N_2\sigma_2}}. \tag{5-11}$$

Each of the exponentials in this equation can be expanded into a series, as follows:

$$e^{-N\sigma} = 1 - N\sigma + \frac{N^2\sigma^2}{2} - \frac{N^3\sigma^3}{6} + \frac{N^4\sigma^4}{24} - \cdots. \tag{5-12}$$

For sufficiently thin foils, only the first two terms need be used for good accuracy. Then

$$\frac{I_1}{I_2} = \frac{1 - (1 - N_1\sigma_1)}{1 - (1 - N_2\sigma_2)}. \tag{5-13}$$

This leads immediately to Equation 5-8 above, i.e., $\sigma_1 = I_1 N_2 \sigma_2 / I_2 N_1$.

SELF-DETECTION CROSS SECTIONS

Self-detection or self-indication cross sections are those determined by using the same material simultaneously for the detector and for the transmission sample (see Fig. 5-7). They are total cross sections of the transmission sample and are calculated from the transmission Equation 5-6. The method is used primarily for studies of resonances. When the resonance width of the scattering foil is much narrower than the spread of energies among the incident neutrons, greater resolution can be attained than by other methods and higher values of the peak of the resonance can be attained.

First, the intensity I is measured when there is no transmitting sample in the beam. Then $I_1 = \int K(1 - e^{-N_s\sigma_s})\, dE$, as in the measurement of scattering cross sections. Then, with the transmitter in the beam, $I_2 = \int K(1 - e^{-N_s\sigma_s})$ $(e^{-N_T\sigma_T})\, dE$, where the subscripts s stand for the scattering material at the detector and the subscripts T stand for the transmission sample. Also, $I_2 =$

$I_1 e^{-N_T \sigma_m}$, where σ_m is the "apparent" or measured cross section. From the three equations above,

$$e^{-N_T \sigma_m} = \frac{\int e^{-N_T \sigma_T} (1 - e^{-N_s \sigma_s}) \, dE}{\int (1 - e^{-N_s \sigma_s}) \, dE}. \tag{5-14}$$

For sufficiently thin scattering and transmission samples, $e^{-N\sigma} = 1 - N\sigma$, as before. Then

$$1 - N_T \sigma_m = \frac{\int (1 - N_T \sigma_s) N_s \sigma_s \, dE}{\int N_s \sigma_s \, dE} = \frac{\int N_s \sigma_s \, dE}{\int N_s \sigma_s \, dE} - \frac{N_s \int N_T \sigma_s^2 \, dE}{N_s \int \sigma_s \, dE}$$

$$= 1 - \frac{N_T \int \sigma_s^2 \, dE}{\int \sigma_s \, dE}, \quad \text{or} \quad \sigma_m = \frac{\int \sigma_s^2 \, dE}{\int \sigma_s \, dE}. \tag{5-15}$$

In order to evaluate the integrals, a relationship between σ_s and E must be used; i.e., the Breit-Wigner dispersion formula for neutron scattering.* When the integrations have been completed, one obtains

$$\boxed{\sigma_0 = 2(1 - 2 \sin^2 \delta)\sigma_m} \tag{5-16}$$

where σ_0 is the scattering cross section of the peak height at exact resonance and σ_m is the measured cross section calculated from the transmission Equation 5-6. $\delta = -R/\lambda$. The geometric "radius of the nucleus is given by $R = 0.14 \, A^{1/3} \times 10^{-12}$ cm and $\lambda = \lambda/2\pi = (2.6 \times 10^6/4\pi E_0)^{1/2} \times 10^{-12}$ cm, where λ is the neutron wave length and E_0 is the energy in ev at exact resonance. This equation ignores the Doppler broadening of the resonance.

For absorption and foil activation experiments, a form of the Breit-Wigner single-level dispersion formula is used in the derivation and leads to $\sigma_0 = 2\sigma_m$, again omitting the Doppler broadening.† The self-absorption method may be used to find the so-called potential scattering cross section of a material by using thick absorber samples.

Experiments

For the present experiments, a selected number of cross sections are to be measured by use of the annular scattering chamber, a beam of neutrons from the CP-5 reactor, and some appropriate samples of gold. Sufficient data will be taken to obtain the following cross sections:

* R. K. Adair, Rev. Mod. Phys., **22**, 249 (1950).
† For an expression which includes the broadening see Bethe and Placzek, Phys. Rev., **51**, 450 (1937).

1. Subcadmium neutron scattering cross section
2. Epicadmium neutron scattering cross section
3. Reactor neutron scattering cross section
4. Subcadmium total cross section
5. Epicadmium total cross section
6. Reactor total cross section
7. Subcadmium absorption cross section

These cross sections are the *average* cross sections over the energy regions specified.

To obtain the total cross section of gold in the epicadmium region, a Cd filter 30-40 mils thick is used to remove the subcadmium neutrons. A detector such as graphite, which has no resonances, is used to scatter the neutrons into the counter. This same detector is also to be used in the case when the Cd filter is removed. A thick sample of gold (50-70 mils) is used as the transmission sample at the position marked "transmitter" in Fig. 5-7.

To obtain the scattering cross sections, thin foils of gold ($\sim$1 mil) are used as detectors and compared with graphite ($\sim$11 mils) in the epicadmium region. Use for graphite: σ scattering = 4.60 barns, which is the average epicadmium scattering cross section obtained by self-detection methods.

For more reliable results in the subcadmium region, it is desirable to use a vanadium foil 1 mil thick as the known sample for comparison, since the coherent scattering amplitude for this material is nearly zero in this region. By this means the effects of crystals are avoided. For less accurate results, graphite may be used. Take σ subcadmium scattering of vanadium = 5 barns.

In the subcadmium region, subtract the scattering cross section of Au from the total cross section of Au to obtain the thermal absorption cross section. This is acceptable because the total cross section is much larger than the scattering cross section.

The following suggested order of taking data is designed to expedite the experiment:

1. Readings with graphite or vanadium as detector:
   (a) Cadmium in beam.
   (b) Cadmium out of beam.
   (c) Cadmium and thick sample of Au in beam as absorber.
   (d) Cadmium out of beam. Thick sample of Au in beam.
2. Thin foil of Au as detector:
   (a) Cadmium in beam.
   (b) Cadmium out of beam.
3. To obtain backgrounds, repeat the above readings exactly as before but without detector foils. Note that 1(a) and 2(a) are the same in this case. Likewise 1(b) and 2(b) are the same.

Dead-time corrections must be made if accurate results are to be expected. The following cross sections are to be determined:

1. Scattering cross sections of gold
   (a) For pile or reactor neutrons
   (b) For epicadmium neutrons
   (c) For subcadmium neutrons
2. Transmission cross sections of gold
   (a) For reactor neutrons
   (b) For epicadmium neutrons
   (c) For subcadmium neutrons
3. Neutron absorption cross section of gold in the subcadmium energy region.

Supplementary Experiments

Some elements possess prominent scattering resonances at low energies such as Mn (345 ev), Co (135 ev), W (20 ev) and Sm^{152} (8.2 ev). When one of these elements is used as the detector, the neutrons scattered into the counter are principally in an energy band around the energy of the resonance, and thus measurements may be made at this energy.

A. Self-Detection Cross Section of Cobalt. Using two very thin foils of cobalt, each about 1 mil or less in thickness, one as detector and the other as the transmission sample, take readings in the epicadmium region with and without the transmission sample in position. From this data calculate the self-detection cross section of cobalt at 135 ev by Equation 5-6. Then, using Equation 5-16, calculate the peak cross section of the resonance.

B. Test of the $1/v$ Law for Boron. Using each of the following detectors (Mn, Co, W, and Sm^{152} about 1 mil thick) in turn, measure the total cross sections of boron (placed in the "transmitter" positions of Fig. 5-7) at their respective energies and determine whether the $1/v$ law holds for boron at these energies. A useful formula for making this check quickly is the following:

$$\sigma_1 = \sigma_2 \sqrt{\frac{E_2}{E_1}}. \tag{5-17}$$

Take the thermal cross section σ_2 of boron at the energy $E_2 = 0.0253$ ev.

C. Transmission Cross Section of Cobalt. Using a 1-mil foil of Co as a detector, and thick samples of Co as transmission samples, measure the transmission cross section of Co in the epicadmium region for successively thicker samples until the transmission is very small, of the order of 10 to 15 per cent. The 8 or 10 thick samples should range in thickness from 25 mils to 2 in. and may be made up of combinations of Co having thicknesses of 25, 50, 100, 200, 400, and 800 mils. Plot on semilogarithmic paper, the net counting rates vs. sample thickness in atoms per cm^2. From the asymptotic part of this curve, determine the cross section. Identify this cross section.

EXPERIMENT 5-2

CROSS-SECTION MEASUREMENTS WITH A CRYSTAL SPECTROMETER

By S. RABOY, G. R. RINGO, and C. C. TRAIL, ANL, Physics Division

INTRODUCTION

A neutron, although generally considered as a particle, has a characteristic wave length given by the De Broglie equation

$$\lambda = \frac{h}{Mv}, \tag{5-18}$$

where h is Planck's quantum constant, M is the mass, and v is the velocity of the neutron. This dualism exists also for other "particles" such as protons

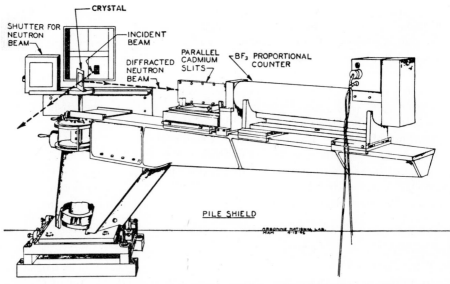

FIG. 5-15. Neutron crystal spectrometer. The paraffin shield is not shown. From W. H. Zinn, Phys. Rev., **71**, 752 (1947).

and electrons and for "waves" such as light, X-rays and gamma rays. The wave length of fast neutrons (1-Mev energy) is 2.86×10^{-12} cm or 2.86×10^{-4} angstroms ($1 \text{ Å} = 10^{-8}$ cm) which is of the order of magnitude of the size of a nucleus; and of thermal neutrons (0.025 ev) is 1.82×10^{-8} cm $= 1.82$ Å, which is, roughly, the size of an atom.

Neutrons, when considered as waves, can be diffracted by crystals just like

X-rays, because their wave lengths are comparable to the spacings between the atoms of crystals. A neutron crystal spectrometer consists of a collimator to produce a narrow beam of neutrons, a table with a graduated circle upon which a crystal is placed, and a collimator and neutron detector on an arm which may be swung around to various angles from the path of the incident

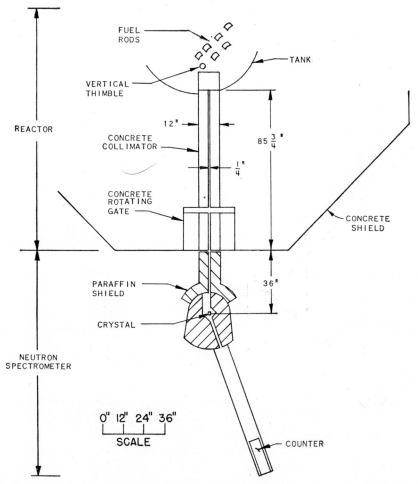

FIG. 5-16. Sketch of spectrometer. This is a cross section of the spectrometer and the reactor taken 42 in. above the floor.

neutron beam. Fig. 5-15 shows such an instrument while Fig. 5-16 indicates its position when using the neutrons from a nuclear reactor.

This type of spectrometer is used chiefly nowadays for two kinds of work: (1) to measure reaction cross sections when it is necessary to record for a relatively long time—more than 10 microsec after the neutron capture—in order to see the reaction; (2) to measure all cross sections in the range from 0.1 to 10 ev, where this instrument gives its highest intensities. For most other cross-section measurements, the various time-of-flight spectrometers are superior.

BRAGG'S EQUATION

Consider a crystal as made up of a large number of planes of atoms regularly spaced a few angstroms apart. When a neutron beam falls on one of these planes, a certain amount is reflected just as light would be reflected from a mirror. The neutron beam, considered as a train of waves moving in the direc-

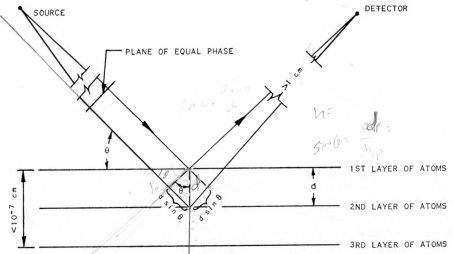

FIG. 5-17. The diffraction of neutrons by atom planes in a crystal.

tion of the beam, has crests and troughs in planes normal to that direction, as indicated in Fig. 5-17. We consider only the waves reflected from the first and second layers of atoms for simplicity. The amplitude of the beam at the detector is the sum of the amplitudes of these two waves if the two are in phase, with crests coinciding with crests and troughs with troughs; otherwise it is less, even zero, if the waves are exactly out of phase. The two waves will be in phase if the differences in their paths, from the plane where they are in phase, to the detector is one wave length, or a multiple of one wave length. From the figure, one can see that this path difference is just $2d \sin \theta$, where d is the interplanar spacing. When the effect of reflections from the other layers of atoms is included, the conclusion is reached that the amplitude of the beam is not just a little less if the waves are not in phase, but is much less, nearly zero, unless the condition stated above is met within very narrow limits. Thus the beam is only appreciable when

$$n\lambda = 2d \sin \theta, \qquad\qquad (5\text{-}19)$$

where n is an integer and is called the order of the spectrum. This is the famous Bragg relation and is the basis for all the work on the determination of crystal structure by X-rays as well as for neutron diffraction.

It is clear from this relation that at any given angle setting of the crystal in the spectrometer with respect to the incident neutron beam, only waves of one particular wave length, and hence of only one energy, or that wave length divided by an integer (n), will be reflected strongly.

The "reflections" involving values of n greater than 1 are not too important in neutron spectrometry because the number of neutrons in the spectrum and the efficiency of the counter which detects them decrease with decreasing wave length. Moreover, the reflectivity of the crystal decreases sharply at the higher orders. These effects, taken together, reduce the second-order "contamination" to about 2 per cent. If necessary, it can be measured and corrected for.

The Crystal Spectrometer

The Argonne crystal spectrometer of Figs. 5-15 and 5-16 consists of a crystal table and an arm for mounting a neutron detector. Both are rotated about a common axis, and the rotation of each is controlled by accurately machined divided circles. They may be locked by means of gears and then rotated together about the same axis. In this case, when the crystal rotates through 1°, the spectrometer arm is made to rotate through 2°.

In its present form, the spectrometer is used as selector of monoenergetic slow neutrons. A highly collimated heterogeneous beam of neutrons from the reactor impinges upon a large single crystal—say, of beryllium—cut along one of its planes—say, the (110) plane. The diffracted beam passes through a second collimator to a neutron detector such as an enriched boron trifluoride (BF_3) counter. Pulses from this counter are amplified in a preamplifier, and then carried by a long cable to an amplifier and scaler rack. Pulses larger than a certain size, which are very apt to be from neutrons reacting with the boron of the counter gas, are registered by the scaler.

A shield (see Fig. 5-16) is necessary around the crystal whenever the neutron flux is so high that people are endangered by scattered radiations or the background counting rate of adjacent experiments is adversely affected.

The Energy of Neutrons Diffracted at a Given Angle

The relationship between the energy E of a neutron and the angle θ at which it is diffracted from a set of (110) parallel planes of a beryllium crystal is obtained as follows: The momentum of a neutron of mass M and velocity v is given by

$$Mv = h\nu/c = h/\lambda = 2\pi\hbar/\lambda, \tag{5-20}$$

where $\hbar = h/2\pi = 1.054 \times 10^{-27}$ erg·sec, ν is the frequency and λ the wave length of the neutrons; c is the speed of light. The mass of the neutrons $M = 1.675 \times 10^{-24}$ gram. Their kinetic energy E is then

$$E = \tfrac{1}{2}Mv^2 = \frac{2\pi^2\hbar^2}{M\lambda^2} \text{ ergs.} \tag{5-21}$$

When the wave length λ is expressed in angstroms, the energy E is expressed in electron volts, and the numerical values above are used, the equation becomes

$$E = 0.0818/\lambda^2 \text{ ev}, \tag{5-22}$$

or

$$\lambda = 0.286/\sqrt{E} \text{ Å}, \tag{5-23}$$

which may be equated to λ of the Bragg equation, Equation 5-19. Then $E = 0.0818 \; n^2/4d^2 \sin^2\theta$, or

$$E = K/\sin^2\theta \tag{5-24}$$

where K is a constant for reflection from a given plane in a given crystal.

At this point, we shall give a brief discussion of the spacing d between the atom planes of crystals. These internal planes can be classified and identified by establishing an imaginary set of coordinate axes in the crystal. Along each

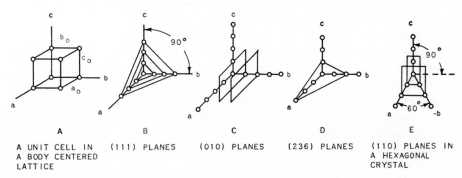

A — A UNIT CELL IN A BODY CENTERED LATTICE

B — (111) PLANES

C — (010) PLANES

D — (236) PLANES

E — (110) PLANES IN A HEXAGONAL CRYSTAL

FIG. 5-18.　A unit cell and Miller indices $(h,\ k,\ l)$ used to designate crystal planes. The circles indicate the centers of atoms.

axis there is a periodic repetition of the atoms. The "unit length," a_0 or b_0 or c_0, is equal to the repeat distance in that direction and is called the lattice constant or lattice period. The entire repeating unit is called a *unit cell* and is the fundamental entity from which the whole crystal is developed. The planes in the crystal are then described in terms of these lattice constants and small integers known as Miller indices, h, k, and l, together with the angles α, β, and γ between the coordinate axes. Miller indices are the smallest integers proportional to the reciprocals of the intercepts of the planes on the axes. For example, in D of Fig. 5-18, the intercepts of the plane with the axes are $3a_0$, $2b_0$, and $1c_0$. The reciprocals of these intercepts are $1/3a_0$, $1/2b_0$ and $1/1c_0$ or, with a common denominator, $2/6a_0$, $3/6b_0$ and $6/6c_0$. The Miller indices are $h = 2$, $k = 3$, and $l = 6$ and the plane is a (236) plane. The symbol (h,k,l) stands for not one but the whole set of parallel planes.

The perpendicular distance d between the planes, for cubic, tetragonal, and orthorhombic crystals in which the three axes are all at right angles to each other, is given by

$$d = 1/\sqrt{\frac{h^2}{a_0{}^2} + \frac{k^2}{b_0{}^2} + \frac{l^2}{c_0{}^2}}, \tag{5-25}$$

which reduces to

$$d = a_0/\sqrt{h^2 + k^2 + l^2} \tag{5-26}$$

for crystals such as rock salt and for copper crystals, which have cubic lattices, i.e., where $a_0 = b_0 = c_0$.

The spacing d between the atomic planes can be determined for a hexagonal crystal such as beryllium from the following equation (see any standard textbook on X-rays):

$$d_{(hkl)} = 1/\sqrt{\frac{4}{3a_0{}^2}(h^2 + k^2 + hk) + \frac{l^2}{c_0{}^2}}. \tag{5-27}$$

For this crystal $a_0 = 2.2855$ Å and $c_0 = 3.5830$ Å.

When Equations 5-19, 5-23, and 5-27 are combined and the numerical values substituted, we find for the (110) planes of beryllium

$$E = 1.565 \times 10^{-2}/\sin^2 \theta \text{ ev.} \tag{5-28}$$

Values of the energy E of neutrons diffracted at angle θ, computed from this equation, are given in Table 5-1.

SPECTROMETER ADJUSTMENT

With the reactor in operation, set the spectrometer arm at some convenient angle such as 12° with respect to the neutron beam from the reactor, and lock it in place. Make sure the crystal table is not locked to the spectrometer arm. Next, locate the desired neutron "reflection" by rotating the crystal. When the angle setting of the crystal planes is not well known, it is possible to rotate the crystal fairly rapidly on its table, say 3° in 1 min of time, while looking for a marked increase in the counting rate of the detector.

After locating the "reflection" roughly, it should be located more accurately

TABLE 5-1. BRAGG ANGLE (θ) VS. NEUTRON ENERGY FOR THE (110) PLANE IN BERYLLIUM

Bragg Angle	Energy (ev)	Bragg Angle	Energy (ev)	Bragg Angle	Energy (ev)	Bragg Angle	Energy (ev)
24'	313.2	4° 6'	3.0645	7° 48'	0.85020	11° 30'	0.39396
30'	195.8	12'	2.9216	54'	0.82900	36'	0.38734
36'	142.4	18'	2.7865	8° 0'	0.80850	42'	0.38084
42'	104.4	24'	2.6587	6'	0.78890	48'	0.37446
48'	82.421	30'	2.5422	12'	0.76991	54'	0.36830
54'	62.640	36'	2.4354	18'	0.75143	12° 0'	0.36225
1° 0'	52.200	42'	2.3478	24'	0.73383	6'	0.35639
6'	42.324	48'	2.2371	30'	0.71670	12'	0.35065
12'	35.590	54'	2.1452	36'	0.70035	18'	0.34508
18'	30.705	5° 0'	2.0605	42'	0.68444	24'	0.33962
24'	26.100	6'	1.9822	48'	0.66923	30'	0.33426
30'	22.695	12'	1.9074	54'	0.65413	36'	0.32906
36'	20.077	18'	1.8358	9° 0'	0.63996	42'	0.32402
42'	17.795	24'	1.7674	6'	0.62614	48'	0.31907
48'	15.818	30'	1.7040	12'	0.61267	54'	0.31421
54'	14.24	36'	1.6449	18'	0.59954	13° 0'	0.30949
2° 0'	12.836	42'	1.5882	24'	0.58695	6'	0.30485
6'	11.686	48'	1.5338	30'	0.57489	12'	0.30034
12'	10.653	54'	1.4815	36'	0.56311	18'	0.29592
18'	9.7267	6° 0'	1.4327	42'	0.55160	24'	0.29156
24'	8.9485	6'	1.3871	48'	0.54056	30'	0.28734
30'	8.2421	12'	1.3431	54'	0.52976	36'	0.28323
36'	7.6019	18'	1.3007	10° 0'	0.51940	42'	0.27919
42'	7.0540	24'	1.2598	6'	0.50927	48'	0.27522
48'	6.5523	30'	1.2225	12'	0.49936	54'	0.27136
54'	6.1171	36'	1.1855	18'	0.48983	14° 0'	0.26756
3° 0'	5.7153	42'	1.1506	24'	0.48052	6'	0.26386
6'	5.3630	48'	1.1169	30'	0.47154	12'	0.26022
12'	5.0192	54'	1.0852	36'	0.46276	18'	0.25668
18'	4.7311	7° 0'	1.0545	42'	0.45431	24'	0.25319
24'	4.4488	6'	1.0248	48'	0.44603	30'	0.24980
30'	4.1983	12'	0.99682	54'	0.43792	36'	0.24646
36'	3.9746	18'	0.96966	11° 0'	0.43010	42'	0.24321
42'	3.7644	24'	0.94394	6'	0.42256	48'	0.24000
48'	3.5672	30'	0.91901	12'	0.41505	54'	0.23684
54'	3.3822	36'	0.89530	18'	0.40792	15° 0'	0.23377
4° 0'	3.2156	42'	0.87240	24'	0.40082		

by recording counting rates at several angles in the vicinity of the peak of intensity. With the crystal set to give this peak, the spectrometer arm and the crystal should be locked together so that they will then rotate at the fixed 2-to-1 ratio.

A convenient form for recording the beam shape is given in Data Sheet 5-1.

DATA SHEET 5-1

BEAM SHAPE MEASUREMENT

Spectrometer Arm Setting (2θ) _____

Crystal Table Angle	Counts

TRANSMISSION MEASUREMENT

The transmission of gold is to be measured over the energy range from 1 to 10 ev. Use a gold foil 1 to 50 mils thick and about 5-10 cms square, located in the path of the neutrons just in front of the counter. The transmission T is found from four measurements according to the equation

$$T = I/I_0 = (R_1 - \gamma_1)/(R_2 - \gamma_2), \qquad (5\text{-}29)$$

in which R_1 is the counting rate with the beam transmitted through the gold sample, R_2 is the counting rate without the sample, and γ_1 and γ_2 are the corresponding counting rates with the crystal rotated to a position 1° off of the peak-intensity position. By this it is meant that the crystal alone is to be rotated 1° off the peak. The spectrometer arm should not be rotated for these measurements. The values of γ_1 and γ_2 give the background due to incoherent scattering and other sources.

In transmission measurements, I/I_0 should be between 0.7 and 0.2. If this becomes smaller, the transmitted beam becomes so weak that it is difficult to measure against the background. If it becomes larger, the calculated cross section will be found to depend on ($I_0 - I$). This is hard to measure when it is a small part of I_0 because of statistical fluctuations. For this reason it is necessary to choose the sample thickness to match the range of cross sections expected. In the case of gold, near resonance, use ~1-mil thickness, and at other energies use 10 to 50 mils.

A convenient form for recording is given in Data Sheet 5-2.

TRANSMISSION MEASUREMENT ON GOLD					
				Crystal 1° Off	
Spectrometer Arm Settings, 2θ	Sample	Open Beam Counts	Transmitted Beam Counts	Open Beam Counts	Transmitted Beam Counts

Transmission Calculations

1. From the measurements of T, calculate the microscopic, total neutron cross sections σ_m of gold at the various energies, using Equation 5-6. This equation can be expressed in the form

$$\sigma_m = -\ln T/N_1, \qquad (5\text{-}30)$$

where $T = I/I_0$ and $N_1 = Nx = (N_0/A)\,(m/a) = $ the total number of atoms per cm² of the sample.

2. Plot the curve of σ_m vs. E. Determine the energy corresponding to the peak of this curve, i.e., the resonance energy of gold, and record on the chart. Compare with published values.

3. The resolution of the spectrometer is limited by the collimation of the beam incident on the crystal. This collimation in turn is determined by a channel ¼ in. wide and 85¾ in. long in the reactor shield. Calculate the spread in θ, and from that, the spread in energy at the Au resonance energy from this cause. Roughly what effect does this spread have on the cross-section curve of Au?

Activation Measurements and Calculations

The second part of this experiment is a direct measurement of activation cross sections as a function of neutron energy. For this purpose indium is suitable because its 57-min period is fairly convenient to count. The experiment consists of placing a series of indium foils in the "reflected" beam at a series of angle settings of the spectrometer and then counting the foils. The spectrometer counter can be used to monitor the flux from the crystal. Then relative values of the activation cross section can be obtained very simply. It must be remembered in calculating the flux that the spectrometer counter has a sensitivity that varies as $1/v$, i.e., directly as the angle of the counter arm with respect to the direct beam.

Indium has several resonances in the region from 1 to 25 ev. Starting the measurement at 1 ev, it should be carried as far up as the flux permits.

Convenient forms for recording the data are given in Data Sheets 5-3 and 5-4.

DATA SHEET 5-3

ACTIVATION MEASUREMENTS				
Spectrometer Arm Setting, 2θ	Time Started	Elapsed Time	Total Counts	Foil No.

DATA SHEET 5-4

FOIL COUNTS				
Foil No.	Time Started	Elapsed Time	Total Counts	Total Counts Minus Background Counts

1. Determine the relative activation cross sections as a function of energy.
2. Plot their values vs. E, and locate the resonances.

REFERENCES FOR EXPERIMENT 5-2

1. A much more precise derivation of the Bragg relation: R. W. James, "The Optical Principles of the Diffraction of X-rays," G. Bell & Sons, Ltd., London (1948), Chapter I.
2. Early experiments: W. H. Zinn, Phys. Rev., **71**, 752 (1947); W. J. Sturm, Phys. Rev., **71**, 757 (1947); Borst, Ulrich, Osborne, and Hasbrouck, Phys. Rev., **70**, 557 (1946).

3. Description of a current instrument: L. B. Borst and V. L. Sailor, Rev. Sci. Inst., **24**, 141 (1953); Sailor, Foote, Landon, and Wood, Rev. Sci. Inst., **27**, 26 (1956).
4. Reports on recent experiments: R. E. Wood, Phys. Rev., **95**, 453 (1954); Allen, Stephenson, Stanford, and Bernstein, Phys. Rev., **96**, 1297 (1954); Sailor, Landon, and Foote, Phys. Rev., **96**, 1014 (1954).
5. General discussion of neutron spectrometers: D. J. Hughes, "Pile Neutron Research," Addison-Wesley Publishing Co., Cambridge, Mass. (1953), p. 159 et seq.
6. Neutron diffraction in general: G. E. Bacon "Neutron Diffraction," Oxford University Press, New York (1955).

CROSS-SECTION MEASUREMENTS WITH CHOPPERS

By J. B. Hoag, ANL, International School of Nuclear Science and Engineering

A steady beam of neutrons of various energies is incident on a rotating shutter. The neutrons pass through this rotor in short bursts of a few microseconds duration and travel to a distant detector, the faster, more energetic

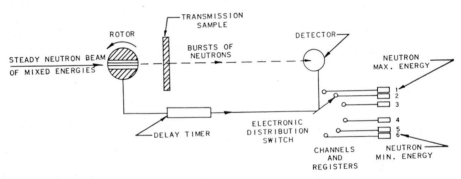

Fig. 5-19. The principle of time-of-flight measurements.

neutrons arriving first, the slower, lower-energy neutrons later on. An energy selection is thus made in terms of the time of flight of the neutrons from the rotor to the detector. The time to reach the detector is measured electronically, usually by distributing the detector pulses to a series of channel circuits, according to the time of flight. Thus Channel 1 of Fig. 5-19 would count only the neutrons of highest energy in the burst while Channel 6 would count only those of some lesser energy. As burst after burst enters the detector, each channel's register adds up the number of neutrons corresponding to its particular energy selection. After a period of time, the register's counts are read and divided by the total time interval, to give the intensity of the neutrons in the original beam at the energies specified by each channel. In this manner, 2, 6, 100, or 1024 intensities are simultaneously determined, according to the number of channels, and the time for collecting the data is shortened.

In order to measure total cross sections, counts are made with and without the transmission sample in place at some point along the flight path, as in Fig.

5-19. Equation 5-6 is used to calculate the cross section for each channel, i.e., for each neutron energy.

If t_1 is the *time of flight* for a flight path of 1 meter (in between the rotor and detector) in microsec/m (microseconds per meter) and v is the velocity of the neutrons, in m/sec, then

$$t_1 = 10^6/v. \tag{5-31}$$

But the energy of the neutrons is $E, = Mv^2/2$, where M is their mass. If this energy is expressed in electron volts, and Equation 5-13 is used,

$$E = 5228/t_1^2 \quad \text{or} \quad t_1 = 72.3/\sqrt{E}. \tag{5-32}$$

Thus the time for a flight path from rotor to detector of l meters will be

$$t = 72.3l/\sqrt{E}. \tag{5-33}$$

For a flight path from rotor to detector of 10 m, the flight time of 1-ev neutrons will be 723 microsec; of 100-ev neutrons 72.3 microsec. These are times that can be measured with electronic devices, the faster neutrons arriving 650.7 microsec ahead of the slower ones.

The *time between bursts* must be great enough that the slowest neutrons in a given burst can reach the detector before the next burst leaves the rotor. The burst time is determined by the speed of rotation n(rps) of the rotor and the number of bursts per rotation. For a single opening in the rotor, there will be two bursts per rotation and the time between bursts will be $t' = \frac{1}{2}n$. With two openings, $t' = \frac{1}{4}n$, etc.

The *burst width,* or time duration of a given burst, is determined by the fraction of time that the neutrons can pass through an opening and by the

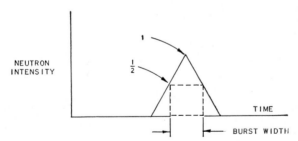

FIG. 5-20. The burst width is one-half the complete time that the shutter hole can pass neutrons.

speed of rotation n of the rotor. If a given opening allows neutrons to pass through during θ degrees of rotation, then the time the shutter is open is $\theta/360n$. This might amount to, say, 5 microsec. However, the intensity of the neutrons is small as the shutter starts to open, rises to a maximum, then decreases to zero as the opening closes. Although of irregular shape in practice, this is symbolized in Fig. 5-20 by the triangle. It is customary to use the time corresponding to one-half the peak intensity to define the burst width. In our example, the base of the triangle of Fig. 5-20 is equal to 5 microsec and the burst width $t'' = \theta/720n$, is 2.5 microsec.

In order to *start* the distribution of neutrons of various energies into their proper channels, a photoelectric cell may be used. Light is reflected from mirrors on the shaft of the rotor (one for each burst) into a photoelectric cell. The electrical output of this cell controls the electronic distribution circuits so that at a suitable time after the burst has left the rotor, the neutrons are fed for a brief time into Channel 1. This brief time is called the "channel time," and is established by the electronic circuits.

In order to open succeeding channels, each to count lower and lower energy groups, several schemes are possible. For *slow choppers*, where the energies of the neutrons are less than approximately 0.4 ev (the cadmium cut-off) a row of photocells is used near the rotor, as in Fig. 5-23. Light reflected from the mirror on the rotor shaft sweeps across the cells in succession. Each cell is separately wired to its appropriate channel.

The energy accepted by each channel of the slow chopper just described can be determined as follows. (1) Choose the value of the energy that the channel is to accept. (2) Compute the time of flight, using Equation 5-33. The flight

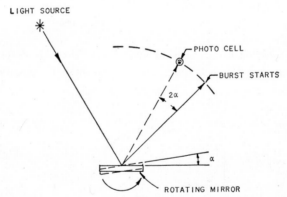

FIG. 5-21. The faster neutrons just reach the detector when the light reaches the photocell.

path l in this equation is to be taken as the distance from the center of the rotor to the center of the detector tube. (3) Compute the proper location of the photocell, as indicated in Fig. 5-21. In this drawing, the solid mirror position is that for the rotor position that just starts the burst on its flight toward the detector. During the time that the neutrons of the desired energy are traveling to the detector, the mirror turns through angle α and the light through angle 2α. The electrical pulse from the photocell then serves to operate an electronic gate which opens the appropriate channel. If T $(= 1/n)$ is the time for one rotation of the rotor, then $\alpha/360 = t/T$, or $\alpha = 360\ nt$, which, from Equation 5-33, gives

$$\alpha = (2.60 \times 10^{-2})\ nl/\sqrt{E}, \qquad (5\text{-}34)$$

where E is in electron volts (ev), n is in revolutions per second, and l is in meters.

Typical rotors for both slow choppers ($E < 0.4$ ev, say) and fast choppers (E ranges up to, say, 100 kev) are shown in Fig. 5-22. Details of a slow rotor are given in Experiment 5-3. The flight path of fast choppers is made considerably greater than for slow choppers—as much as 60 m—and usually is in

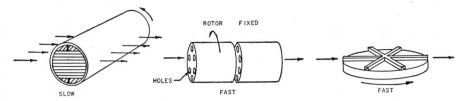

FIG. 5-22. Types of rotors for "chopper" or time-of-flight measurements.

an evacuated tube or one filled with helium to cut down losses of neutrons by scattering.

The photocells of the slow chopper described above and in Experiment 5-3 are merely a convenience in measuring the time intervals and hence the energies of the neutrons. With *fast choppers* it is generally necessary to use more complicated electronic means of timing. There are several such methods, one of which may be briefly described as follows.* Electrical pulses from an oscillator, whose period is equal to the desired channel width, are passed through a gate which is opened by a keying signal corresponding to the time the shutter is opened and is turned off by a pulse from the detector. These oscillator pulses are counted with a scaler. Since they are of known duration (the period of the oscillator), their number is directly proportional to the flight time and, hence, establishes the channel number.

---

* See D. H. Wilkinson, Proc. Camb. Phil. Soc., **46**, 508 (1950) (the application of Wilkinson's system to a chopper was made by L. M. Bollinger); R. W. Schumann and J. P. McMahon, "Argonne 256 Channel Pulse Height Analyzer," Rev. Sci. Inst., **27**, 675 (1956); R. W. Schumann, "1024-Channel Neutron Time of Flight Analyzer," Rev. Sci. Inst., **27**, 686 (1956).

USE OF A LOW-SPEED NEUTRON CHOPPER IN TOTAL CROSS-SECTION MEASUREMENTS

By W. H. McCorkle, Director, Reactor Operations
Division, ANL

The neutron chopper is a device for interrupting a collimated beam of neutrons at a definite but adjustable frequency. A neutron detector whose counting rate may be switched to different registering channels at adjustable known times after a pulse of neutrons passes through the interrupter or rotor will serve to measure the number and time of flight from rotor to detector of different energy groups of neutrons. When the frequency of the chopper and the switching of the counting registers are properly synchronized, the energy of the neutron bands and the associated counting rates may be determined with considerable accuracy and resolution.

APPARATUS

A relatively simple "slow chopper" for making cross-section measurements with low-energy neutrons has been developed.* The essential parts of the chopper are indicated in Fig. 5-23.

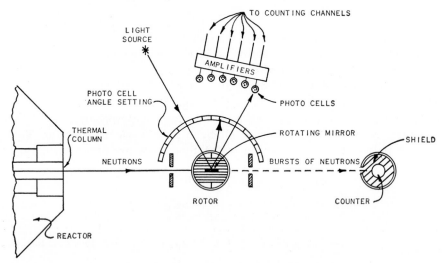

FIG. 5-23. A simple form of a slow neutron chopper.

* Fermi, Marshall, and Marshall, Phys. Rev., 72, 193 (1947); Brill and Lichtenberger, Phys. Rev., 72, 585 (1947).

The Rotor. A rotating cylinder, as in Fig. 5-22, which acts as a shutter for the beam of neutrons from a reactor or other source. A sandwich of alternate sheets of 6-mil cadmium and 30-mil aluminum are mounted in a 2-in.-diameter steel tube about 6 in. long which can be rotated. The aluminum sheets serve as the openings for neutrons passing diametrically through the cylinder. The cadmium sheets block off essentially all neutrons in the subcadmium region (below approximately 0.4 ev). Two $\frac{1}{16}$-in. cadmium sheets are placed the length of the tube at the center and perpendicular to the Cd-Al sandwich. The remaining space in the rotor is filled with aluminum. One end of the shaft of the rotor is extended outward beyond its ball bearings and is flattened and polished on opposite sides to serve as the two mirrors to reflect light to the photocells.

The Neutron Counter. This is a BF_3 proportional counter located at a known distance from the rotor, with its long axis at right angles to the neutron beam. A slot approximately $\frac{1}{2}$ in. wide and several inches long is provided in its shield to admit the neutrons. The counter operates continuously.

Channels. The set of channels is used to record the counts from neutrons of various energies at each burst. Six channels are used in this experiment, but more could be employed. The neutron counts are switched into the various channels at the proper times by means of a gating circuit activated by signals from the set of photocells.

Photocells. The set of photocells is used to adjust the time, after a burst of neutrons leaves the rotor, during which each channel is sensitive. The photocells are activated by a beam of light reflected from the mirror on the rotor. The angle through which the rotor turns after each burst before the light activates the photocells is adjustable. All the photocells are mounted on a common, movable arm whose angle setting thus determines the time of flight and hence the energy of the neutrons for each channel.

Channel Adjustment. The sensitive time of each channel can be adjusted in either of two ways. One method is to have each channel left open for a given time after its corresponding photocell pulse arrives, the time to be determined by an electronic circuit. The other method for adjusting each channel's sensitive time, which is used in this experiment, is to turn off a given channel by the photocell pulse which turns the next channel on.

Motor. An adjustable-speed motor drives the rotor. The faster the rotor is driven, the shorter the burst time, and therefore the greater the resolution, but of course the lower the counting rate. Since the time of flight is determined in part by the rotation frequency, the latter must be known accurately. The rotor frequency can be magnetically synchronized at 60 rps or an integral fraction of 60 rps. The synchronization can be indicated on an oscilloscope tachometer.

Sequence. The sequence of events is as follows: (1) The neutrons pass through the rotor in a short burst. They reach the counter at various times later, depending on their velocities. (2) Light is reflected by the mirror on the rotor shaft into each of the photocells in succession, a short time after the burst. Each photo pulse turns on its appropriate counting channel. (3) Each channel is turned off by a pulse from the next photocell. During the time interval that each channel is open, its scaling circuit records the number of neutrons of the corresponding energy interval.

DATA SHEET 5-5

Measure-ment No.	Sample	rps of Rotor	Photocell Setting	Approx. Energy Range (milli-ev)	Monitor Clicks	Time (approx.)
1 [a]						
2	B + Al Out In	180	120.5°	145-60	25 25	15 sec
3	"	"	100.5°	60-33		
4	"	60	130.5°	30-10		
5	"	"	110.5°	10-5		
6 [a]						
2'-6'	Al only[b] Out In					
7	Beryllium Out In	60	120.5°	16-7	100 400	1 min 4 min
8	"	"	100.5°	7-3.5		2 min 2 min
9 [a]						

[a] *Background Check.* Turn the motor off. Rotate the shutter (rotor) to closed position. Set the gate switch to BACKGROUND CHECK. Take readings for 100 monitor clicks. This count should be multiplied by 1/90 to correct for the fraction of the time the channel is open.

[b] The effect of the aluminum blank is to be subtracted from the corresponding boron-plus-aluminum (B + Al) effect.

Measurements may be repeated for gold or other materials in which you may be interested.

MEASUREMENTS

1. The total cross sections of boron and of beryllium* at various energies are to be determined.

2. The characteristics of the chopper are to be determined at low energies (5 to 10 milli-ev).

Cross-section measurements are made by measuring the fraction of neutrons transmitted, and use of Equation 5-6. To make this measurement, the counting rates are measured with the sample in and out of the beam. The rates of counting are normalized to each other by means of a monitor located inside the thermal column of the reactor or other source supplying the low-energy neutrons for the experiment. Illustrative data are shown in Data Sheet 5-5.

DATA SHEET 5-6

CHOPPER CHARACTERISTICS AT LOW ENERGIES

Measurement No.	Rotor rps	Photocell Setting	Approx. Energy Range (milli-ev)	Monitor Clicks	Time (approx.)
10	120	40.5°	4.5-6.5		
11	120	60.5°	6.5-9		
12	60	90.5°	3-5		
13	30	140.5°	4-9		

INTERPRETATION OF DATA

1. Plot the cross section of boron: (a) as a function of energy, on semilog paper; (b) as a function of $1/v$, on linear paper; (c) any other materials studied, as functions of energy, on semilog paper.

2. (a) Plot the cross section of beryllium as a function of energy. (b) Plot the transmitted neutron intensity for beryllium as a function of neutron wave length λ, and compare with Fig. 3 in Fermi and Marshall, *loc. cit.* λ, in Å, $= 3968/v = 0.286/\sqrt{E}$, where E is in electron volts and v is in m/sec.

3. At a given energy, if the rotor speed is doubled, the burst length is decreased one-half, the counting period (per channel) is decreased one-half, and the burst frequency is doubled. This should result in a decrease by one-half

* E. Fermi and L. Marshall, Phys. Rev., **71**, 672 (1947).

in the counting rate. Compare the data of measurements 5, 10, 11, 12, and 13. They should show that at high rotor speeds some of the low-energy neutrons are cut off by the shutter before they can get through it. Plot the "relative transmission" of the rotor as a function of energy, at rotor speeds of 30, 60, and 120 rps, assuming the relative transmission to be unity at 30 rps for energies above 4 milli-ev.

Questions

If the boron cross section were measured at lower energies than those used in this experiment (this would take too long because the transmission would be so small) it would not show any sudden decrease as occurs in the case of beryllium. Why is this so? Repeat for the other materials studied.

SUGGESTED ADDITIONAL EXPERIMENTS

Experiment 5-4. Measurement of absorption cross sections by the "danger coefficient" method.

Experiment 5-5. Measurement of absorption cross sections by the "pile oscillator," local flux variation method.

Experiment 5-6. Measurement of absorption cross sections by the "pile oscillator," total flux variation method.

Chapter 6

EXPERIMENTS USING AN OPERATING REACTOR

In addition to the measurements of cross sections, as described in the preceding chapter, many other constants and parameters of use in the design of nuclear reactors can be determined by using an operating reactor. Several experiments of this type are described in detail below and others are listed at the end of this chapter.

EXPERIMENT 6-1

DISADVANTAGE FACTOR OF A SIMULATED FUEL ASSEMBLY

By H. BRYANT, ANL, Reactor Engineering Division

INTRODUCTION

In the core of a thermal, heterogeneous reactor, where the fuel and moderator are distinctly separate from each other, the thermal neutron flux inside a fuel element is *less* than that in the moderator. There are several important advantages of lumping the fuel into plates, rods, tubes, etc., separate from the moderator, but the resultant increased value of the neutron density in the moderator and the lowered value in the fuel are disadvantages, as will be explained below.

It is the purpose of this experiment to determine the thermal neutron disadvantage factor, DF, defined by:

$$\mathrm{DF} \equiv \frac{\bar{\phi}_M}{\bar{\phi}_F}, \qquad (6\text{-}1)$$

where $\bar{\phi}_M$ is the average thermal neutron flux in the moderator and $\bar{\phi}_F$ is the same quantity in the fuel.

A small section of a heterogeneous core is constructed, as shown in Figs. 6-1 and 6-2, using the same fuel, moderator, volume ratios, and geometry as in a

FIG. 6-1. A fuel-moderator assembly.

full-sized reactor. In addition, metal foils are supported transversely through the assembly. When exposed to the neutrons in an operating reactor's thermal column, the foils are activated. Subsequent measurements of the activity of each of the foils, after removal from the thermal column and from the assembly,

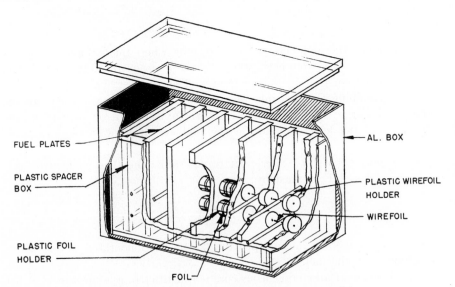

FIG. 6-2. Diagram of a fuel-moderator assembly.

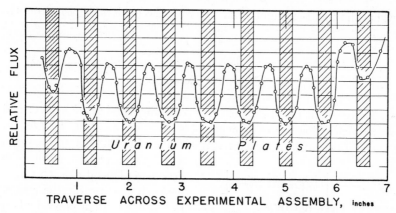

FIG. 6-3.   The thermal neutron flux distribution in a heterogeneous assembly of natural-uranium plates in a light-water moderator. Volume of moderator to volume of fuel = 2:1. Exposed in the CP-5 thermal column.

give the data for a plot of the distribution of the fission-producing neutron flux through the fuel elements and moderator, as in Figs. 6-3 and 6-4. From these, the average flux in the moderator and fuel is obtained. Then the disadvantage factor is computed, using Equation 6-1.

Note that the thermal density is greatest in the moderator. Thus the neutron absorption in this region is augmented. This is known as the excess neutron absorption in the moderator. Moreover, in the fuel, where the thermal neutron density is least, the chance of fission is reduced. Both of these considerations are disadvantageous. For heterogeneous fuel-moderator arrangements of practical interest, the disadvantage factor is approximately 1.5. For a homogeneous

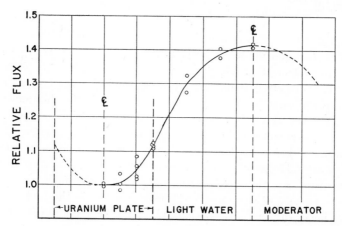

FIG. 6-4.   Intracell neutron flux as measured by copper foil activation. Water to metal ratio = 2:1. Disadvantage factor = DF = 1.32/1.04 = 1.27.

core, where the fuel is intimately mixed with the moderator, the disadvantage factor is 1.

NEUTRON ECONOMY

The effective multiplication factor, k_{eff}, is the number of neutrons at the end of one generation for each neutron at the beginning of that generation. If k_{eff} is equal to unity, the reactor will operate in a steady state because there will be one neutron left to cause a fission at the end of each generation for each one starting the generation. If k_{eff} is less than unity (subcritical condition), there will not be enough neutrons left at the end of a generation to continue the fission chain, and the reactor power will decrease. If k_{eff} is greater than unity (supercritical condition), the power of the reactor will continue to rise.

As indicated in the following equation and in Fig. 6-5, k_{eff} may be considered as made up of six factors:

$$k_{\text{eff}} = \eta \epsilon \mathcal{L}_f p \mathcal{L}_s f, \qquad (6\text{-}2)$$

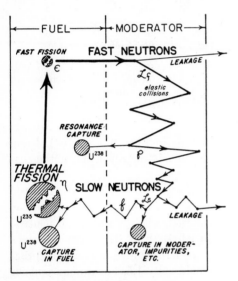

FIG. 6-5. Illustrating neutron economy during one generation (by J. B. Hoag).

where η is the number of neutrons produced by thermal fission for each thermal neutron absorbed in the fuel. Some of the neutrons absorbed in the fuel are captured by U^{238}, while others cause fission in U^{235} with the release of ν fast neutrons. In Equation 6-2, ϵ is the multiplicative effect of fast fission, p is the fraction of neutrons that escape resonance capture during their slowing-down process, $\mathcal{L}_f$ is the fractional number of fast neutrons that do *not* leak out of the reactor, $\mathcal{L}_s$ is the same for the slow neutrons, and f is the thermal utilization of the fuel, i.e., the ratio of the number of thermal neutrons absorbed in the fuel to the number captured in all other materials in the reactor.

For thermal neutron fission in natural uranium (whose isotopic ratio, N^{235}/N^{238}, $= 0.00717$), $\eta = 1.36$, i.e., for every neutron absorbed in this fuel, 1.36 fast neutrons are produced. Actually, each fission of U^{235} produces 2.48 fast neutrons ($= \nu$), but some of the thermal neutrons in the fuel are captured in U^{238} and hence do not cause fission. The value of ϵ for natural uranium is close to 1.03, i.e., the fast fissions add approximately 3 per cent to the number of neutrons. The fraction of neutrons that escape capture in the uranium resonance region depends on the structure of the core materials but may be taken as approximately 0.87 ($= p$) in our example. The thermal utilization factor f may be taken as about 0.9; i.e., 90 per cent of the neutrons that have slowed down to thermal energy will enter the fuel and 10 per cent will be captured by all the other materials in the reactor. The values above give, for the "infinite multiplication factor," $k_\infty = \eta\epsilon pf = 1.36 \times 1.03 \times 0.87 \times 0.9 = 1.09$, i.e., for an infinitely large reactor (no leakage) of the type chosen, each generation would increase the number of neutrons by 9 per cent. However, the leakage of fast and slow neutrons from the sides of the core, even with reflector materials, can easily reduce this value so that the effective multiplication, $k_{\text{eff}} = k_\infty \mathcal{L}_f \mathcal{L}_s$ is equal to unity, the value required for steady-state operation of the reactor.

The Thermal Utilization Factor, f

The number of thermal neutrons absorbed in the fuel is given by $N_F\sigma_F$, where N_F is the number of fuel nuclei (say, U^{235}) per cm^3 and σ_F is the microscopic absorption cross section of the fuel nuclei for thermal neutrons. The number absorbed in the moderator is given by $N_M\sigma_M$. Hence, if the core of the reactor is made of a homogeneous mixture of fuel and moderator and there are no impurities or other materials present, $f = N_F\sigma_F/(N_F\sigma_F + N_M\sigma_M)$, which may be written in the form

$$f = \left[1 + \frac{N_M\sigma_M}{N_F\sigma_F}\right]^{-1}. \tag{6-3}$$

However, in a heterogeneous reactor the volume of the fuel elements, V_F, and of the moderator, V_M, are not necessarily equal. If the neutron density were uniform throughout the core, Equation 6-3 could be modified

$$f = \left[1 + \frac{N_M\sigma_M V_M}{N_F\sigma_F V_F}\right]^{-1}. \tag{6-4}$$

In the experiment which follows, it is found that the neutron density in a heterogeneous reactor is not uniform throughout the core. Equation 6-4 is then to be modified as follows:*

$$f = \left[1 + \frac{N_M\sigma_M V_M \bar{\phi}_M}{N_F\sigma_F V_F \bar{\phi}_F}\right]^{-1}, \tag{6-5}$$

where $\bar{\phi}_M/\bar{\phi}_F$ is the disadvantage factor, as defined in Equation 6-1. Then

$$f = \left[1 + \frac{\bar{\Sigma}_{aM}}{\bar{\Sigma}_{aF}} \times \frac{V_M}{V_F} \times \text{DF}\right]^{-1}, \tag{6-6}$$

where $\bar{\Sigma}_{aM}$ and $\bar{\Sigma}_{aF}$ are the macroscopic absorption cross sections of the modera-

---

*S. Glasstone and M. Edlund, "The Elements of Nuclear Reactor Theory," D. Van Nostrand Co., Inc., Princeton, N. J. (1952), p. 264.

tor and fuel, respectively, averaged over a Maxwellian distribution of the thermal neutrons.*

As an example of Equation 6-6, consider the case of a $2:1$ light-water-moderator natural-uranium-fuel lattice. In this case $\bar{\Sigma}_{aM}$ is approximately 0.02 and $\bar{\Sigma}_{aF} \simeq 0.3$. Take DF as 1.5. Then

$$f = [1 + (0.02/0.3)(2/1)1.5]^{-1} = 1.2^{-1} = 1/1.2 = 0.83.$$

THEORY

In certain cases, it is possible to compute the disadvantage factor from theoretical considerations. Let ϕ_s be the value of the neutron flux at the surface of the fuel. Add and subtract ϕ_s from Equation 6-5. Then

$$f = \left[1 + \frac{\Sigma_M V_M}{\Sigma_F V_F}\left(\frac{\phi_s}{\bar{\phi}_F}\right) + \frac{\Sigma_M V_M}{\Sigma_F V_F}\left(\frac{\bar{\phi}_M - \phi_s}{\bar{\phi}_F}\right)\right]^{-1}, \qquad (6\text{-}7)$$

which may be represented by

$$f = \left[1 + \frac{\Sigma_M V_M}{\Sigma_F V_F}F + (E - 1)\right]^{-1}, \qquad (6\text{-}8)$$

where $E - 1$ is called the excess absorption and F and E are called the lattice functions. Expressions for the lattice constants have been derived using simple diffusion theory for several cases such as flat-plate and cylindrical geometries.† F and E depend on the thermal diffusion lengths of the neutrons in the fuel and moderator and on the geometry of the unit cells of the lattice structure.

It should be realized that the determination of the neutron flux distribution in a nuclear reactor, either by theory or by experimentation, results in some uncertainty. The equations just cited are based on diffusion theory and are not strictly applicable to a light-water moderator. "Adjusted" values of Σ are sometimes used to compensate for the shortcomings of the diffusion theory, while preserving the relatively simple form of the equations. In general, the simple diffusion theory overestimates the value of f. The use of transport theory and of spherical harmonic expansions gives more accurate expressions for f. However, the equations are complicated and need advanced computational techniques for their evaluation. The task of exploring the effects of various parameter changes on the design of reactors involves an extensive program using digital computers. A limiting factor in reactor design today is the magnitude of these computations.

Consequently, experiments of the type described here are needed. A simple way of testing the approximations used in diffusion theory is to compare its

---

*J. A. Harvey and J. E. Sanders, "Progress in Nuclear Energy," Series I, "Physics and Mathematics," McGraw-Hill Book Co., Inc., New York (1956), p. 1.

† Glasstone and Edlund, *op. cit.*, pp. 264-272.

predicted neutron distribution in a reactor lattice with that actually measured. In many cases the experimental work is used to guide the theoretical studies by emphasizing the important physical features of the problem. Once the validity of a theoretical approach has been verified, latitude and certainly come to the reactor design.

On the other hand, the experimental results can be in error. The disturbance of the flux pattern due to the detecting device, the foils, has been kept to a minimum in the experiment described here. This perturbation occurs in both the moderator and fuel, so that the flux ratio or disadvantage factor is not too seriously affected. Another source of error is that due to the capture of neutrons in the resonance region of copper (the foil material) ; there are of course some neutrons of these energies in the "thermal" column where the assembly is irradiated. However, this activity occurs in both the moderator and fuel foils so that the correction to the disadvantage factor from this cause is not too serious. In other words, the copper foils may be considered as $1/v$ detectors.

APPARATUS

In the experimental assembly unit of Figs. 6-1 and 6-2, the natural-uranium fuel plates are 0.25 in. thick and 4.0 in. square. They are held in place in slots in a plastic (Lucite) spacer box which in turn is placed in a 2S aluminum box. The spacer box is nearly filled with distilled light water which serves as the moderator. The moderator-to-fuel ratio (V_M/V_F) is 4 : 1; about 1.5 liters of water are used.

Two kinds of "foils" are used in the assembly shown in Fig. 6-1: (1) cylindrical "foils" of copper wire of 0.030 diameter placed in holes in the fuel plates and in the moderator between the plates; and (2) copper wafers approximately 0.001 in. thick and $\frac{5}{8}$ in. in diameter, sandwiched between plugs of uranium in the fuel plates and between solid discs of Lucite in the moderator region; (3) a copper tape can also be used. Waterproof plastic tape is used to prevent water seepage into the fuel plate interior. The Lucite of the spacers has nearly the same neutron properties as the water which it displaces. It is necessary to expose a large number of foils (say 40 plane and 10 cylindrical) in order to determine the average neutron flux with reasonable accuracy (see Figs. 6-3 and 6-4).

Other lattice assemblies can be used. An alternate form of mounting the flat plates is shown in Fig. 6-6. Volume ratios of 1 : 1, 2 : 1, and 3 : 1 have been used satisfactorily, as well as fuel rods of various diameters, spacing, and clustering. In one version an aluminum box was used to hold an assembly of 37 natural-uranium rods each of 1-cm diameter, arranged in hexagonal lattices of 1 : 1, 2 : 1, 3 : 1, and 4 : 1 moderator-to-fuel volume ratios. Techniques have been developed for measuring f, p, and ϵ upon exposure of this assembly in the

Fig. 6-6. A convenient mount for the uranium-water assembly.

thermal column of a reactor.* Obviously, enriched uranium can be used as the fuel and heavy water as the moderator, so that the variety of assemblies that can be tested is very large.

The completed assembly is irradiated in the thermal column of a reactor such as CP-5, as shown in Fig. 6-7 (see also Fig. 5-5). With a thermal flux of approximately 10^9 neutrons/(cm^2)(sec), an irradiation time of three hours will bring the copper activity to a sufficiently high level for satisfactory counting. The cadmium ratio (see Chapter 1) should have been measured in the thermal column. At the location of the assembly shown in Fig. 6-7, the (gold) resonance flux amounted to approximately 10^5 neutrons/(cm^2)(sec). The cadmium ratio is then $10^8/10^5 = 1000$, indicating that the neutrons are reasonably well thermalized.

As detailed below, great care must be taken to avoid excessive radiological exposure while inserting and removing the assembly, and in removing and counting the foils. Fig. 6-8 shows the instructor removing an irradiated assembly while a radiological health physicist monitors the work.

A Geiger counter or a scintillation counter is used to measure the activity of the "detector" foils. Incidental equipment consists of a balance to obtain the weight of each foil and a calculator for processing the data. A scanning coun-

---

* A. Z. Kranz, "Measurement of Thermal Utilization, Resonance Escape Probability and Fast Fission Factor of Water Moderated, Slightly Enriched Uranium Lattices," WAPD-134 (Sept. 1955); A. Z. Kranz and G. G. Smith, "A Second Report on Measurements of f, p, and ϵ of Water Moderated, Slightly Enriched Uranium Lattices," WAPD-151 (May 1956).

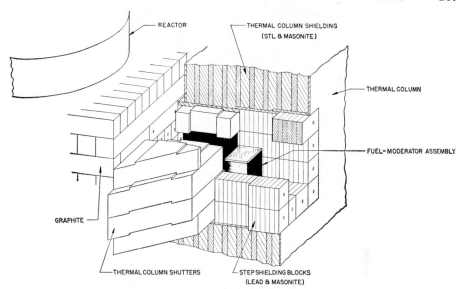

FIG. 6-7.   The location of the fuel-moderator assembly in the thermal column of the reactor CP-5.

ter has proved to be of great assistance in measuring the activity along the length of the copper wire. The wire may be cut into sections, before or after assembly, (1) with pieces inside the moderator and (2) with pieces in the fuel. The net activity of the cylindrical foils represents the average flux in the corresponding medium. The ratio of the two activities, $\bar{\phi}_M/\bar{\phi}_F$, gives the disadvantage factor directly.

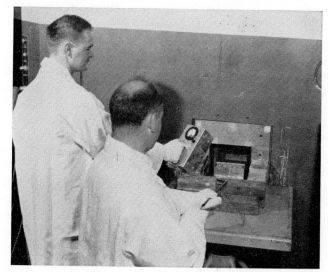

FIG. 6-8.   Removal of an irradiated assembly from the reactor.

The thermal neutron irradiation of the two stable isotopes of copper, Cu^{63} and Cu^{65}, produces the radioactive isotopes Cu^{64} and Cu^{66}. By waiting at least one hour after stopping the irradiation before counting, the Cu^{66}, with a half-life of 5.5 min,[*] will have decayed to such an extent that its contribution to the observed counts will be negligible. The Cu^{64} has the convenient half-life of 12.9 hr for counting. This time is short enough to give high activity buildup during short exposures and yet long enough to permit adequate counting for several hours after shutdown of the irradiation. Cu^{63} is present as 31 per cent of natural copper and has a thermal neutron absorption cross section of 4.3 barns.[†] A larger cross section would poison the core and perturb the flux. A smaller cross section would have necessitated higher power irradiations.

EXPERIMENTAL PROCEDURE

1. The plane foils are punched, marked with an identifying number and weighed. 2. The cylindrical foils are cut, and if necessary, forced to proper diameter, using dies. 3. The foils are positioned in the uranium plates. 4. The plates are installed in the plastic spacer box. 5. the moderator foils are positioned. 6. The prepared assembly is placed in the aluminum container. 7. The moderator is added. 8. The lid is fastened on.

9. An Irradiation Request Form is completed and authorization obtained from the Director, Division of Reactor Operations, for the irradiation in the thermal column. 10. Arrangements are made to have the Radiation Safety Representative stand by to monitor the area in front of the thermal column as the shielding is removed. 11. The Reactor Operators on duty are contacted. Submit the approved Irradiation Request Form to them and enlist their aid in removing the shielding from the thermal column in order to install the experimental assembly.

12. Remove the shielding from the thermal column back to the shutter, making an opening 8×8 in. 13. An aluminum sheet is placed on the floor of the thermal column, and the assembly is placed on it and positioned so as to be just outside the shutter. 14. A beam catcher (see Fig. 5-6) is placed immediately in front of the opening. This precaution is taken to safeguard not only yourself but other researchers in the reactor room. 15. The assembly is irradiated by opening the shutter. 16. The shutter is closed to complete the irradiation. 17. The beam catcher is removed. 18. The assembly is removed by sliding the aluminum sheet onto a hydraulic utility table, as shown in Fig. 6-8. 19. The shielding is reinserted in the thermal hole.

20. The assembly is taken out to a storage area and the foils removed, with care taken to record the position and the number of each foil. Use long-handled tweezers and continue monitoring during this step. 21. The foils are washed in distilled water. 22. Those cylindrical foils that were in the uranium are to be

---

[*] G. T. Seaborg and I. Perlman, Rev. Mod. Phys., **20**, 585 (1948).
[†] R. K. Adair, Rev. Mod. Phys., **22**, 249 (1950).

etched slightly in dilute nitric acid to remove an outer layer which acted as a "catcher" foil for fission-product recoils. Wash in distilled water. Four baths are provided. First, immersion in the acid (2 parts water, 1 part concentrated HNO_3 at 50°C) for 10 sec. Second, a quick dip in a second beaker of the same dilute acid. Third, a rinse in distilled water. Fourth, a second rinse in a separate beaker of distilled water. Then dry. **23.** Remove the foils to the counting room. **24.** Weigh the cylindrical foils.

25. The irradiated assembly must be stored with adequate shielding. The water moderator must be treated as active material.

26. After approximately one hour from shutdown, when the short-lived activity has decreased to negligible value, count each of the foils, as discussed in the next section. **27.** The counting data is recorded and processed, using a calculator. **28.** The results are discussed.

DATA AND COMPUTATIONS

Inspection of Data Sheet 6-1 will show the procedure for counting the foils and the corrections to be made for the counter background, the differences in weights of the foils, and the decay of the activity. The foils are weighed either before or after irradiation; but after the acid, if so treated. Choose for the "standard foil," the one which was located in the center of the central moderator region. The "foil factor" is the ratio of the weight of a given foil to that of the standard. The activity is to be divided by this number in order to normalize the foils to a common weight.

Zero time may be taken as at the beginning of the count of the standard foil. Since all of the copper foils are slowly losing activity, the activities of all later measurements must be increased so as to bring them all back to their activity at the same (zero) time. A decay curve of Cu^{64}, whose half-life is 12.9 hr, is plotted. From this the "decay factor" is entered in the Data Sheet. The activity (next to last column) is divided by the decay factor to get the final corrected activity (last column on the right). Inasmuch as any one counting time is so short, allowance for the decay of Cu^{64} need not be made during these intervals.

The background counting rate is taken periodically while counting the foils. The BG rate to be subtracted in all cases from the "gross counts per min" is the average of all values taken over the entire counting time. After this correction, the adjustments for foil weight and the decay can be made.

At least 10,000 counts should be taken on each foil in order to reduce statistical fluctuation errors. The sample-to-counter geometry is adjusted, by trial and error, so as to minimize the counting losses. See the section Dead Time and Resolving Time in Chapter 2.

Using the corrected activities of the plane foils (the last column in Data Sheet 6-1), plot a flux distribution like that in Fig. 6-3. Average the values of the flux in the moderator and fuel and divide as in Equation 6-1 to obtain the

DATA SHEET 6-1

Plate thickness _____   Date _____

Volume ratio _____   Time of irradiation _____

Time at end of irradiation _____

Standard foil _____

Foil location:

			Time at Start Count-ing	Decay Factor	Counter #1		Gross Counts, per min	Activity After Correction for:		
Foil: Cu. Plane								Back-ground	BG and Weight	BG, Wt., and Decay
Number	Weight, mg	Factor			Total Counts	Min				
BG			10:18		285	1	285			
Std. 20	42.4	1.000	10:31	1.000	12,531	2	6265	5988	5988	5988
1	43.8	1.033	10:36	0.995	17,913	3	5971	5694	5512	5540
2	43.3	1.021	10:42	0.990	11,496	2	5748	5471	5358	5412
⋮										
7										
BG			11:05		262.4	1	262.4			
20	42.4	1.000	11:07	0.970	10,014	2	5007	4730	4730	4876
8										
⋮										
11										
BG										
20										
12										
⋮										
40										
BG										
⋮	⋮	⋮	Average Background = 277					⋮	⋮	⋮
⋮	⋮	⋮	COPPER WIRE (ON COUNTER #2)					⋮	⋮	⋮
BG			10:18		123	5	24.6			
Std. M3	129.4	1.000	10:25	1.000	13,205	1	13,205	13,180	13,180	13,180
F1	32.65	0.2519	10:29	0.996	13,181	5	2636	2611	10,398	10,439
M1	128.2	0.9892	10:35	0.992	11,798	1	11,798	11,773	11,903	11,998
⋮										
BG										
M3										
⋮										
F6										
M3	129.4	1.000	11:30	0.942	12,003	1	12,003	11,978	11,978	12,715
BG			11:32		116	5	23.2			
Average Background = 24.6										

disadvantage factor. Also average the corrected activities of the wire foils and again calculate the DF.

Use your values of DF, and V_M/V_F, in Equation 6-6, together with cross-section data from the literature, to calculate the thermal utilization factor, f.

Time permitting, or from the results of other groups of students, plot the disadvantage factor and the thermal utilization factor as a function of the volume

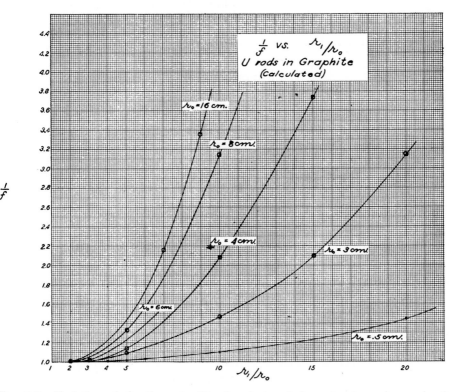

FIG. 6-9. Variation of the thermal utilization factor, f, for natural uranium rods of various radii and separations in a graphite moderator.

ratio. An example of this type of study is shown in Fig. 6-9, where r_0 is the radius of the uranium and r_1 is the radius of the unit cell.

It is recommended that the student peruse Appendix 2, Reactor Summary Tables, of the "Reactor Handbook," Vol. I (AECD-3645) to note the values of f, p, and k_{eff} for various types of reactors.

REFERENCES FOR EXPERIMENT 6-1

Thermal Utilization: (1) S. Glasstone and M. Edlund, "The Elements of Nuclear Reactor Theory," D. Van Nostrand Co., Inc., Princeton, N. J. (1952) Chapter 9; (2) "The Reactor Handbook," Volume I, Physics, Declassified Edition, Chapter 1.5;

(3) D. J. Hughes, "Pile Neutron Research," Addison-Wesley Publishing Co., Cambridge, Mass. (1953); (4) A. Weinberg, "Science and Engineering of Nuclear Power," Addison-Wesley Publishing Co., Cambridge, Mass. (1949), Vol. II, Chapter 6; (5) Ivan C. Atkinson and Raymond L. Murray, "Optimizing Multiplication Factors of Heterogeneous Reactors," Nucleonics, **12**, No. 4, 50-56 (1954); (6) G. F. von Dardel, "A Study of the Interaction of Neutrons with Moderating Materials," Phys. Rev., **94**, 1272 (1954).

Foil Activation: (7) S. H. Fitch and J. E. Drummond, "Neutron Detector Perturbations," Report LRL-95, Livermore Research Laboratory, Livermore, California (February 1954); (8) Robert C. Axtmann and James S. Stutheit, "Scintillation Counting of Natural Uranium Foils," Nucleonics, **12**, No. 7, 52-53.

EXPERIMENT 6-2

SHIELDING EXPERIMENTS

By M. Grotenhius,* Assistant Director, International School of Nuclear Science and Engineering

Introduction

One of the many problems associated with the design and operation of reactors is the attenuation of the radiation which is given off. This radiation, which for shielding purposes may be limited to neutrons and gamma rays as is indicated in Fig. 6-10, must be reduced to levels in which people, instruments, and equipment can function properly. It is desirable, if not necessary, to predict these radiation levels during the design stages by arranging materials around the reactor so as to control the escaping radiation.

There are two types of shields which have been given serious attention— the monolithic type, usually concrete, and the composite shield, usually hydrogenous material to attenuate neutrons and a heavy metal for gamma-ray attenuation. Concrete has been utilized † in stationary reactor shields where low cost is a primary consideration; the composite type has been employed in situations where space and weight are the primary considerations.

At the present time the neutron‡ and gamma-ray spectra§ are well known. The fundamental processes of neutron‖ and gamma-ray attenuation¶ are also

* It would not have been possible to set up this experiment without a great deal of assistance. It is a pleasure to acknowledge, in particular, the valuable assistance rendered by J. W. Butler for technical advice, H. Bryant for instrumentation, T. Brill for electronics, and E. E. Hamer for mechanical design.

† J. F. Hogerton, et al., "Reactor Handbook," AECD-3645, Vol. I, Appendix 2.

‡ T. Rockwell, III, "Reactor Shielding Design Manual," TID-7004 (Mar. 1956), p. 32.

§ Rockwell, *ibid.*, TID-7004, p. 34; F. H. Clark, "Decay of Fission Product Gammas," NDA-27-39 (Dec. 30, 1954); P. Mittleman, "Gamma-Rays Resulting from Thermal Neutron Capture," NDA-10-99 (Oct. 6, 1953); Nucleonics, **13**, 50 (1955).

‖ Rockwell, *op. cit.*, TID-7004, pp. 5 and 48; "Reactor Handbook" AECD-3645, p. 667.

¶ Rockwell, *op. cit.*, TID-7004, p. 7; "Reactor Handbook," AECD-3645, p. 637; H. Golstein, "Calculations of the Penetrating Gamma Rays," NDA-15C-41 (June 30, 1954); U. Fano, "Gamma Ray Attenuation," Nucleonics (Aug., Sept., 1953).

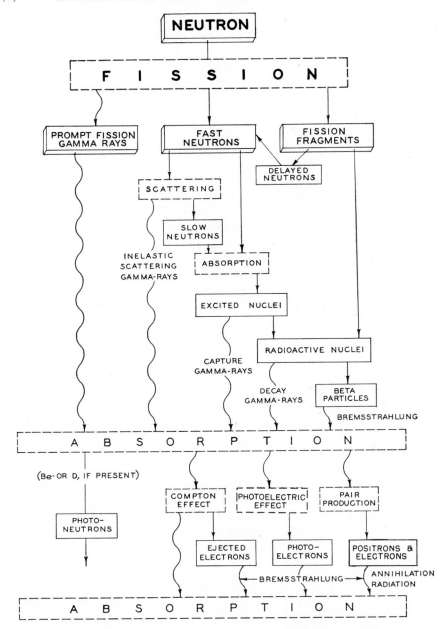

FIG. 6-10. Neutrons and gamma rays are the main radiations which must be attenuated by the shield of a nuclear reactor.

well known. However, the combination of all this knowledge in a form usable for designing a reactor shield becomes a complex problem. As a consequence, shield design has been heavily dependent upon experimental data, particularly when the weight and volume of the shield must be kept to a minimum.

Experimental data for shielding purposes may of course come from surveys of existing reactor shields as well as from fundamental experiments such as the determination of cross sections* or spectra. There are also facilities† designed and operated for the express purpose of testing shield configurations and materials. Concrete shields have been designed on the basis of data obtained from bulk attenuation experiments,‡ which have so far resisted interpretation in terms of fundamental nuclear information. It has been found, however, that a composite shield containing a large proportion of hydrogenous material may be successfully analyzed in terms of fast-neutron "removal" cross sections.§ These will be discussed in a later paragraph.

Notable examples of shielding facilities in present operation are the Lid Tank Facility and the Bulk Shielding Facility at Oak Ridge National Laboratory. The Lid Tank Facility is a tank of water $7 \times 7 \times 11$ ft, in which slabs of material may be arranged. The source of radiation is a natural-uranium disc exposed to thermal neutrons from the X-10 reactor. The Bulk Shielding Facility is a larger tank of water in which a reactor core is suspended. It was built primarily to obtain readings through shield thicknesses comparable to an operating shield. Brookhaven National Laboratory has a Lid Tank Facility similar to that of Oak Ridge.‖ Water is an obvious choice for these experiments because of its value as a typical hydrogenous material as well as being a convenient medium in which to work.

REMOVAL CROSS SECTIONS

In addition to measuring the radiation that passes through shielding configurations, the Lid Tank Facility is used to determine fast-neutron "removal" cross sections¶ for shield materials in a hydrogenous medium and an experimental function which describes the attenuation of fission neutrons in water. "Removal" cross sections thus determined have been tabulated for many materials commonly used in shielding reactors.** In magnitude they are often two-thirds to three-quarters of the total neutron cross section for neutrons above

---

* D. J. Hughes, and J. A. Harvey, "Neutron Cross Sections," BNL-325 (July 1, 1955).

† Hogerton, op. cit., AECD-3645, p. 671; H. P. Sleeper, Jr., "A Critical Review of ORNL Shield Measurements: Neutron Attenuation," ORNL-436 (Dec. 21, 1949).

‡ Hogerton, op. cit., AECD-3645, p. 674.

§ Hogerton, AECD-3645, p. 673; Rockwell, TID-7004, pp. 6, 58, 75.

‖ A. C. Rand, "Mechanical Features of the Brookhaven Shielding Facility," BNL-139 (Dec. 1951).

¶ G. P. Chapman and C. L. Storrs, "Effective Neutron Removal Cross Sections for Shieldings," AECD-3978 (Sept. 19, 1955).

** T. Rockwell, III, op. cit., TID-7004, p. 7.

1 Mev. The attenuation of fast neutrons in an actual composite shield is then obtained by applying the experimental information in the proper geometry and thickness of materials.

In order to measure a removal cross section, a neutron flux traverse must be measured both parallel and perpendicular to the neutron beam in the water. This procedure is repeated behind a slab of material located in the water. There will be a reduction in the neutron flux in that portion of the parallel traverse in which the fast and thermal neutron fluxes are in equilibrium. The concept of the "removal cross section" for this material is based on the assumption that there is exponential attenuation of fast neutrons within this material. The amount of attenuation must be determined from that part of the data where the fast and thermal neutron fluxes are in equilibrium. In this region the curves representing the neutron flux, with the slab and without the slab, will be parallel. This is true whether the detector measures thermal or fast neutron flux. For infinite plane geometry, the microscopic removal cross section σ_r may then be calculated by the equation,

$$\sigma_r = \frac{1}{Nt} \ln \left(\frac{\phi_1}{\phi_2} \right) \text{ barns,} \tag{6-9}$$

where t = slab thickness, N = atoms/cm^3 of material $\times$ 10^{-24}, ϕ_1 = neutron flux in the water, and ϕ_2 = neutron flux behind an equal amount of water, with the slab in place.

Because the geometry is not that of an infinite-plane collimated source, or because the beam is spread owing to scattering, it is not quite proper to use the centerline fluxes in the above formula. Instead, the following integrated flux should be used.

$$\phi = K \int_0^\infty r \, \phi(r) \, dr, \tag{6-10}$$

where ϕ is the corrected flux at the point where σ_r is being calculated, $\phi(r)$ is the flux traverse perpendicular to the beam, K is a proportionality constant, and r is measured from the beam centerline.

It is recognized that the removal cross section is not truly a constant. However, for practical consideration and within the limits of criteria indicated in the reference*, it may be treated as such.

Strictly speaking, "removal" theory does not apply when the materials are located in media other than water. It may, however, be extended to include other hydrogenous media with reasonable assurance of a good answer. A similar type of calculation may also be utilized when calculating fast-neutron leakage through a concrete shield. A comforting coincidence that supports this type of calculation is that the computed "removal" cross section for concrete has about the same value as the reciprocal of the measured relaxation length for fast

* Rockwell, TID-7004, pp. 6, 58, 75.

neutrons in concrete. Then too, a reactor that is shielded with concrete usually does not have too strict limitations on space or weight, and doubts may be dispelled with an extra measure of concrete.

OBJECTIVES

The design of a reactor shield may be divided into five related problems:

1. Attenuation of fission neutrons
2. Attenuation of fission gamma rays
3. Production of thermal neutrons in the shield materials
4. Production and attenuation of secondary gamma rays
5. Heat generation in reactor components

Other problems to be considered include the attenuation of radiation caused by neutron activation of coolant and structural materials, and the reduction of streaming from cracks and holes in the shield. It is the solution of these problems that determines the adequacy of a particular shield design.

The facility used in the following experiment is designed to test the shielding properties of water and materials located in a water medium. It will serve to illustrate principles involved in the solution of the problems suggested. Particular emphasis will be placed on fast-neutron attenuation, the slowing down of fast neutrons to thermal energies, and the production of capture gamma rays. While related experiments are beyond the time limitations of this experiment, arrangements can be made for additional experiments. These additional experiments could include instrument calibration, buildup experiment with Co^{60} gamma-ray source,[*] heat generation in iron, reactor gamma-ray attenuation, experiments with slabs of other materials of interest, and measurements of radiation from holes in a reactor.

DESCRIPTION OF APPARATUS

Source. The source of radiation is a reactor such as CP-5, operating at about 1 megawatt. The radiation from the core is allowed to pass through a 4-in. beam hole to the water tank located at the mouth of the hole (Fig. 6-11). The beam is partially controlled by a movable door which consists of 4 in. of lead and $5\frac{1}{2}$ in. of heavy concrete, lined with Boral [†] (Fig. 6-12). In addition there are semipermanent boral-lined lead plugs that may be inserted in the beam hole to control the thermal neutrons and gamma rays that reach the tank (Figs. 6-12 and 6-13). These plugs will have relatively little effect on the fast-neutron flux.

---

[*] G. R. White, "The Penetration and Diffusion of Co^{60} Gamma-Rays in Water Using Spherical Geometry," Phys. Rev., **80**, 154 (1950).

[†] Boral is a composite of boron carbide, B_4C, in an aluminum matrix, with an aluminum cladding. See V. L. McKinney and T. O. Rockwell, "Boral: A New Thermal Shield," ORNL-242, AECD-3625 (July 1949).

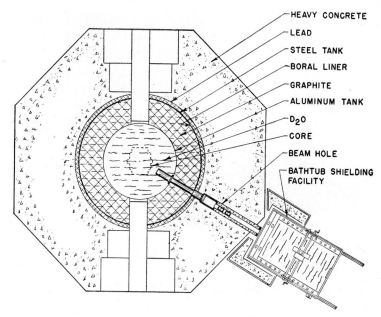

HEAVY CONCRETE
LEAD
STEEL TANK
BORAL LINER
GRAPHITE
ALUMINUM TANK
D_2O
CORE
BEAM HOLE
BATHTUB SHIELDING FACILITY

FIG. 6-11. Plan view of bathtub shielding facility at the CP-5 location.

Normal operation is with one plug in the beam hole. The beam is thus filtered by 2 in. of lead and a layer of boral.

Water Tank. A tank of water is located outside the beam hole (Figs. 6-14 and 6-15). The radiation passes from the beam hole into the water tank through a plastic window (polyethylene, ¾ in. thick). Additional shielding is provided at the sides of the tank by means of heavy concrete in steel forms, and at the back of the tank in the form of two 4-in.-thick iron slabs. These are the same iron slabs that will be tested as shielding materials. These slabs and any other that are to be tested are located in the tank by pins which fit into holes in the

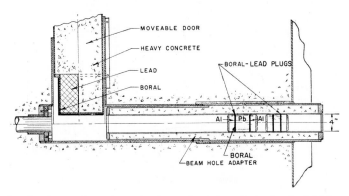

MOVEABLE DOOR
HEAVY CONCRETE
LEAD
BORAL
BORAL-LEAD PLUGS
Al   Pb   Al
4"
BORAL
BEAM HOLE ADAPTER

FIG. 6-12. Sectional view of a 4-in. beam hole for the bathtub shielding facility.

FIG. 6-13.   Beam-hole adapter and lead-boral plugs.

rails on either side of the tank. The positioning of these slabs is accomplished by the overhead crane.

Instrumentation. The instruments are placed in an aluminum can (Fig. 6-16) suspended at the end of an aluminum tube. The voids around the instruments are filled with plastic (Lucite) to simulate water. The wiring passes from the instruments through the tube and then to the instrument panel. The instruments may be located at any position within the tank by means of a traversing mechanism (Fig. 6-17) operated by manual cranks. The position may be noted by the scales permanently mounted within the tank.

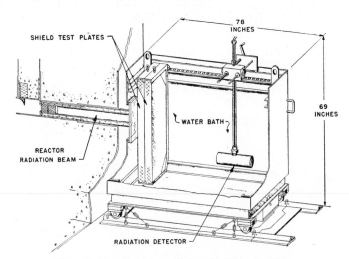

FIG. 6-14.   Drawing of the shielding facility.

There are three basic instruments involved in this experiment: a fast-neutron detector, a thermal-neutron detector, and a gamma-ray detector. Only pertinent details will be given here.

The fast-neutron detector is the Raychronix F-1 fast-neutron dosimeter* shown in Figs. 6-18 and 6-19. A feature of this detector is that it measures a quantity proportional to the fast-neutron dose-rate. If located in a region where

FIG. 6-15.   The shielding facility at ANL.

the gamma background is high, this instrument must be shielded with a few inches of lead.

Thermal neutrons can be detected with a U^{235} fission counter, as shown in Fig. 6-20. Baer and Bayard† give full details of this instrument. A feature is its operation as a counter at low fluxes, and as a chamber at high fluxes.

---

* G. S. Hurst et al., "A Count Rate Method of Fast Neutron Tissue Dose," Rev. Sci. Inst., **22**, 981 (Dec. 1951).

† W. Baer and R. T. Bayard, "A High Sensitivity Fission Counter," Rev. Sci. Inst., **24**, No. 2, 138 (Feb. 1953).

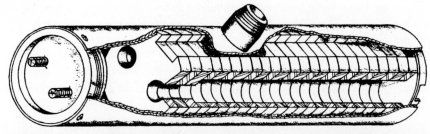

FIG. 6-16. Instrument can for bathtub shielding facility.

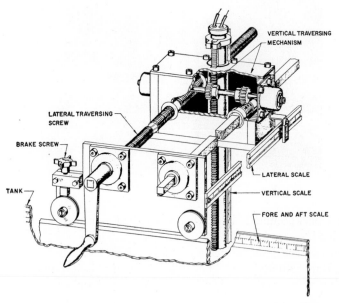

FIG. 6-17. Traversing mechanism for bathtub shielding facility.

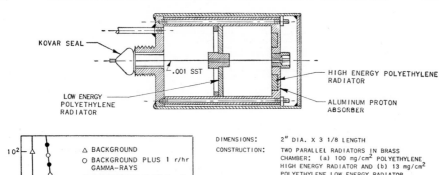

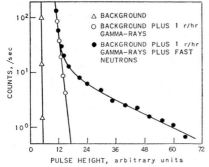

DIMENSIONS: 2" DIA. X 3 1/8 LENGTH

CONSTRUCTION: TWO PARALLEL RADIATORS IN BRASS
                CHAMBER: (a) 100 mg/cm^2 POLYETHYLENE
                HIGH ENERGY RADIATOR AND (b) 13 mg/cm^2
                POLYETHYLENE LOW ENERGY RADIATOR
                COVERED WITH 50 mg/cm^2 ALUMINUM PROTON
                ABSORBER

FILLING: 13.2 cm Hg METHANE, 30.0 cm Hg ARGON

SENSITIVITY: APPROX. .013 counts/n/cm^2 PROPORTIONAL
                TO HUMAN TISSUE SENSITIVITY TO 0.2–10
                Mev NEUTRONS

OPERATING V: 1400 VOLTS

PULSE HEIGHT: UP TO 750 mv, DEPENDING UPON NEUTRON
                ENERGY

DISCRIMINATION: APPROX. 6–1 GAMMA PULSE HEIGHT DIS-
                CRIMINATION

DIRECTIONALITY: 2–1

Fig. 6-18.   Fast-neutron dosimeter.

Fast Neutron Dosimeter

Fission Counter

Gamma-Ray Chamber

Fig. 6-19.   Neutron and gamma-ray detectors.

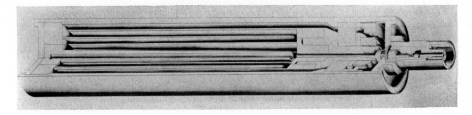

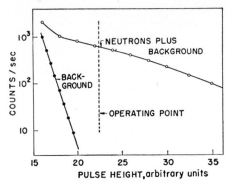

Electrode spacing: .15 in.
Operating voltage: 300 volts
Coating: 2 mg/cm^2
Filling: Nitrogen 2 atmospheres
Total of 1.6 grams of enriched U^{235}
Sensitivity: 0.7 counts per unit thermal
            neutron flux in a background
            of 5 cps, 1.2 x 10^{-13} amp per
            unit thermal neutron flux
Alpha current: 1.2 x 10^{-8} amp
Volume: 152.3 cc

FIG. 6-20. Fission counter. The same construction and operation is used for a *gamma-ray chamber* with the following changes: U^{235} coating—none; sensitivity—4.2 × 10^{-11} amp/r/hr.

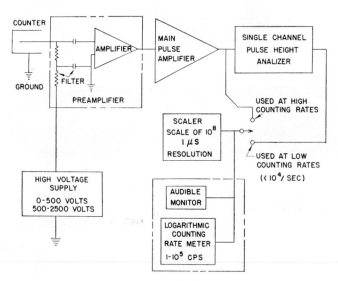

FIG. 6-21.   The pulse channel.

The gamma-ray dose rate can be measured with an instrument constructed identically like the fission counter except for the U^{235} coating (see Fig. 6-20).

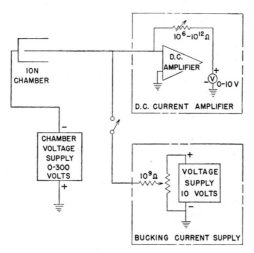

Fig. 6-22. The current channel.

Block diagrams, Figs. 6-21 and 6-22, show the electronic equipment used and the way in which the instruments are connected to it.

Geometry Used at ANL. The x axis is taken horizontally in a direction parallel to that of the beam. The front of slab No. 1, nearest the reactor, is 76.5 in., the front of the second slab is 72.5 in., and the rear of the latter is 68.5 in. from the zero of the x scale. The distance from the front of the instrument can to its vertical center lines is 9 in. The y axis is taken horizontally across the can, at right angles to the beam. The z axis is vertical, its zero located 7 in. above the horizontal centerline of the instrument can. The instrument can has, on its front end, ⅛-in. Al and ⅛-in. plastic. The horizontal centerline of the detectors are offset 1 ³⁄₁₆ in. from the horizontal centerline of the can. The diameter of the holes in which they are placed is 2 in.

Experimental Procedure

1. Locate the instruments with respect to the coordinate system, from the dimensions and location of the instruments in the can.
2. Open the beam-hole door and survey the exterior of the tank with a gamma-ray survey meter. This is done to insure that there is adequate protection for the experimenters.
3. Make a vertical and horizontal traverse for fast neutrons, thermal neutrons, and gamma rays at two positions—midway in the tank and at the far end of the tank.
4. Take readings of fast neutrons, thermal neutrons, and gamma rays on the beam-hole centerline throughout the length of the tank.

5. Place one 4-in. iron slab in the tank at the position nearest the reactor and repeat steps 2, 3, and 4.

6. Repeat step 5 with two adjacent 4-in. iron slabs in the tank.

7. Repeat step 5 with the slabs in another location.

CALCULATIONS AND PROBLEMS

1. Compare fast and thermal neutron curves in the three sets of measurements.

   a. Does measurement of thermal neutrons yield information about the fast neutrons?

   b. Why does the thermal-neutron flux peak behind the iron?

   c. Calculate a fast-neutron removal cross section for iron.

2. Note the gamma-ray curves.

   a. Calculate the gamma-ray relaxation length for H_2O and also for Fe.

   b. Is the gamma-ray absorption coefficient for water different when the iron is in the tank? Why?

   c. Compare the sharpness of the gamma beam with that of the neutron beam.

3. Estimate the intensity of the water capture gamma rays and iron capture gamma rays at the sides and end of the tank and compare with the gamma-ray survey reading.

4. Calculate the shielding necessary for an operating reactor.

BIBLIOGRAPHY FOR EXPERIMENT 6-2

REPORTS

Aronson, R., J. Certaine, H. Goldstein, and S. Preiser, "Penetration of Neutrons from a Point Isotropic Fission Source in Water," NYO-6267 (Sept. 22, 1954).

Aronson, R., J. Certaine, and H. Goldstein, "Penetration of Neutrons from Point Isotropic Monoenergetic Sources in Water," NDA-15C-60 (NYO-6269) (Dec. 15, 1954).

Beghian, L. E., et al., "The Inelastic Scattering of Fast Neutrons by Light Nuclei," Phys. Rev., 77, 286 (1950).

Davisson and Evans, "Gamma Ray Absorption Coefficients," Rev. Mod. Phys., 24, 79 (1952).

Dixon, W. R., "Buildup Factors for the Transmission of Co^{60} Gamma-Rays Through Concrete and Lead," Phys. Rev., 85, 498 (Feb. 1952).

Durham, F. P., "Heat Transfer and Thermal Stresses in Nuclear Reactor Shells," LA-1590 (Sept. 1953). Dep. (mc).

Engberg, C. J., "Radiation Shields and Shielding," TID-3032 (Sept. 1952).

Gallaher, R. B., and A. S. Kitzes, "Summary Report on Portland Cement Concretes for Shielding," ORNL-1414 (March 2, 1953). Dep.

Garrett, C., and G. N. White, "Buildup Measurements on Co^{60} Gamma-Radiation in Iron and Lead," Phys. Rev., 95, 889 (Aug. 15, 1954).

Grace, M. A., et al., "The Inelastic Scattering of Fast Neutrons," Phys. Rev., **82**, 969 (1951).

Grodstein, Gladys White, "X-ray Attenuation Coefficients from 10 kw to 100 mev," NBS Circular 583 (April 30, 1957).

Grotenhuis, M., and J. W. Butler, "Experimental Boiling Water Reactor (EBWR) Shield Design," ANL-5544 (Aug., 1956).

Gugelot, P. C., and M. G. White, "On the Shielding Qualities of Different Concrete Mixtures," Jour. App. Phys., **21**, 5 (1950).

Hayward, E., and J. H. Hubbell, "An Experiment in Gamma-Ray Backscattering," NBS-2264 (Feb. 10, 1952).

Hayward, E., and J. H. Hubbell, "The Albedo of 1 Mev Photons," Phys. Rev., **93**, 955 (1954).

Le Caine, J., "A Table of Integrals Involving the Functions $E_n(x)$," National Research Council of Canada #1553, MT-131, Ottawa.

Moteff, J., "Miscellaneous Data for Shielding Calculations," APEX-176 (Dec. 1, 1954).

Moteff, J., "Fission Product Decay Gamma-Ray Spectrum," APEX-134.

Nelms, A. T., "Graphs of the Compton Energy-Angle Relationship and the Klein-Nishina Formula from 10 Kev to 500 Mev," NBS Circular 542 (Aug. 28, 1953).

Peebles, G. H., "Attenuation of Gamma-Rays," Part I, J. Appl. Phys., **24**, 1271 (Oct. 1953; Part II, 1437 (Dec. 1953).

Placzek, G., "The Functions $E_n(x) = \int_1^\infty du e^{-xu} u^{-n}$," National Research Council of Canada #1547, MT-1, Ottawa.

Rockwell, T. R., III, "Construction of Cheap Shields," AECD-3352 (Jan. 16, 1950).

Rockwell, T. R., III, and A. S. Kitzes, "Theoretical and Practical Aspects of Shielding," ORNL-710 (Sept. 29, 1950).

Roys, P. A., K. Shure, and J. J. Taylor, "Penetration of 6 Mev Gamma-Rays in Water," (WAPD-T-163) Phys. Rev., **95**, 911 (1954).

Senftle, F. E., and W. Z. Leavitt, "Activities Produced by Thermal Neutrons," Nucleonics **6**, #5, 54, May (1950).

Shure, K., P. A. Roys, and J. J. Taylor, "Penetration of 6 Mev Gamma-Rays in Lead and Iron," (WAPD-T-170) Phys. Rev., **95**, 610A (1954).

Simon, A., and C. E. Clifford, "Attenuation of Neutrons by Air Ducts in Shields (Revised)," ORNL-1217 (Mar. 8, 1954). Dep.

Taylor, J. J., and F. E. Obenshain, "Flux from Homogeneous Cylinders Containing Uniform Source Distributions," WAPD-RM-213 (Dec. 7, 1953).

Taylor, J. J., "Applications of Gamma Ray Buildup Data to Shield Design," WAPD-RM-217 (Jan. 25, 1954).

Untermyer, S., and J. T. Weills, "Heat Generation in Irradiated Uranium," ANL-4790, AECD-3454 (Feb. 25, 1952). Dep. (mc).

Voress, H. E., "Radiation Shields and Shielding," TID-3032, Supp. 1 (Dec. 1, 1954).

Watt, B. E., "Energy Spectrum of Neutrons from Thermal Fission of U^{235}," Phys. Rev., **87**, 1037 (1952).

Way, K., "Decay of Fission Product Gamma-Rays," Phys. Rev., **70** (1946).

BOOKS

Blizzard, E. P., in Annual Review of Nuclear Science, **5**, 73 (1955).

Glasstone, S., "Principles of Nuclear Reactor Engineering," D. Van Nostrand Co., Inc., Princeton, N. J. (1955).

Goldstein, H., "The Attenuation of Gamma Rays and Neutrons in Reactor Shields," Division of Reactor Development, USAEC.

NBS Handbook 59, "Permissible Dose from External Sources of Ionizing Radiation," National Bureau of Standards, Washington, D. C. (Oct. 24, 1954).

Price, B. T., C. C. Horton, and K. T. Spinney, "Radiation Shielding," Pergamon Press, New York. International Series of Monographs on Nuclear Energy, Div. X, Vol. 2.

Stephenson, R., "Introduction to Nuclear Engineering," McGraw-Hill Book Co., Inc., New York (1954).

EXPERIMENT 6-3

RADIATION LEAKAGE THROUGH A STEPPED SHIELDING PLUG

By H. C. STEVENS, ANL, Reactor Operations Division

INTRODUCTION

In most reactor shields there are various types of removable portions called "shielding plugs." They facilitate various operations on the reactor or its component parts, such as refueling, repairing, construction, instrumentation, the insertion of samples, and the opening of beam holes, in the case of an experimental reactor.

Most of the shielding plugs present a problem to the reactor shield itself in that they all have a finite gap or space between mating surfaces. A direct gap through a reactor shield will provide an area of leakage of radiation, sometimes referred to as "streaming." Generally speaking, the entire shield being

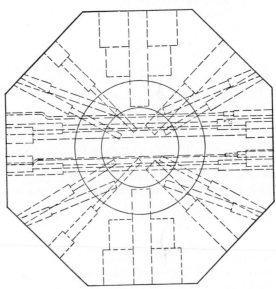

FIG. 6-23. Top view of CP-5 reactor, showing steps in the various openings, as well as an offset duct.

adequate, the room background will be proportional to the area of leakage.

Since most shielding plugs are rather large and heavy, the problem of holding extremely fine tolerances between mating surfaces becomes very costly and time-consuming during fabrication and requires extreme care in handling

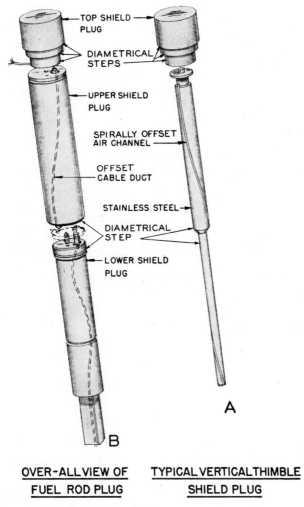

OVER-ALL VIEW OF   TYPICAL VERTICAL THIMBLE
FUEL ROD PLUG   SHIELD PLUG

Fig. 6-24.   Typical reactor plugs.

thereafter. There are various methods of reducing radiation leakage around shielding plugs without the necessity of holding fine tolerances. One of the simplest methods used in shielding a straight opening is to use a step along the air channel, between the mating surfaces. This is done by increasing the size of the shielding plug in abrupt steps (at least once) as it recedes from the center of the reactor, as seen in the following figures. The step eliminates any direct, straight line opening through the reactor shield; requiring that the radiation either penetrate a dense material or be scattered at least twice. In either case, the final radiation will be reduced.

The most common forms of stepped shielding plugs are (1) the round or cylindrical types and (2) the rectangular or block types. The cylindrical shielding plug usually consists of two or more cylinders of different diameters whose axes are common or parallel. The difference in diameters forms a "diametral step." These cylinders are made of or filled with dense absorbing material and may or may not be joined together. The dimensions, weight, and ease of handling will determine how the plug is to be made. The advantages of the cylindrical plugs are that they may be made of pipe or tubing and may be easily and inexpensively turned on a lathe.

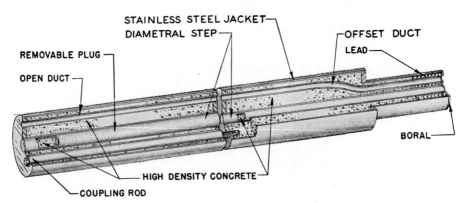

Fig. 6-25.   A plug for a grazing hole in the CP-5 reactor.

The rectangular block stepped plugs are a series of two or more blocks whose rectangular cross sections differ so as to have as few common axial planes as possible. These blocks may or may not be joined together. The rectangular block is usually used where it is desired to open only a portion of a possible large opening in a shield.

Both of these types of shielding plugs have been used successfully in the Argonne reactors, where by the very nature of the reactors (for research), there is a wide variety of accessible openings in the reactor shields (see Fig. 6-23).

In addition to the use of the step on a shielding plug itself, there are usually small offset service ducts through a reactor shield. These small ducts remain open at all times and carry such items as air for cooling, samples to be irradiated, and instrument cables.

A common use of the duct is found in the form of a spiral tube, either buried within the shield or shield plug, or where space is at a premium, in the form of a spiral groove cut into the surface of a cylindrical plug. An example of the spiral groove is shown in Fig. 6-24A, where an air passage for the cooling of samples within a reactor core is spirally slotted into a stepped stainless-steel shielding plug. The number of slots must not be increased to the point where

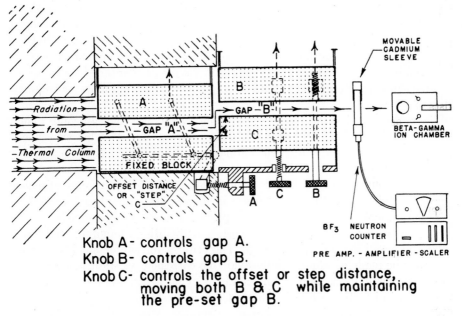

Knob A- controls gap A.
Knob B- controls gap B.
Knob C- controls the offset or step distance,
     moving both B & C while maintaining
     the pre-set gap B.

FIG. 6-26.   Adjustable stepped shielding plug.

there is an insufficient mass of shielding material present. Figs. 6-24B and 6-25 show offset cable ducts within shield plugs.

DISCUSSION

This experiment is primarily concerned with the effect of a step or offset in a shielding plug—in particular, with regard to the tolerance between the plug and its mating surface. This will be accomplished under specific conditions where the change in radiation level through a shielding apparatus will be due to both tolerances and offset. The results will illustrate the usefulness of stepped shielding and how it may be used to subdue radiation leakage in a simple, inexpensive manner.

Two pairs of matched shielding blocks will be used to form a controlled tolerance and offset step combination (see Fig. 6-26). The shielding blocks are matched to fit tightly together, so that when closed, there will be no radiation leakage except that which is transmitted through the blocks themselves. There are two pairs of blocks to provide the offset or step mechanism. Rectangular blocks are selected instead of cylindrical plugs because of the ease in varying the tolerances and offsets. Yet the results will serve to illustrate the similar offset on a cylindrical plug with a diametral step.

It is interesting to note that as a general rule the horizontal surfaces on the bottom side of the shield plugs do not cause a leakage problem. The weight of a shielding plug resting on a reasonable smooth surface will offer a high resistance to leakage. This can eliminate one of the four surfaces to be stepped, where rectangular block shielding is used. This is of less value where cylindrical shielding is used horizontally, since there is then only a line of contact between the cylindrical plug and the cylinder wall. Gravity can be relied on as an aid in some shielding problems to minimize alignment gaps and reduce or eliminate radiation leakage.

The problem to be studied is the radiation leakage through air voids. There are some specific references to work done with air ducts.* This experiment, however, is devoted to a practical application of shielding where the air duct involved is irregular.

It is obvious that one should avoid, whenever possible, the requirement of extreme tolerances of mating surfaces in stepped shielding plugs as a solution of radiation leakage, especially when a proper offset step will simplify most of the problems of manufacture (time, cost, and facilities), handling, and maintenance, as well as radiation leakage. The criteria for simple shield plugs are that they be made of commercially available corrosion-resistant materials and require a minimum amount of machining, including an allowance for small amounts of distortion while handling. Corrosion is another problem which is reduced greatly with the use of larger tolerances. Most reactor openings will have some air pockets in the inner reactor vicinity. These pockets usually contain air whose primary ingredients—water vapor, nitrogen and oxygen— are available for corrosion that might well weld a tightly fitted shield plug in place. The formation of corrosive nitric acid in stagnant air in a reactor is not uncommon. It is also obvious that calculations of radiation streaming through the air ducts formed by common shield plugs would be very difficult, possibly fruitless.

This experiment considers the step quality in a particular situation, but it does not locate the most efficient use of the step. As a general rule, a shielding step is located midway through the thickness of the reactor shield. Where there is more than one step, the steps are usually spaced equally between the limits of the total shield traversed.

DESCRIPTION OF APPARATUS

The apparatus is shown in Figs. 6-26 and 6-27, installed in the thermal column of a reactor. The addition of two heavy concrete shield blocks was

* A. Simon and C. E. Clifford, "Attenuation of Neutrons by Air Ducts and Shields," ORNL-1217 (Rev) (March 8, 1954).

found to be necessary, one above and one below the portion of the apparatus protruding from the thermal column, in order to reduce radiation leakage affecting the safety of the experimenters.

There are three components which move to give the desired experimental conditions. The thermal column shutters open and close to allow a beam of reactor radiation to enter the shield apparatus used in this experiment. The apparatus itself is composed of four movable shielding blocks, each 17½ in. long, mounted on a stainless-steel plate. The blocks are linked together in pairs

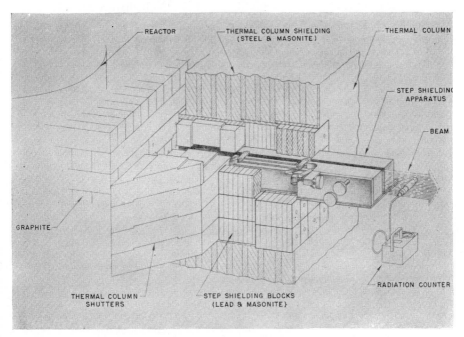

FIG. 6-27.   Step shielding experimental apparatus.

so that a gap may be established between blocks of each pair, keeping the mating surfaces parallel at all times. The external pair of shield blocks may be moved as a unit, maintaining any established gap between the blocks, to produce a step in the gap set by the internal pair of blocks. The blocks may be positioned to give any gap up to 1¼ in. in width and an offset up to 2 in.

The materials used are noncorrosive stainless-steel plates and a concrete mixture of limonite iron ore and portland cement.* Both materials are common reactor shield-plug constituents. Iron ore and steel punchings are often used to increase (inexpensively) the density of a concrete shield. The stainless-steel plate is a commercial product used to contain the concrete. Stainless steel is used because of its corrosion resistance and durability. Stainless steel contain-

* "The Reactor Handbook," AECD-3647 (March 1955), Vol. 3, Sec. 1.

STEPPED SHIELDING PLUG TEST

Background, with thermal column shutter closed:

Neutrons, total _____   Date _____

Neutrons, epicadmium _____   High voltage _____

Gamma _____   Pulse height _____

Sensitivity mult. _____

Thermal column shutter open _____ in.

Openings, in.			Radiation		
In-Pile Blocks	Rear Blocks	Offset	Neutrons, Total, cts/min	Neutrons, Epi-Cd, cts/min	Gamma mr/hr
0	0	0			
0	1 1/4	0			
1	0	0			
1/32 "	1/32 "	0 1/32			
1/16 "	1/16 "	0 1/16			
3/32 "	3/32 "	0 1/8			
1/8 "	1/8 "	0 5/32			
1/4 "	1/4 "	0 5/16			
3/8 "	3/8 "	0 7/16			
1/2 "	1/2 "	0 9/16			
3/4 "	3/4 "	0 1/16 1/8 1/4 3/8 1/2 5/8 3/4 7/8 1			

ing nickel and chromium does not have the "neutron window"* that is found in iron or ordinary steel.

Two types of radiation-detection equipment are used to measure the escaping beam. A BF_3 neutron chamber is used to detect thermal and epicadmium neutrons, the latter when a cadmium sleeve is placed around the counter. The neutron-counter components are the typical preamplifier, amplifier, voltage supply, scaler, register and timer. An additional counting-rate meter and audio-scaler are used to help the experimenter quickly recognize changes in neutron intensity while operating the experimental mechanisms. The radiation to be detected consists of fast and slow neutrons and gamma rays. The latter are measured with a portable ionization chamber.

In addition to the stepped shielding apparatus, the effectiveness of existing shield plugs in the reactor itself may be investigated.

METHOD OF TESTING

All of the radiological precautions detailed in Experiment 6-1 must be followed.

The apparatus is placed in the thermal column of a reactor such as CP-5, as shown in Fig. 6-27. With the shielding blocks closed tightly together, the thermal-column shutter is opened approximately 2 in., allowing a beam of mixed radiation to impinge on the apparatus. The radiation consists of 10^8 to 10^9 slow neutrons/(cm²) (sec), 10^5 to 10^6 fast neutrons/(cm²) (sec), and approximately 30 r/hr gamma rays. The background of this beam is then measured with the instruments appropriate to each of these irradiations.

A straight-through beam slot is then set up, with each of the gaps listed in Data Sheet 6-2. Measurements of the intensities of the three escaping beams are made for each gap. Also, at each gap setting the outer pair of blocks is to be moved to form a step. The amount of offset giving the greatest decrease in intensity of radiation for each slot width is to be recorded. In addition to this offset, intermediate positions of offset equal to any of the previously measured straight-through gaps may be taken as positions of measurement.

CONCLUSION

A most useful interpretation of the results may be obtained in graphical form. The width of the gap is to be plotted against the offset which gave the maximum decrease in leakage radiation. Inspection of the graph should lead to a very general rule of thumb. An additional graph may be plotted to show the effect of the final slot width as compared to the initial slot width.

Other interesting facts may be observed from the data itself, always bearing

---

* D. J. Hughes et al., "Neutron Cross Sections," AECU-2040 (May 15, 1952).

in mind the conditions of the experiment, i.e., the materials used, the dimensions of the apparatus, and the source of radiation.

If time permits, investigate the use and efficiency of some of the shield plugs used in the reactor.

SUGGESTED ADDITIONAL EXPERIMENTS USING AN OPERATING REACTOR

1. Measurement of the "danger coefficient."
2. Absorption cross sections by the over-all flux oscillation method.
3. Absorption cross sections by the local flux oscillation method.
4. Survey of the background activity around a reactor.
5. Measurement of backscattering and albedos.
6. Measurement of the periods of the delayed neutrons from fission products.
7. Measurement of the number of neutrons emitted per fission. (ν)
8. Measurement of the light emission from irradiated rock salt.
9. Resonance disadvantage factor.

Chapter 7

SOME CHARACTERISTICS OF
OPERATING REACTORS

THE NEUTRON FLUX DISTRIBUTION

By W. H. McCorkle, Director, Reactor Operations Division, ANL

Introduction

When a reactor is being designed, it is essential to gather considerable detailed knowledge of the neutron flux distribution which may be expected throughout the reactor, either from theoretical considerations or from exponential and critical assembly experiments. Likewise, for an operating reactor and especially for a research reactor it is very valuable to have among other things a detailed record of the neutron fluxes throughout available regions of the reactor. The magnitudes of many effects which will be produced on experimental installations and materials put into the reactor will depend on the values of the neutron fluxes at the locations where the devices or materials are to be positioned. Hence it is our desire to investigate in some detail the magnitude and distribution of the neutron flux as one of the important characteristics of a nuclear reactor.

When irradiation thimbles or channels are provided in a reactor such as the CP-5 research reactor (see Fig. 7-1), it is very desirable to know the neutron flux distribution through such facilities. It is possible to use a number of different materials and techniques for making neutron flux surveys through the accessible regions of a reactor. A relative measure of the flux along an irradiation thimble, in conjunction with careful absolute flux measurements as described in detail in Experiment 3-1 at one or more of the positions covered by the relative survey, will provide for given conditions of the reactor operations a reliable flux calibration of the facility.

For relative measurements in high neutron fluxes, it would generally be desirable to employ some material or materials which are not highly susceptible to the action of neutrons and which at the same time retain the produced effects

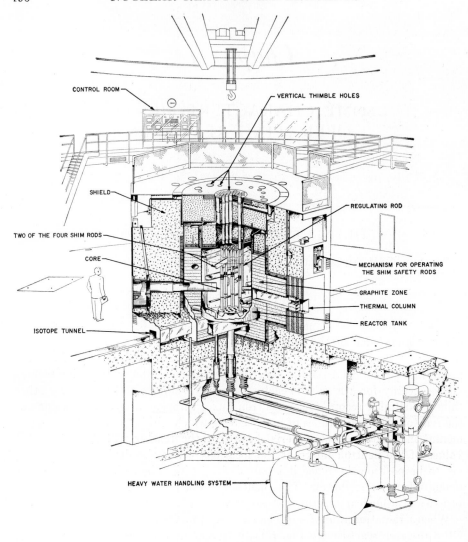

FIG. 7-1. Cut-away view of the CP-5 reactor.

long enough for convenient measurement. Several different scanning techniques have been developed.* For convenience, the one selected in this instance uses the activation of a relatively small wire, approximately 30 mils in diameter, made from an alloy of aluminum, manganese, and cobalt. The alloy contains ½ per cent of manganese and ½ per cent of cobalt by weight in the aluminum.

* W. Bernstein, E. H. Foster and J. J. Floyd, AECU-1621 (1951); F. Schroeder, IDO-16051 (Sept. 1954).

Thus the aluminum serves to uniformly disperse the atoms of manganese and cobalt and also to provide the means of supporting these atoms in the neutron fluxes to be compared. The radioactivity induced in the aluminum has a half-life of only 2.3 min, while the manganese activity has a half-life of 2.6 hr and the cobalt activities possess half-lives of 10.7 min and 5.3 years. A relatively short time after the exposure to the neutron fluxes, the manganese activity and the long-lived cobalt activity are effectively the only ones remaining. Thus, by supporting a length of the alloy wire on a holding device made of a material

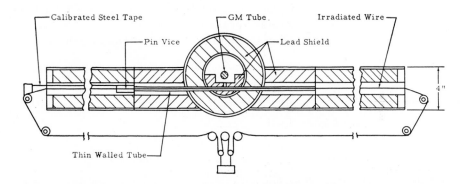

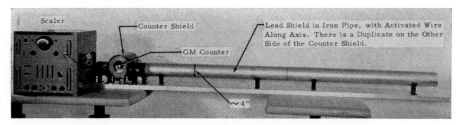

FIG. 7-2. Apparatus for scanning activated wire for relative flux measurements.

which will not become very radioactive, such as a strip of dry wood as free from resin as possible, it is possible to insert the wire along the axis of the thimble and then withdraw it from the flux region at recorded times, to provide useful activations in the wire proportional to the neutron fluxes. To indicate the relative activations, the wire is drawn through a lead shield containing a counting tube, arranged, as shown in Fig. 7-2, so that the radioactivity of the wire is shielded from the tube except for a narrow slot in the shield just beneath the counting tube. By moving the wire in known small steps through the shield, the counting rates are observed and coordinated with the position of the wire in the thimble. A curve is plotted relating counting rate and axial position along the thimble to give the relative flux distribution.

PROCEDURE FOR BOTH ABSOLUTE AND
RELATIVE FLUX MEASUREMENTS

The gold foils used in the absolute flux measurement and the alloy wire used in the relative flux measurement should be irradiated near the beginning of the day to comparatively high intensity. They should then be allowed to decay until near the end of the day, when the counting measurements are made on them. This will increase the accuracy of the timing.

Convenient forms for recording the data are shown in Data Sheets 7-1 and 7-2.

DATA SHEET 7-1

Counter Used _____				
Data for Plateau Curve		Flux Determination		
Volts	Cts/Min	Gold foil No.		
		Covered with		
		Wt. foil		
		Time placed in pile		
		Time removed from pile		
		t_0 (counting timer started)		
		Background		
		Time started count		
		Time ended count		
		Observed counts		
		Absorber used		
		Background		
		t_2 = Time since removal from pile to time t_0 + time from t_0 to midpoint of counting time, in min.		

Dead time calibration

Background _____

Position	Counts	Time
A		
(A + B)		
B		

Background _____

Dead time correction = _____

DATA SHEET 7-2

WIRE SCANNING					
Position	Time	Obs. Cts.	Position	Time	Obs. Cts.

Step 1: Foil and Wire Activations. Place a weighed standard gold foil in a numbered small aluminum envelope. Then with a small piece of masking tape, attach the envelope to a thin wood strip so that it may be placed in an isotope thimble at a known position relative to the pile face. With the reactor operating steadily, insert the foil to position at a noted time. About 15 min later, note the time and quickly and smoothly remove the strip of wood with the foil. Put the wood strip with the foil aside under a shield or behind a stack of lead bricks while a second wood strip is being prepared with the alloy wire to make a flux survey in the same isotope thimble. The alloy wire should be placed as straight as possible on the wood strip and secured by small pieces of masking tape, with small pads of paper between the wire and the tape. Index the wire and the wood strip so that the position of the wire relative to the reactor face will be well defined. When everything is ready, insert the wood strip with the wire to the proper position at a noted time. Approximately 15 min later note the time and quickly withdraw the wire into the long shield provided. Disconnect that portion of the wood strip which extends out of the shield and then move the wire and shield aside to allow the necessary decay before counting.

Next, prepare a standard gold foil in a cadmium case (shaped like a pill box). Attach it to another wood strip and insert at a noted time into the same location used for the gold foil in aluminum. About 45 min later, note the time and quickly and smoothly withdraw the cadmium-covered foil and set it aside in a lead shield (pile of lead bricks, 2 to 4 in. thick).

While the short-lived activities induced by the neutron bombardments are decaying, attention may be given to preparing the counting equipment.

Step 2: Calibration and Testing of Counters. Since the time available for making the neutron flux measurements and survey is often limited, certain of the steps required for standardization and intercalibration of the counters and absorbers have been performed by the instructor in advance, as shown by the tables and figures in Experiment 3-1. Thus, in preparation for the flux measurements by the foil counting technique, the student is expected only to verify the counting rate vs. the voltage plateau of his counter, the dead time determination, the counting rate with the long-lived test standard, and if time permits, the intercalibration of the foil holders and absorbers by use of the active foils provided, without employing the elaborate overlap illustrated in the tables just mentioned.

Step 3: Flux Determination by Foil Counting. About 2 hr before the end of the laboratory period, obtain the gold foils which were irradiated in the isotope thimble. Arrange for one group to count the foil which was in cadmium while another group counts the foil which was in aluminum. Each reading should use at least 10,000 counts. Clean each foil by swishing it through acetone before placing it in a foil holder. Always select the thickest absorber to cover the foil before placing the foil under the counting tube. If the counting rate is too low, use Table 3-5, Experiment 3-1, to guide you in selecting an appropriate absorber. Interchange foils with the other group and repeat the counting procedure.

By using your counting data along with the tables provided, it is now possible to calculate the total neutron flux as indicated by the gold foil at the selected position in the isotope thimble, the cadmium ratio for the gold foil as covered with cadmium in your experiment, and the epicadmium and the subcadmium neutron fluxes as indicated by gold foils at the chosen thimble position.

Step 4: Total Neutron Flux Survey. As soon as the gold foils are counted and returned to the proper containers, both groups should proceed to the location of the wire scanner to obtain the flux survey data. Place the thick lead absorber over the slot in the scanner shield, then position the shield containing the activated alloy wire so that the wire may be threaded through the scanner shield. Attach the pin vise on the exit side of the scanner to the wire and position the index on the wire with the index on the scanner. This adjustment will place the wire so that the counting tube is positioned over that part of the wire which was at the inner surface of the biological shield of the reactor. Advance the wire through the scanner by 6-in. steps. Pause at each step to record the counting rate (with 10,000 counts taken each time) and the time after removal of the wire from the isotope thimble. These data will provide the information for calculating the relative neutron fluxes along the isotope thimble. When the flux calculations from the gold-foil data are combined with the activated-wire flux survey, a curve may be drawn showing the magnitudes of the neutron fluxes at the various positions along the isotope thimble.

EXPERIMENT 7-2

REACTOR POWER MEASUREMENT

By W. H. McCorkle, Director, Reactor Operations Division, ANL

Introduction

There are reactors for which the power may be determined quite readily by calorimetric methods. There are also some reactors for which the power determination by this method may be impractical. Where the arrangement is such that the heat transfer entails elaborate accounting techniques for the heat transfer, some other method than calorimetry may be employed.

Calorimetric Methods

For most reactors which are operated at considerable power, the heat is transferred from the core of the reactor to an exterior system by processes which may supply this heat almost entirely to a flowing stream of liquid or gas. In these cases, the power level under steady-state operation may readily be determined by observing the flow rate W, or gpm, of the fluid used for cooling, its temperature rise Δt as it passes through the reactor, and its specific heat c_p. Then,

$$P = K_1 W \, \Delta t \, c_p = K_2 \, (gpm) \, \Delta t \, c_p, \tag{7-1}$$

where K_1 and K_2 are constants which depend on the units used; W may be lb/hr or grams/sec etc.

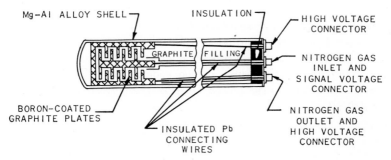

Fig. 7-3. A PCP counter.

However, to follow a reactor in its rise to power, more rapidly responsive means must be employed. For this purpose an ionization chamber is used which has large-area, boron-coated electrodes in a small volume, such as the parallel circular-plate (PCP) type,* shown in Fig. 7-3 together with its circuit in Fig. 7-4. It is located in the reflector and produces an ionization current pro-

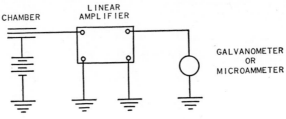

FIG. 7-4.   A power recorder.

portional to the reactor power, as shown in Equation 1-17. The ion current, after suitable linear amplification, will operate a galvanometer (or even a microammeter). The power-indicating galvanometer must be calibrated against the power production as determined calorimetrically for steady-state operation. It may then be used under conditions of variable power.

OTHER METHODS

For other reactors than those that may be calibrated by direct calorimetric means, the power production may be determined by neutron density measurements made through the characteristic regions of the reactor. When properly weighted, averaged, and used in Equation 1-17, they will provide the answer which is sought. Usually this determination is very difficult and requires quite complete knowledge of the flux distribution in the reactor in all directions.

THE EXPERIMENT (7-2)

(Under the guidance of the instructor)

1. Establish the reactor at some selected moderate power level and maintain at this power level until thermal equilibrium has been established. While waiting, compute the constant of proportionality in Equation 7-1. Then observe the inlet and outlet temperatures of the coolant, and the flow rate. Apply Equation 7-1 to calculate the power. Observe the corresponding power-galvanometer deflection.

2. Repeat the procedure for several other power levels in the operating range and plot a curve of galvanometer deflection vs. power.

* R. K. Abele and J. C. Gundlack, AECD-3494.

REACTIVITY, PERIOD, AND INHOURS

By J. B. Hoag, ANL, International School of Nuclear Science and Engineering

When one uranium-235 nucleus is fissioned, an average of $2\frac{1}{2}$ neutrons are ejected. One of these is needed to start the second generation of fissions, i.e., to perpetuate the chain reaction. The others are lost by capture or leakage, or in the conversion of uranium-238 to plutonium-239. The *effective multiplication* k_{eff} is defined as the number of neutrons at the end of one generation for each neutron at the beginning of that generation. It is equal to unity for a critical reactor operating in a steady power state; is less than unity for a subcritical and greater than unity for a supercritical reactor.

The *excess multiplication* δk is the gain of neutrons each generation for one neutron at the start of that generation. Since one neutron is needed to start the second generation,

$$\delta k \equiv k_{eff} - 1. \tag{7-2}$$

It is zero for a critical reactor, negative for a subcritical, and positive for a supercritical reactor. The *reactivity* ρ is defined by

$$\rho \equiv \frac{\delta k}{k_{eff}}. \tag{7-3}$$

When a thermal reactor is designed, more than the critical mass of fissile fuel is built in than is needed to just barely keep the reactor in operation. This *excess reactivity* $\Delta\rho$ is then offset by the introduction of absorbing material, say cadmium or boron, in the form of control, regulating or shim rods or plates, so that the steady operation can be obtained or so that the neutron flux may be increased or decreased. Some excess reactivity is also needed to correct for the formation of fission products, some of which have high absorption cross sections for neutrons and would cause the eventual shutdown of the reactor.

Suppose a thermal reactor is operating at steady power (i.e., constant neutron flux, constant neutron density), with the control rod in a given position part way in the reactor. When the rod is partly withdrawn, say 1 in., thus removing some of the neutron-absorbing material, an excess of neutrons is produced each generation, and their density, the flux, and the power start to rise. When the power has reached a new, higher, desired level, the control rod is reset to its original position to maintain the steady state.

The time it takes for the neutron density or flux or the power to increase by a factor e (the base of Naperian logarithms) is defined as the *reactor period, T*. The power will increase e-fold its former value in T sec. T is sometimes referred to as the "e-folding time." If a reactor is operating with a period of 5 sec, then in two periods the power will have increased $e^2 = 7.38$ times in 10 sec, which is sufficient to allow mechanical movement of the control rod to prevent a runaway, without attendant melting and destruction of the core of the reactor. Hence, too short a period is undesirable. On the other hand, if the period is excessively great, it will take too long to start up or shut down the reactor.

The period can be measured by observing the rate of change of current from a neutron detector located in the reactor. There are also meters which give the period directly.* As indicated in Fig. 7-5, a boron-coated counter tube is located in the neutron flux of a reactor. In order to cover the wide range of fluxes encountered in startup and operation of a reactor, the diode is used. Its effect is to make the output of the d-c amplifier proportional to the logarithm of the counter's ion current. Up to this point, the circuit is a "log-n" meter. The RC circuit passes a current through the meter M which is inversely pro-

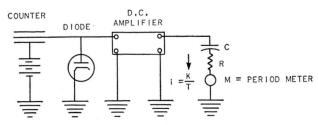

FIG. 7-5. The principle of a period meter.

portional to the reactor period. The meter's scale is then calibrated in terms of reactor period, usually with the pointer at the center of the dial, for infinite period, corresponding to stable reactor power. Deflections to the right give positive periods, corresponding to rising reactor power, and deflections to the left are calibrated in negative periods for decreasing power.

The period of a reactor depends not only on the number of excess neutrons produced each generation, as expressed by δk, but also on the number of generations each second. This depends on the average lifetime of the neutrons. In a thermal uranium-graphite reactor, the "prompt" neutrons born in a fission are slowed down in the moderator to thermal energy in about 10^{-5} sec. They then diffuse around in the core for about 10^{-3} sec before capture in the fuel to cause another fission. There are then about 1000 $(1/10^{-3})$ generations each second of prompt neutrons.

In addition, approximately 0.73 per cent of the neutrons have a delayed emission. They originate in various stages in the decay series of the fission products and have a weighted-average time of decay of about 0.1 sec, from U^{235}. Although there are relatively few delayed neutrons, they act as a buffer which, within limits, slows up *changes* in the power level of a reactor. Provided, for a U^{235} thermal reactor, k_{eff} is kept below 1.0073 (the "prompt critical" condition), the delayed neutrons will exert their influence, there will be only

---

* Glasstone, "Principles of Reactor Engineering," p. 291.

10 generations (1/0.1) each second, and the period of the reactor will be long enough to be manageable.

The relationship between the reactivity ρ and the period T for a reactor which is not far above the critical condition of operation is given by*

$$\rho = \frac{l}{Tk_{eff}} + \sum_{i=1}^{m} \frac{\beta_i}{1 + \lambda_i T},\tag{7-4}$$

where l is the average lifetime of thermal neutrons in a finite reactor of definite composition, and is less than the lifetime in the pure moderator. The effective multiplication constant k_{eff} is essentially unity because the reactor is near critical. In Equation 7-4, Σ is the summation from $i = 1$ to $i = m$ of the delayed-neutron groups and is *not* the macroscopic cross section. The absolute yield β_i is the fraction of all the fission neutrons in the i-th delayed group. Also, λ_i is the decay constant of the precursor (or first member) of the i-th delayed group of neutrons.

Substitution in Equation 7-4 of the values of β and λ for the five major groups of delayed neutrons of uranium 235 gives, with l and T in seconds,

$$\rho = \frac{l}{T} + \frac{0.00085}{1 + 1.6T} + \frac{0.00241}{1 + 0.455T} + \frac{0.00213}{1 + 0.154T} + \frac{0.00166}{1 + 0.0315T} + \frac{0.00025}{1 + 0.0125T}.$$
$$\tag{7-5}$$

For example: for a U^{235} reactor with $l = 10^{-3}$ sec and $T = 10$ sec, $\rho = 0.00421$. When averaged values of these five groups are used, $\beta = 0.0073$ and $\lambda = 0.080$, $\rho = l/T + 0.0073/(1 + 0.080T) = 0.00415$, in this case—an approximate value which is close to the more accurate value from Equation 7-5.

It is desirable to establish a unit of reactivity, ρ_1, for a given reactor. This is customarily done by choosing the stable reactor's period as one hour. This unit is called the inverse-hour or *inhour*. With $T = 3600$ sec, the U^{235} equation (7-5) becomes

$$\rho_1 = \frac{l}{3600} + 2.677 \times 10^{-5}.\tag{7-6}$$

For a particular reactor for which $l = 10^{-3}$ sec, $\rho_1 = 2.70 \times 10^{-5}$.

In order to compute the reactivity in inhours:

$$Ih = \frac{\rho}{\rho_1},\tag{7-7}$$

where ρ is given by Equation 7-4 and ρ_1 is given by the same equation, in which $T = 3600$. In the example cited, where the fuel is U^{235}, $l = 10^{-3}$ and $T = 10$ sec, the reactor has a reactivity of $Ih = 0.00421/(2.70 \times 10^{-5}) = 156$. For a reactor of long period (low reactivity), the following approximations may be used: $Ih = 3600/T = 3.91 \times 10^4 \rho$, or $\rho = 0.092/T = 2.56 \times 10^{-5} Ih$.

* Glasstone, *ibid.*, p. 236; calculation of l, p. 190; values of β and λ, p. 230.

A graph relating inhours, reactivity, and period for a heavy-water, enriched-uranium reactor is given in Fig. 7-6.

STARTUP, CALIBRATION OF CONTROL RODS, AND SHUTDOWN OF A REACTOR

By W. H. McCORKLE, Director, Reactor Operations Division, ANL

INTRODUCTION

Before normal operation of a reactor, it is required that it first be carefully loaded to critical (see Experiment 4-7). Then the desired reactivity is added by further loading, for the routine operation of the reactor. Briefly, the process of loading to critical consists of placing a neutron source, such as a Po-Be source, on one side of the core, with a sensitive neutron detector, such as a fission counter (see Experiment 6-2), on the opposite side, before the fissile fuel material is loaded into the reactor. The fuel assemblies are then inserted one by one into the core of the reactor and a plot is made of the reciprocal counting rate y vs. number of fuel assemblies x. There results an approximately straight line with negative slope, which, extrapolated to the x axis, predicts the critical loading.

In a reactor, there are adjustment rods known as *control rods*. The process of loading to critical requires that after each fuel assembly is added, the control rods be carefully withdrawn and the resultant counting rate for that loading determined. The control rods are reinserted before the next fuel element is added. This process is repeated step by step as each of the fuel assemblies are added. When the critical loading has been approached and then calculated by extrapolation of the curve, and the control rods are fully inserted, further fuel assemblies are added to supply the reactivity necessary for the routine operation of the reactor. The reactivity should always be considerably less than that which the control rods can suppress.

INITIAL STARTUP OF REACTOR AND CALIBRATION OF CONTROL RODS

When the reactor, with an extraneous neutron source present, has been loaded to *slightly* over critical and the control rods then completely inserted, the control rods are to be calibrated over a small portion of their operating range in the following manner. The reactor is brought to critical by careful withdrawal of the control rods until an easily detected low power level is obtained. The control rods are then adjusted for a steady state of the reactor. The control rod under calibration is then removed some small measured or indicated amount. The reactor period is observed on an ionization chamber-fed galvanometer. The control rod is then reinserted to a point somewhat below critical in order to suppress the reactor power to the original critical level. Then the control rod is adjusted to its initial setting and the reactor power goes back to its original value. The control rod is again withdrawn, somewhat farther this time, and the period again observed by timing the movement of the galvanometer deflection (or with a period meter) after which the power is returned to its original value. This is repeated step by step, until the reactor period becomes undesirably short, say 10 to 20 sec. In this manner, the control rod position is related to the reactor period over a small range of motion of the rod.

In order to continue the calibration of the control rod, it is now necessary to select a higher position of the control rod than that originally chosen. To accomplish this, other control rods or neutron absorbers are added or inserted farther into the reactor, to such an extent that the rod under calibration may be withdrawn farther without rendering the reactor supercritical. The new position of the rod should be somewhat below the highest position used in the previous work. The procedure is again repeated over an additional small range of the rod under calibration. It should be apparent that with only a small amount of reactivity supplied to the reactor, only a small portion of the uppermost range of the control rod can be calibrated.

To accomplish further calibration of the control rod, and to enable the reactor to operate routinely, more reactivity must be supplied by adding more fuel. By reference to the curve made during loading to critical and to the curve for the small range of calibration already accomplished, the effect of an additional fuel assembly can be estimated. Sufficient control and safety rods should have been provided originally in the design of the reactor to assure control of several times the reactivity that will be loaded into the reactor. It is then possible, by the insertion of one or more additional fuel assemblies, to provide the reactivity necessary for routine operation of the reactor and to enable the control-rod calibration process to be continued for the other control or shim rods. This is done carefully step by step.

Other methods may also be used to calibrate the control rods. In particular, the reactor may be brought up to a steady low operating-power level of a few watts and then be suddenly shut down by dropping a control rod to the IN position. By observing the drop and decay of the neutron flux in some instrument hole of the reactor, the effect or worth of the sudden control-rod motion may be determined. A neutron-detecting chamber feeding a quick response instrument such as a Brush Recorder will supply information from which the per cent $\delta k/k$ or inhour worth of the control rod may be calculated by the "rod drop method." By dropping the control rods from different positions, data may be obtained for calibrating the control rods.

A curve is now plotted like that in Fig. 7-6, but for the particular reactor at hand. Equation 7-4—or its special case for uranium-235, Equation 7-5—relates the period with the reactivity. Equation 7-7 (together with the special case for U^{235}, i.e., Equation 7-6) relates the reactivity with inhours.

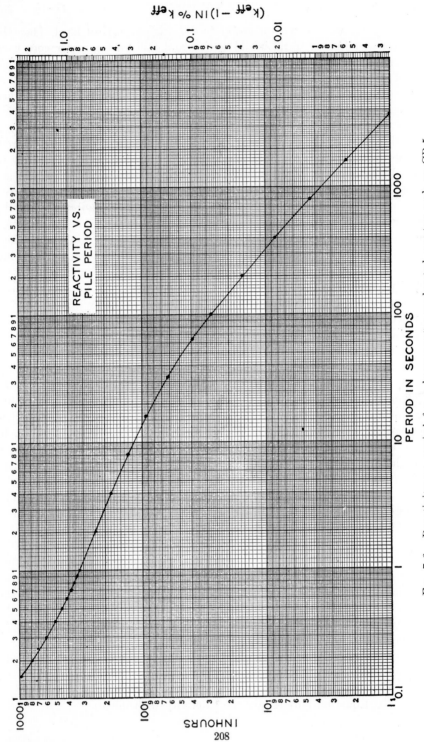

FIG. 7-6. Reactivity vs. period for a heavy-water-moderated reactor such as CP-5.

The final step is to plot a curve for each control rod as in Fig. 7-7, relating the reactivity controlled or supplied by that rod (inhours change from the stable critical condition $(Ih = 0)$, to the position of the rod in inches, centi-meters, or other units measured from its position at criticality.

The reactor may then be routinely brought up to full power operation. If the

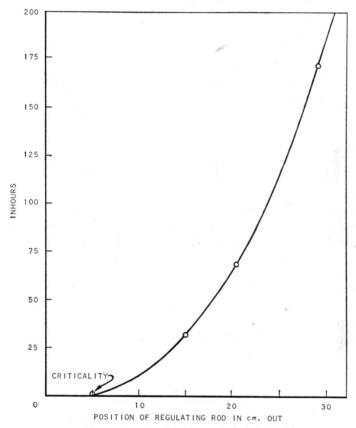

FIG. 7-7.   The reactivity supplied by a given control rod.

reactor is one in which photo-neutrons may be produced in the reactor to serve as a neutron source, as in the case of heavy water or one containing beryllium, then, after a sufficient time of operation at moderate power, the extraneous source may be removed (following shutdown of the reactor, of course; this shutdown is accomplished by inserting the control and safety rods).

Routine Startup and Shutdown of the Reactor

With the control rods of the reactor calibrated and with either an inherent or extraneous neutron source provided, the reactor may be taken up to power from its shutdown condition by slowly withdrawing the safety rods to their ready positions, followed by small stepwise withdrawal of the several shim rods and the regulating rod, maintaining approximately symmetrical positions for all the shim rods, one with respect to another, and also for the regulating rod with respect to the shim rods. The multiplication of the neutrons is followed with the period meter and/or the ionization-chamber-fed galvanometer while the reactor is still subcritical. If the motion of the shim or regulating rod under withdrawal is stopped while the reactor is in this condition, the galvanometer spot will come to rest and the period meter will return to the infinite-period position.

The slow adjustment of the shim rods and the regulating rod is continued. There will come a time when, with the rods stationary, the period meter or galvanometer will not indicate an infinite period, but some finite, large value. This indicates that the reactor is slightly above critical. The shim rods' positions should then be left as they are, and the regulating rod adjusted slightly to set the period to a moderate value. In this state, the power of the reactor is slowly rising and may be followed by the power-indicating galvanometer or other power-indicating means. When the desired power level is obtained, the regulating rod should be run in slightly and adjusted until the power level remains constant and the period meter returns to the infinite-period position. If the reactor is provided with a means of automatic control, it may now be used to automatically adjust the control- or regulating-rod to maintain the selected power level.

The reactor may be shut down by one or more methods. To slowly reduce the power to the zero or shutdown level, gradually insert the shim and regulating rods. To shut the reactor down quickly, the scram button is pressed, thereby releasing the safety rods. They will then be quickly and automatically inserted and shut the reactor down.

The Experiment (7-3)

(Under the guidance of the instructor)

With the reactor loaded for routine operation, but in the shutdown position, calibration of a shim rod and/or a regulating rod may be accomplished much as in the preceding description.

1. Slightly withdraw the shim rods and the regulating rods until the reactor is barely subcritical. This may be determined by observing the motion of the galvanometer spot. If the reactor is slightly above critical, motion of the galvanometer spot will continue even when the rod motion is stopped. If the rod under calibration is then inserted slightly so that the reactor is rendered subcritical, the galvanometer spot will slowly drop. Adjustments may thus be made of the rods not under calibration, so as to render the reactor just critical at the

setting of the rod to be calibrated. Calibration is then accomplished as previously described.

2. Following this procedure, calibrate either the shim rod or regulating rod, as the instructor designates, over a fairly wide range of its motion.

3. NORMAL OPERATING STATE—Shut the reactor down by the method suggested by the instructor; then proceed to take the reactor up to power, following the steps used in setting the reactor at critical for the calibration procedure. Then adjust the regulating rod as previously mentioned, to give a reactor period of 30 or 40 sec. Allow the reactor power to rise slowly, adjusting the range of the power-indicating galvanometer as necessary to follow the behavior of the reactor. When the reactor has risen to within a few per cent of its normal power level, proceed to insert the regulating rod slowly and to adjust it so as to level the reactor off at the normal power level.

4. Now shut the reactor down by a different method than you used the first time.

EXPERIMENT 7-4

MEASUREMENT OF THE TEMPERATURE COEFFICIENT OF REACTIVITY

By W. H. McCORKLE, Director, Reactor Operations Division, ANL

INTRODUCTION

In different fields it has been observed that important properties change when the temperatures of materials are changed. For example, some materials are found to have their electrical resistivities increased with increasing temperature, while for others a decrease of resistivity may occur. Somewhat similarly, expansion with increasing temperature is usually observed. Thus, some materials are said to have positive temperature coefficients of resistivity, etc., while others may have negative temperature coefficients over approximately the same ranges of temperature. The dynamic behavior of a reactor is associated with an important property known as its reactivity. This property may possess a positive temperature coefficient for some reactors and a negative temperature coefficient for others; or for a given reactor, the coefficient may be negative over certain temperature ranges and positive over other ranges. Since the inherent safety of operation of a reactor is so dependent on the control of reactivity, it is essential to have information about its coefficient over various temperature ranges.

DISCUSSION

Rather gross reactivity changes may be caused by the movement of neutron absorbers and fissile material in and near the core of a nuclear reactor. Alterations of reactivity may also be produced by changes of the moderator used with thermal reactors. Those reactors which have the moderator, the fissile material, and the neutron absorbers in solid form would usually not be expected to undergo reactivity changes, owing to voids appearing in the moderator. On the other hand, liquid-moderated reactors might be quite subject to this effect, owing to boiling of the moderator or the formation of sizable volumes of its vapor. In general, however, changes of this nature would be similar to the bodily removal of solid moderator from regions of a reactor. Such effects are not to be considered at this time. The more gradual changes of reactivity, occasioned by moderate changes of temperature, form the effect which we will refer to as the *temperature coefficient of reactivity*.

The parts of an operating reactor will usually not all be at the same temperature. Furthermore, the relative changes in temperature of the different parts may not be entirely the same for different operating conditions. However, if attention is focused on some part of the reactor, such as the moderator in the core, one may say that the increase of ρ for each degree rise in temperature of the moderator could be called the temperature coefficient of reactivity. Since the reactivity is zero for a just critical reactor, the coefficient is usually expressed either as per cent excess k per °C or as inhours per °C. When the moderator is a liquid which is also circulated and used as the coolant, one may measure the temperature of the moderator either as it leaves or as it enters the reactor, for different equilibrium conditions of operation.

The reactivity is defined in terms of the period, such that one inhour of reactivity will just enable the reactor in one hour to rise in power or to increase its neutron density at a given point in the reactor by the factor e (the base of natural logarithms). Thus, the reactivity possessed by the reactor for different temperatures of the moderator may be determined provided it is possible to measure the minimum reactor periods attainable at the different temperatures. This yields the information required for calculating the temperature coefficient of the reactor.

For a given type of reactor the period is related to the reactivity by an equation involving delayed neutron periods* and, when applicable, photo-neutron periods associated with the actions of fission products. The production of photo-neutrons in certain moderator or core materials will have periods associated with the decay and growth of the gamma rays with energies above the threshold values for photo-neutron emission. Fig. 7-6 shows a curve of reactivity vs. reactor period for a heavy-water-moderated and -cooled reactor such as CP-5.

The over-all temperature coefficient of reactivity is a net of contributions from the moderator, the fuel material, the control absorbers and other poisons in the reactor. Increasing the temperatures of these various constituents of a reactor causes increases in the widths of resonances for absorption and also

---

* D. J. Hughes, et al., Phys. Rev., **73**, 11 (1948).

for fission. Other more obvious changes are also associated with varying temperatures. The change of lattice spacing for heterogeneous reactors and general dimensional changes with temperature will have some influence on reactivity. In liquid-moderated reactors, such as the CP-5 research reactor of the Argonne National Laboratory, the change in density of the moderator, and consequently in the leakage of neutrons from the reactor core, is probably the effect of greatest significance in causing changes in reactivity with temperature.

Some of the changes with temperature conceivably will give positive temperature coefficients, while others will produce negative temperature coefficients. In the case of the CP-5 heavy-water-moderated reactor, the resultant temperature coefficient over the normal operating temperature range is negative and of a magnitude which may be rather easily determined.

The CP-5 reactor is arranged so that 5 sec is the shortest period which is allowed by the safety device incorporated in the reactor period meter. However, the necessary reactivity loaded into CP-5 for normal operations is considerably more than would give reactor periods above 5 sec. Thus, it becomes necessary to measure changes in reactivity by adjustments in the position of a calibrated neutron absorber such as the regulating rod. This requires that the reactor periods be measured for small increments in position of the regulating rod until in a stepwise fashion the motion of the regulating rod has covered a range sufficient to compensate for reactivity changes which would be encountered in the determination of the temperature coefficient. Usually the regulating rod would be calibrated over its full range of motion for normal operation of the reactor and this calibration could be used in determining the temperature coefficient.

EXPERIMENTAL PROCEDURE

Because the demand is great for use of the CP-5 reactor by numerous scientists, it will not usually be possible to recalibrate the regulating rod for each group of experimenters who may be interested in determining the temperature coefficient of reactivity. Hence, for these measurements, the most recent calibration of the CP-5 regulating rod will be supplied from the records of the operating staff.

Several equilibrium operating conditions will be established. These will be attained (by the reactor operators) by adjusting the cooling water flow between the main heat exchanger and the cooling tower so as to raise the equilibrium temperature of the heavy water flowing through the reactor. The reactor is provided with an automatic control system which will adjust the position of the regulating rod to maintain the power level of the reactor steady to about $\pm\frac{1}{2}$ per cent despite changes in the temperature. By observing the temperature indicators for the flow of heavy water into and out of the reactor, the mean of the inlet and outlet temperatures of the heavy water at equilibrium may be obtained. This will be the temperature of the moderator. The corresponding position of the regulating rod will, through its calibration curve, give the reactivity which the regulating rod is suppressing. By forming a data table relating regulating-rod position to the moderator temperature and then by reference to the calibration curve for the regulating rod, the information may be obtained to plot a curve of reactivity available vs. temperature of the moderator. The slope of this curve at any point will then yield the temperature coefficient of reactivity at the corresponding temperature.

A suggested form for the collection of the data is given in Data Sheet 7-3.

DATA SHEET 7-3

TEMPERATURE COEFFICIENT OF REACTIVITY

Operating Power Level of Reactor _____ kw

Level of D_2O in Reactor Tank _____ in.

D_2O Flow Rate Through Reactor _____ gal/min

Shim Rod Settings				Reg. Rod Setting	D_2O Temp.	
No. 1	No. 2	No. 3	No. 4		In	Out

Average Value of Temperature Coefficient _____ $(\% \ \delta k/k)/C°$

EXPERIMENT 7-5

THE DETERMINATION OF HEAT GENERATION IN IRRADIATED URANIUM

By D. R. PATTERSON and R. J. SCHILTZ,* ANL, Reactor Engineering Division

I. INTRODUCTION

Fission-product decay energy is an important consideration in the design, operation, and use of a nuclear reactor from the standpoint of shutdown cooling

* It would not have been possible to set up this experiment without a great deal of assistance. Members of the Heat Engineering Section assisted with technical advice, while the fabrication and assembly of equipment was ably handled by V. Shoemaker. In addition, the extra efforts put forth by E. W. Rylander, J. T. Weills, and R. A. Stella are sincerely appreciated.

as well as for shielding considerations. In a high-power reactor this decay energy may be sufficient to melt the core if adequate means for cooling after shutdown are not provided.

Studies were begun early in the history of reactor development which were aimed toward determining the rate of energy release from fission product decay. These studies have continued up to the present time as more information has become available concerning the fission products. Several different methods have been used successfully to obtain this information, but the spread of values still remains considerable. The apparatus used in this experiment will measure the fission-product decay energy as it appears in the form of heat conducted away from a sample of natural uranium irradiated in the neutron and gamma-ray flux of an operating reactor such as CP-5.

II. Decay Energy of Fission Products

A. General. When a nucleus fissions, it may split into any of about twenty pairs of product nuclei. Most of these are unstable and undergo radioactive decay to a stable end product. In general, there are several transitions before stability is reached and each of these transitions has its own method of decay and lifetime. Radioactive decay of fission products is therefore a complicated process.

The distribution of fission energy from uranium is given by Glasstone* as in Table 7-1. Since the neutrinos do not interact appreciably with matter, the 10

TABLE 7-1. APPROXIMATE DISTRIBUTION OF THE
PRIMARY FISSION ENERGY

Kinetic energy of fission fragments	168 Mev
Instantaneous gamma-ray energy	5
Kinetic energy of fission neutrons	5
Neutrino energy	~10
Beta particles from fission products	7
Gamma rays from fission products	6
Total fission energy	201 Mev

Mev does not contribute to the production of heat in a reactor. It is seen from the table that the beta decay and gamma decay of fission products together account for 13 Mev or 6.8 per cent of the 191 Mev available for heat production, approximately equally divided between the two. Neutron absorption, without subsequent fission, releases additional energy in the form of prompt gamma rays, amounting to about 7 Mev. This is followed by a delayed release of energy of about 2 Mev from the radioactive products formed by neutron capture; as

* S. Glasstone, "Principles of Nuclear Reactor Engineering," D. Van Nostrand Co., Inc. Princeton, N. J. (1955) p. 22; S. Glasstone and M. C. Edlund, "Elements of Nuclear Reactor Theory," D. Van Nostrand Co., Inc. (1952) p. 71.

from U^{239} and Np^{239} decay. In all, then, the *delayed* heat production amounts to approximately 15 Mev out of a total of about 198 Mev, or 7.6 per cent.

The rate of energy release, or decay power, from fission products is a function of the operating power, the length of operation, and the time after shutdown. The rate of energy release per fission may be expressed by the following general equation

$$\text{Mev/sec} \cdot \text{fission} = C\ T^n_F, \tag{7-8}$$

where C and n are constants and T_F is the time since fission, in seconds.

Referring to Fig. 7-8, the increment of energy release rate dE at a time T_s

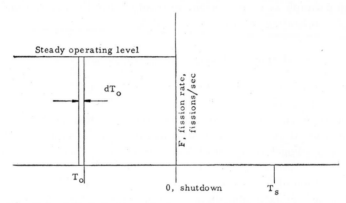

Fig. 7-8.   The fission rate during steady operation of a reactor.

after shutdown as a result of fissions that occurred during the incremental time dT_o is

$$dE = C\ (T_s - T_o)^n\ F\ dT_o, \tag{7-9}$$

where F is the fission rate, i.e., the number of fissions per second. Integration of this expression over the operating time from $-T_o$ to zero (shutdown) gives the following equation for the decay energy rate:

$$E = -\frac{CF}{n+1}\ [T_s^{n+1} - (T_s + T_o)^{n+1}]\ \text{Mev/sec.} \tag{7-10}$$

Assuming 200 Mev/fission as the energy of fission, the operating energy release, in Mev/sec, will be 200 times the fission rate F. Using this value in Equation 7-10, we obtain

$$\frac{P_s}{P_o} = \frac{-C\ (5.0 \times 10^{-3})}{n+1}\ [T_s^{n+1} - (T_s + T_o)^{n+1}], \tag{7-11}$$

where P_s is the shutdown or decay power in watts, and P_o is the operating power, in watts. This form of the equation for decay heating is most useful for nuclear engineering work.

The results of many fission-product decay studies, as given in the form of Equation 7-10, may be converted to the more useful form of Equation 7-11. It is to be noted that the various equations of this type, with their numerical values of C and n, are usually valid over restricted limits of time and may be greatly in error outside those limits.

Brief descriptions of some of the methods used to determine the energy of fission-product decay are given below, together with their results. A comparison of these results is presented in Fig. 7-9. For more complete descriptions see the article by Coryell and Sugarman.*

B. Counting Studies. One of the earliest attempts to determine the decay energy of fission products was made by Borst.† Samples were irradiated by a neutron source and decay curves obtained with an electroscope and a Geiger-Müller counter using various thicknesses of absorber. Curies of activity per fission were then obtained from the counting rate and fission rate. Since the average energy could be determined from the absorption curves, the decay energy rate could then be calculated for each irradiation time.

Based on values obtained by Borst, calculations were made by Wheeler which show the energy liberation as a function of time of irradiation and time after shutdown. A comparison of results with those of other sources is made in Fig. 7-9. A correlation of this data has been made by Way and Wigner‡ as follows:

$$\text{Mev/sec} \cdot \text{fission} = 5.6T^{-1.26}, \text{ from 20 min to 30 days,} \qquad (7\text{-}12)$$

$$\text{Mev/sec} \cdot \text{fission} = 98.0T^{-1.41}, \text{ from 50 to 100 days,} \qquad (7\text{-}13)$$

where T is the time in seconds since fission. Conversion of these two equations to the type of Equation 7-11 yields the following:

$$\frac{P_s}{P_o} = 10.78 \times 10^{-2} [(T_s)^{-0.26} - (T_s + T_o)^{-0.26}], \qquad (7\text{-}14)$$

$$\frac{P_s}{P_o} = 1.195 [(T_s)^{-0.41} - (T_s + T_o)^{-0.41}]. \qquad (7\text{-}15)$$

Other counter studies of gamma decay energy for very short irradiations were made by Sugarman and associates.§ This work owes its greatest importance to the fact that little work has been done for very short irradiation times. Fig. 7-10 gives a comparison with results of another study described in Part E.

C. Calculations from Decay Chains of Fission Products. If sufficient data were available, it would be possible to determine the decay energy of each

* C. D. Coryell and N. Sugarman, "Radiochemical Studies—The Fission Products," National Nuclear Energy Series IV-9, McGraw-Hill Book Co., Inc. (1951), Book I.

† L. B. Borst, "Estimates of Amount of Radiation and Accompanying Energy Liberation from Fission Products," National Nuclear Energy Series IV-9, McGraw-Hill Book Co., Inc., New York (1951). Page 34.

‡ K. Way and C. P. Wigner, "Rate of Decay of Fission Products," *ibid.*, Paper 43.

§ N. Sugarman, S. Katcoff, B. Finkle, N. Elliot, and J. D. Knight, "Decay of Gross Fission Products After Short Irradiations: III. Counter Studies of Gamma Activity and Energy," *ibid.*, Paper 37.

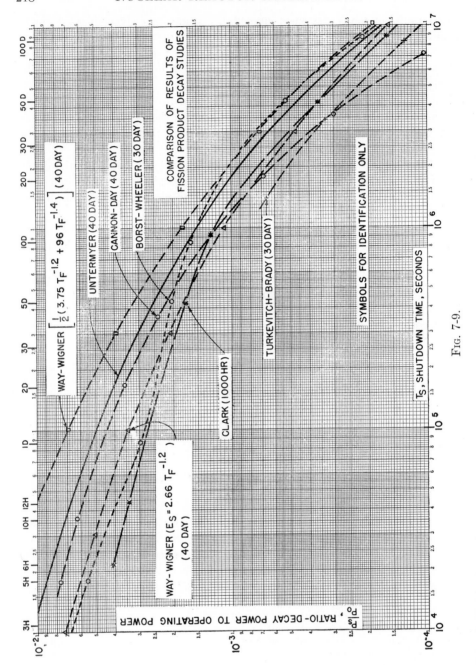

COMPARISON OF RESULTS OF
FISSION PRODUCT DECAY STUDIES

WAY-WIGNER $\left[\frac{1}{2}(3.75\,T_F^{-1.2} + 96\,T_F^{-1.4}) \right]$ (40 DAY)

UNTERMYER (40 DAY)

CANNON-DAY (40 DAY)

BORST-WHEELER (30 DAY)

CLARK (1000 HR)

TURKEVITCH-BRADY (30 DAY)

WAY-WIGNER ($E_S = 2.66\,T_F^{-1.2}$) (40 DAY)

SYMBOLS FOR IDENTIFICATION ONLY

T_S, SHUTDOWN TIME, SECONDS

$\frac{P_d}{P_o}$, RATIO-DECAY POWER TO OPERATING POWER

FIG. 7-9.

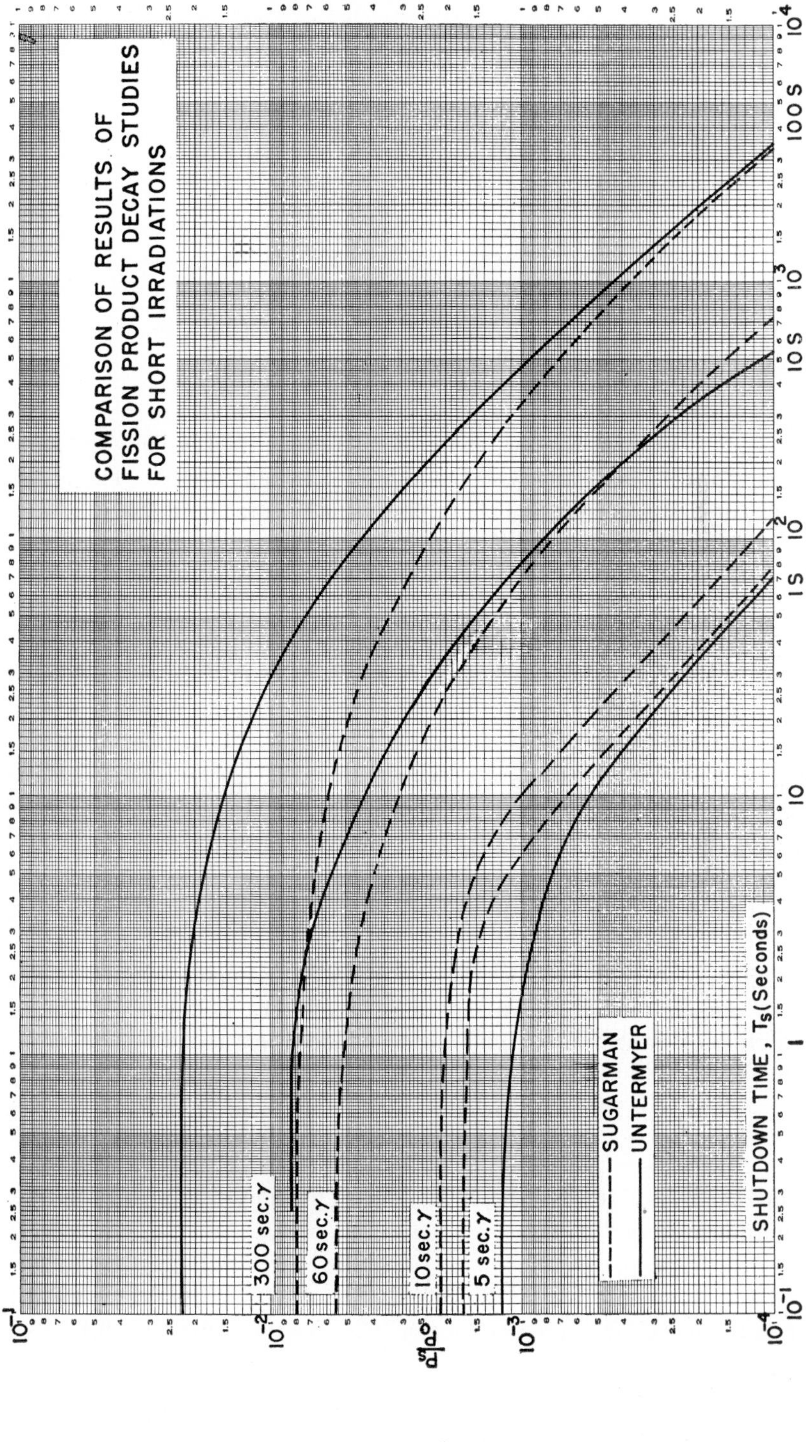

COMPARISON OF RESULTS OF
FISSION PRODUCT DECAY STUDIES
FOR SHORT IRRADIATIONS

SHUTDOWN TIME, T_s (Seconds)

SUGARMAN
UNTERMYER

300 sec.γ

60 sec.γ

10 sec.γ

5 sec.γ

$\dfrac{dP}{dp}$

FIG. 7-10.

nuclide produced in fission, including nuclides produced by radioactive decay. The energy of each of these nuclides could then be added together to determine the total decay energy of the fission products. The decay energy of each nuclide which has reached saturation activity can be expressed as follows:

$$\text{Decay energy rate, Mev/sec} \cdot \text{watt} = ygef, \qquad (7\text{-}16)$$

where y = yield of fission product in per cent of fissions, g = branching fraction in a given decay chain in per cent, e = energy of a given radiation in Mev, and f = fission rate per operating watt = 3.1×10^{10} fissions/sec·watt.

When a decay chain has reached saturation, the rate of production of the first nuclide in the chain is equal to the rate of decay of that nuclide and any subsequent nuclide in the chain. That is to say:

$$y_i F = \lambda_1 N_1 = \lambda_2 N_2 = \cdots \lambda_n N_n, \qquad (7\text{-}17)$$

where y_i is the yield of the i-th chain, F = fission rate (fissions/sec), λ = the decay constant in sec^{-1} and N = the number of atoms present. The number of atoms of the first member of a chain present at saturation is then:

$$N_{1,\,\text{sat}} = \frac{y_i F}{\lambda_1}. \qquad (7\text{-}18)$$

The number of atoms present of the first member of a chain after a time of operation, T_o, and shutdown time, T_s, is given by the following expression:

$$N_{1(T_o,\,T_s)} = \frac{y_i F}{\lambda_1} (1 - e^{-\lambda_1 T_o}) e^{-\lambda_1 T_s}. \qquad (7\text{-}19)$$

Then from Equations 7-18 and 7-19, the fraction of saturation activity present for the first member of a decay chain after T_o operation and T_s shutdown is:

$$A_{1(T_o,\,T_s)} = \frac{N_{1(T_o,\,T_s)}}{N_{1,\,\text{sat}}} = (1 - e^{-\lambda_1 T_o}) e^{-\lambda_1 T_s}. \qquad (7\text{-}20)$$

This expression may also be used for succeeding nuclides in a decay chain where precursive nuclides have short half-lives—say, of the order of minutes. The fraction of saturation activity for a nuclide which is a daughter of a long-lived nuclide is:

$$A_{2(T_o,\,T_s)} = \frac{\lambda_1 \lambda_2}{\lambda_1 - \lambda_2} \left(\frac{1 - e^{-\lambda_2 T_o}}{\lambda_2} e^{-\lambda_2 T_s} - \frac{1 - e^{-\lambda_1 T_s}}{\lambda_1} \right). \qquad (7\text{-}21)$$

From Equation 7-16, the decay rate of any nuclide after operating time, T_o, and shutdown time, T_s, is then:

$$\text{Decay energy rate, Mev/sec} \cdot \text{watt} = ygefA. \qquad (7\text{-}22)$$

For beta decay, the average energy has been assumed as 0.4 times the maximum energy.* One of the first attempts to determine the fission-product decay energy by this method was made by Brady and Turkevitch.† Only those products with significant yield and half-lives greater than 8 days were used in the calculations. Determinations were made for decay times from 16 to 240 days and for various operating times from 5 days to infinity. Correlation by Way and Wigner ‡ yielded the following expression:

$$\text{Beta and gamma energy, Mev/sec} \cdot \text{fission} = 29.4T^{-1.35}. \qquad (7\text{-}23)$$

This expression is valid for times between 16 and 340 days. Upon integration the following expression may be obtained:

$$\frac{P_s}{P_o} = 0.42[(T_s)^{-0.35} - (T_s + T_o)^{-0.35}]. \qquad (7\text{-}24)$$

As more information has become known concerning yields, half-lives, energies, and decay schemes, other studies§ have been made to increase the range and accuracies of this type of study. Results from Brady and Turkevitch and those from Clark|| are compared in Fig. 7-9 with results of studies using other methods. The total decay energy for Clark is obtained by doubling the value for gamma decay energy.

D. Statistical Methods. By considering the fission products as a sort of statistical assembly, Way and Wigner¶ made calculations of the total energy emitted per second at any time after fission has taken place. These theoretical calculations are based on several empirical relationships and the expression derived for the total energy is:

$$\text{Mev/sec} \cdot \text{fission} = 3.75T^{-1.2} + 96T^{-1.4} \qquad (7\text{-}25)$$

where T is the time in seconds since fission. This expression includes beta, gamma, and neutrino energy and is based on the assumption that the neutrino energy is equal to twice the beta energy. If we consider the beta and gamma energies equal, then the beta and gamma energy should equal one-half the values given by Equation 7-25. Integration of the above expression yields:

$$\frac{P_s}{P_o} = 93.8 \times 10^{-3}[(T_s)^{-0.2} - (T_s + T_o)^{-0.2}] + 1.2[(T_s)^{-0.4} - (T_s + T_o)^{-0.4}]$$

$$(7\text{-}26)$$

* E. L. Brady and A. Turkevitch, "Project Handbook," Report CL-697, D-6 (March 1945), Chapter 3.
  † *Ibid.*
  ‡ K. Way and E. P. Wigner, Phys. Rev., **70**, (1946).
  § P. R. Gillette, "Activity of Fission Products," HW-17415 (April 1950); I. L. Faller, T. S. Chapman, and J. M. West, "Calculations on U²³⁵ Fission Product Decay Chains," ANL-4807 (May 1952); J. Moteff, "Fission Product Decay Gamma Energy Spectrum," APEX 134 (1953); F. H. Clark, "Decay of Fission Product Gammas," NDA-27-39 (December 1954).
  || Brady and Turkevitch, *op. cit.*; F. H. Clark, *op. cit.*
  ¶ Way and Wigner, "Rates of Decay."

Handy rule-of-thumb expressions* derived from the above calculations are given as follows:

$$\text{Gamma decay energy, Mev/sec} \cdot \text{fission} = 1.26T^{-1.2} \qquad (7\text{-}27)$$

$$\text{Gamma + beta decay energy, Mev/sec} \cdot \text{fission} = 2.66T^{-1.2} \qquad (7\text{-}28)$$

Integration of expression (7-28) yields the following:

$$\frac{P_s}{P_o} = 66.5 \times 10^{-3}[(T_s)^{-0.2} - (T_s + T_o)^{-0.2}] \qquad (7\text{-}29)$$

Equations 7-27 and 7-28 are considered accurate within a factor of 2, for times between 10 sec and 100 days.

Equations 7-26 and 7-29 are compared with results of other studies in Fig. 7-9. Values of Equation 7-26 are divided by 2 in order to eliminate the neutrino energy which would not be apparent in decay heating.

E. Calorimetric Studies. A calorimetric study of fission product decay energy has been made by Day and Cannon† with results in good agreement with

*Clark, *op. cit.*

† R. A. Day and C. V. Cannon, "Direct Calorimetric Study of Fission Product Decay in Active Studies," National Nuclear Energy Series IV-9, McGraw-Hill Book Co., Inc., New York (1951), Paper 41.

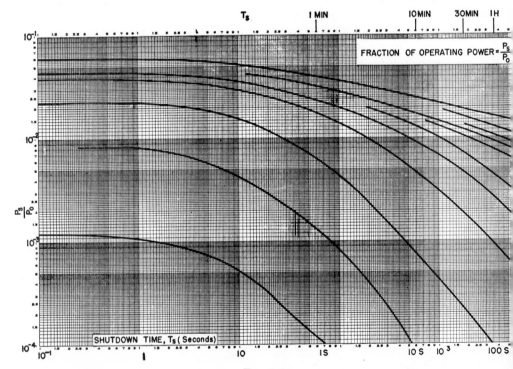

Fig. 7-11.

other data (see Fig. 7-9). Slugs approximately 1 in. diameter and 4 in. long were irradiated in the Clinton pile and the energy, in the form of heat released after removal from the pile, was measured with a water calorimeter. Irradiation time extended from 1 to 22 days and measurements of decay energy were made from 30 min to 60 days after discharge.

The escaping gamma radiation was measured with an electroscope and the gamma escape energy calculated from these measurements. Way* calculates the gamma escape to be about 20 per cent of the gamma decay which corresponds to approximately 10 per cent of the total beta and gamma decay energy. Curves as given in Fig. 7-9 do not include a correction for gamma energy escape from the calorimeter. Consequently these curves may be low but are still within probable accuracy of the measurements.

Correlation of this data† yields the following equation:

$$\text{Beta and gamma energy, Mev/sec} \cdot \text{fission} = 5.1T^{-1.23} \qquad (7\text{-}30)$$

* K. Way, "Calculation of Gamma Wattage Escaping from the Slug in the Calorimetric Experiments," National Nuclear Energy Series IV-9, McGraw-Hill Book Co., Inc., New York (1951), Paper 42.

† Way and Wigner, "Rate of Decay."

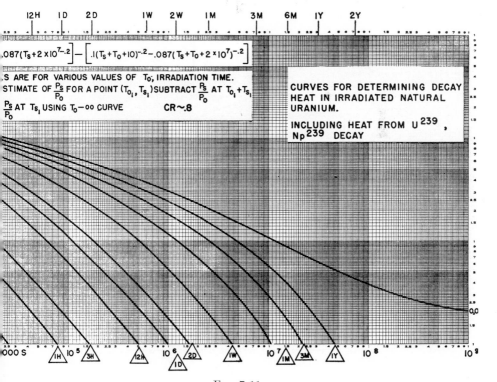

Fig. 7-11.

This equation holds good for times from 1 hr to 100 hr. Upon integration, we obtain:

$$\frac{P_s}{P_o} = 0.110\left[(T_s)^{-0.23} - (T_s + T_o)^{-0.23}\right] \tag{7-31}$$

Another experimental approach has been used [*] which is the basis for the design of the experiment to be performed here. In the experiment performed by Untermyer, the heat conducted away from a uranium slug was measured both during and after irradiation. These values were corrected for errors and then used to obtain the desired ratio of shutdown power to decay power.

In addition to the experimental work of Untermyer, a correlation of existing data into the general form Equation 7-10 was made by Untermyer and Weills. This correlation was made for decay energy of natural uranium and thus included the contribution of decay energy from U^{239} and Np^{239}.

The equation is as follows:

$$\frac{P_s}{P_o} = [0.1(T_s + 10)^{-0.2} - 0.087(T_s + 2 \times 10^7)^{-0.2}]$$

$$- [0.1(T_s + T_o + 10)^{-0.2} - 0.087(T_s + T_o + 2 \times 10^7)^{-0.2}] \tag{7-32}$$

[*] S. Untermyer and J. T. Weills, "Heat Generation in Irradiated Uranium," ANL-4790 (February 1952).

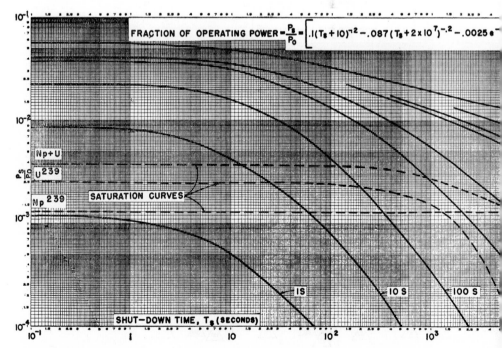

FRACTION OF OPERATING POWER $= \dfrac{P_s}{P_o} = \left[.1(T_s+10)^{-.2} - .087(T_s+2\times10^7)^{-.2} - .0025 e^{-}\right.$

Np+U

U^{239}

Np^{239}

SATURATION CURVES

1 S   10 S   100 S

SHUT—DOWN TIME, T_s (SECONDS)

Fig. 7-12.

A series of curves for different irradiation times was plotted from these equations. They are shown in Fig. 7-11. Because of the range and convenience of these curves, they are very valuable in reactor engineering problems where decay heating is a consideration. However, caution must be exercised in their use because they are subject to considerable error at very long or very short decay times. Fig. 7-9 gives a comparison of results from other studies with the curves of Untermyer and Weills.

In addition to the curves for natural uranium, Fig. 7-12 gives curves for decay heat from U^{235} only, which would omit the factor for U^{239} and Np^{239} contribution.

III. APPARATUS

A. General Description. Of the two experimental methods for determining the decay heat from fission products, which have been briefly described in the preceding section of this report, the method of Untermyer was selected as the basis for the present experiment. Although the basic principle of the experiment remains the same, the apparatus and procedure have been altered appreciably to increase the accuracy.

A uranium specimen is embedded in the end of an aluminum rod which serves

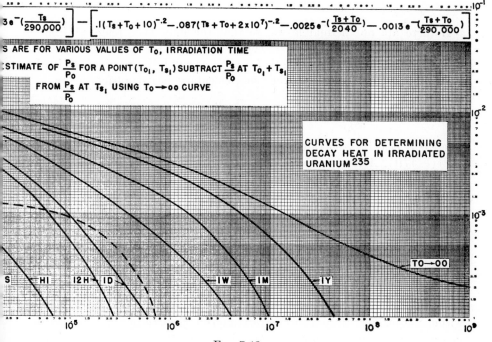

FIG. 7-12.

to conduct heat from the specimen to a cold sink. The specimen and conductor are sealed in a vacuum-tight vessel to assure, so far as possible, that the only heat escaping from the sample is that which is conducted along the aluminum rod to the cold sink. A thermal radiation shield is also incorporated inside the vacuum to reduce losses from radiation. Fig. 7-13 is a diagram of the sample assembly.

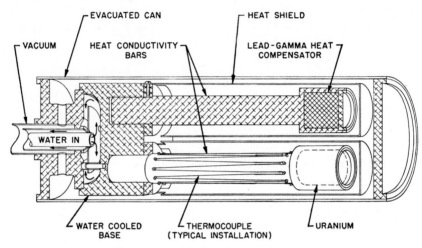

FIG. 7-13.   The irradiation assembly.

If there are no thermal losses, so that the only heat removed from the uranium sample is that which is conducted along the aluminum conductor, then the temperature drop along that conductor will be proportional to the heat generation during steady state. From elementary heat-transfer theory

$$q = kA \frac{dt}{dx}, \tag{7-33}$$

where q = heat transfer rate in Btu/hr, k = thermal conductivity in Btu/(hr) (ft^2) (F$°$) (ft), A is cross-sectional area in ft^2, and dt/dx is the temperature gradient in F$°$/ft. It is seen that the temperature drop is proportional to the rate of heat generation in the sample.

The ratio of temperature drop at any time T_s after shutdown to that during operation is assumed to be equivalent to P_s/P_o, which is the quantity desired. Thus

$$\frac{P_s}{P_o} = \frac{\Delta t_s}{\Delta t_o}. \tag{7-34}$$

There will be some heating in the sample which is due to the high gamma flux within the reactor. In order to correct for this, a piece of lead identical with the uranium sample has been mounted in the apparatus, as in Fig. 7-13. The

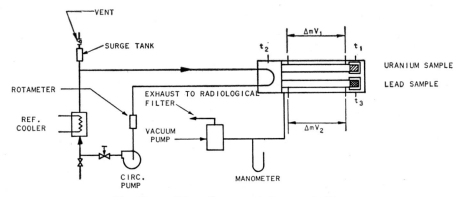

FIG. 7-14.   Flow diagram of the test facility.

gamma heating in the lead is then electrically subtracted from the total value obtained in the uranium sample. This assumes, of course, that the gamma absorption in lead is equivalent to that of uranium, which is not precisely correct. The lead sample conductor also acts as a compensating control for heat-sink temperature changes.

Fig. 7-14 shows the flow diagram of the system. De-ionized water is used as the cooling medium for the cold sink and is recirculated through the system by means of a small circulating pump. A refrigerated cooler is used as a heat exchanger for the cooling water. Fig. 7-15 gives a pictorial view of the assembled apparatus.

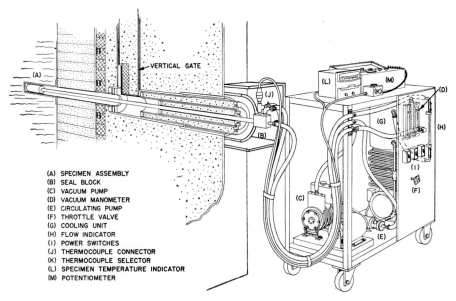

(A) SPECIMEN ASSEMBLY
(B) SEAL BLOCK
(C) VACUUM PUMP
(D) VACUUM MANOMETER
(E) CIRCULATING PUMP
(F) THROTTLE VALVE
(G) COOLING UNIT
(H) FLOW INDICATOR
(I) POWER SWITCHES
(J) THERMOCOUPLE CONNECTOR
(K) THERMOCOUPLE SELECTOR
(L) SPECIMEN TEMPERATURE INDICATOR
(M) POTENTIOMETER

FIG. 7-15.   Experimental apparatus arrangement.

The experiment is designed for use in one of the CP-5 horizontal holes which has a vertical gate. The apparatus is inserted in the reactor to the point of desired flux, which is expected to be about 5×10^{12} neutrons/(cm²) (sec). After the desired operating time has been reached, the apparatus is withdrawn into the shield plug and the gate is closed. The closed gate reduces the neutron flux by a factor of approximatly 1000. The decay heat is then measured with the sample in the withdrawn position.

The time of irradiation is to be from 12 to 24 hr. With this apparatus, reasonable accuracy can be obtained for P_s/P_o down to values of 10^{-3}. This means that for an irradiation time of 12 to 24 hrs, values may be obtained for decay times out to 1 day.

B. Temperature Measurement. During transient conditions such as those encountered after the sample has been removed from the neutron flux, the temperature slope dt/dx is proportional to the heat generation only when dx is infinitely small and at the source of heat generation, and the heat is generated

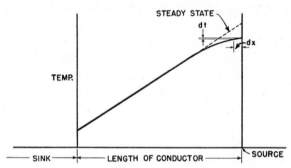

FIG. 7-16.   Temperature distribution during transient conditions.

as a plane source. This is illustrated in Fig. 7-16. It is obvious that these conditions are physically impossible to attain. Consequently, any measurements taken during transient conditions will be in error. For this equipment, heat capacity effects introduce transient conditions for approximately 25 min after removal of the sample assembly from the reactor.

The maximum temperature allowable at the sample is the limiting factor in the temperature drop attainable. It was decided to limit the sample temperature to approximately 600°F. Factors determining this maximum temperature were diffusion of fission gas from the sample, and strength of the aluminum conductor, which acts as a horizontal cantilever support for the uranium sample.

In a matter of an hour or so after shutdown, the decay heat in the uranium, and consequently the temperature drop in the conductor, will have fallen to a small fraction of that during operation. For this reason, a 10-point thermopile has been incorporated in the design rather than a single thermocouple, thus multiplying the signal by a factor of 10. Fig. 7-17 shows the conductor containing the uranium sample with the thermopile attached. The conductor for the lead sample is assembled in the same manner.

The thermopiles for the two conductors are wired in such a manner that the emf from the conductor containing the lead sample is subtracted from that of the uranium sample. The potentiometer reads the difference of the two potentials ($\Delta mv_1 - \Delta mv_2$, in millivolts; see Fig. 7-14). It will not be necessary to convert these potentiometer readings to temperature. The desired ratio of shut-down power to operating power (P_s/P_o) will be equivalent to the ratio of the millivolt readings during shutdown to the millivolt readings during exposure to the neutron flux.

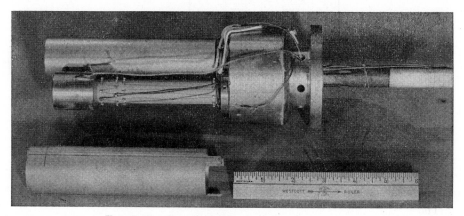

FIG. 7-17.   Sample holder and conducting arm.

The thermocouple wires may be iron and constantan, uninsulated, No. 36 gauge. Junctions for the thermopiles are made by staking a $\frac{1}{16}$-in.-diameter anodized aluminum pin into a hole in the conductor. This pin projects above the surface of the conductor and the two wires are attached to it to serve as a thermocouple junction. The hole in the conductor is also anodized prior to insertion of the pin and the two anodized surfaces act as electrical insulation between junction and conductor. The two terminal lead wires of the junctions are brought out through the vacuum tube. Corrections for emf's developed along these lines are negligible.

A thermocouple is used to measure the temperature at the surface of the aluminum surrounding the uranium sample. This thermocouple is connected to a temperature indicator to give a continuous reading of sample temperature. The temperature of the cold sink is also measured with a thermocouple attached to the potentiometer through a selector switch.

C. Cooling System. In order to maintain the cold-sink temperature as nearly constant as possible, water as coolant is circulated across the cold sink. For the desired temperature drop in the conductor arm, the heat generation is about 200 watts (682.6 Btu/hr). The water is circulated with a small pump and passes through a refrigerated heat exchanger where it is cooled before returning to the cold sink. The water is circulated through concentric tubes into the cold sink and back out. Fig. 7-13 shows the arrangement whereby water flows through

an inner tube to the cold sink and passes back out along an annulus formed
by a second tube. A third tube forms an outer annulus which is used to maintain a vacuum on the system. Spacers are used to keep the water tubes centered in the vacuum tube. This arrangement should prevent any condensation
on the cooling lines within the reactor. The tubes are brought out of the pile
through a seal block (see Fig. 7-18) for connection to external apparatus.

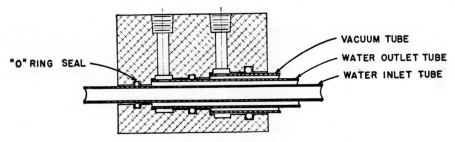

Fig. 7-18. A seal block.

The heat exchanger can be a replacement unit for a water fountain, having
a capacity of about 2500 Btu/hr. A closed recirculating system was selected as
the means for cooling in order to eliminate the problem of disposing of a steady
stream of slightly activated water.

D. Safety. To prevent the specimen from becoming overheated, the specimen temperature is connected to the reactor scram circuit to cause shutdown
of the pile should the specimen temperature rise above 650°F owing to loss of
coolant or for any other reason.

The shielding of the circulating system is not necessary, since the water is
relatively free from contamination and does not become activated. The water
may be changed periodically if corrosion products build up to the point of
presenting a health hazard. The circulation rate of the water will be low (approximately 1 gal/min) and should give sufficient time for the induced activity
in the water to decay to a tolerable level. If shielding of the circulating water
does prove necessary, portable shielding can be used.

The shield plug has been designed to permit ready insertion and withdrawal
of the apparatus from the pile. The standard shield plug has been replaced with
an arrangement of two concentric plugs as shown in Fig. 7-15. The inner plug
has been shortened to permit the apparatus to be withdrawn into the shield
and the gate closed. This plug extends beyond the face of the reactor a few
inches so that the over-all length of shield is only a few inches shorter than
that of the standard plug.

The circulating water in the two inner tubes provides shielding at this point,
but the vacuum annulus provides a means for neutron escape. If the "stream-

ing" of neutrons through this annulus is sufficient to produce a hazard, a neutron beam catcher may be used over the end of the apparatus where it protrudes from the pile. This was not found necessary on the CP-5 installation.

To assure that no activity escapes to the reactor room, the vacuum pump exhaust is connected to the reactor radiological filter.

IV. Test Procedure

A. Assembly and Filling of System. With the vertical gate closed, the specimen assembly and connected concentric tubes are first inserted in the pile with the outer shield plug in place. The inner plug is then slipped over the tubing and bolted to the outer plug. Thermocouple leads are soldered to the connector, and the seal block assembled. The flexible hose is clamped to the inlet and outlet water connections. The unit is now ready to be filled with cooling water.

To fill the apparatus, the cooling water system is first evacuated and the de-ionized water is then drawn in to the desired depth in the surge tank.

B. Startup Procedure. With the assembly in the withdrawn position and the vertical gate closed, startup is accomplished as follows:

1. Fill the reference junction with ice.
2. Start the vacuum pump and allow sufficient time for a suitable vacuum to be obtained.
3. Open the throttle valve wide open.
4. Turn on the circulating pump power switch.
5. Turn on the refrigerator power switch.
6. Check all connections for any leaks in system.
7. Check all thermocouple readings to see if they are reasonable.

The apparatus is now ready to be inserted in the reactor for the beginning of the irradiation. For the first irradiation it will be necessary to proceed cautiously with the insertion in order to determine the depth into the reactor that will give the required heat generation. After the vertical gate has been raised, the sample is inserted slowly into the reactor until the temperature of the specimen reaches approximately 600°F at equilibrium. It was found that the outer end of the unit should be approximately 1 ft inside the D_2O in CP-5 operating at 1 Mev where the flux is of the order of 10^{12} neutrons/(cm²) (sec).

C. Withdrawal and Removal. When the required time of irradiation has been obtained, the specimen is withdrawn into the shield plug and the gate closed. Required readings are then taken of the decay heat in the specimen.

For complete removal of the apparatus from the reactor, a horizontal coffin with 8 in. of lead shielding and a 5½-in.-diameter bore is used. The system is first evacuated of water and the connections at the seal block are removed. The coffin is then rolled up to the face of the reactor, and the sample and inner shield plug are drawn into the coffin. The coffin gate adjacent to the reactor is then closed. The specimen can then be transported to storage or disposal as the case may be.

D. Data Required. For the in-pile portion of the experiment, the following data are required hourly and should be recorded on Data Sheet 7-4.

1. Temperature drop along conductor from uranium sample, minus drop along conductor from lead sample—$\Delta mv_1 - \Delta mv_2$ (Fig. 7-14) millivolts.
2. Temperature of uranium sample, t_1 °F.
3. Temperature of cold sink, t_2 °F.
4. Temperature of lead sample, t_3 °F.

NOTE: The cooling water flow rate and the pressure in the vacuum system should remain constant during the test.

In addition, the following data should be recorded for each run:

1. Date
2. Run number
3. Time of insertion in neutron flux
4. Time of removal from neutron flux

DATA SHEET 7-4

Date_____   Run No. _____

Time of Insertion _____   Time of Removal from Reactor _____

Time	Time Since Insertion, hr	$(\Delta mv_1 - \Delta mv_2)$, millivolts	Uranium Temp., °F	Sink Temp., °F	Lead Temp., °F

After the sample has been removed from the neutron flux, $\Delta mv_1 - \Delta mv_2$ is recorded on Data Sheet 7-5 at a frequency as follows:

0-20 min (no valid readings because of transient conditions).
20-30 min after removal—readings every 5 min.
30-60 min after removal—readings every 10 min.
1-3 hr after removal—readings every 30 min.
3-12 hr after removal—readings every hour.
12-24 hr after removal—readings every 2 hr.

DATA SHEET 7-5

Date _____ Run No. _____

Time of Specimen in Reactor _____ Time of Removal from Reactor _____

Approximate Time Since Removal	Time	$(\Delta mv_1 - \Delta mv_2)$, millivolts	Uranium Temp., °F	Sink Temp., °F	Lead Temp., °F

V. RESULTS

A. Comparison of Data. Millivolt readings during operation $(\Delta mv_1 - \Delta mv_2)_o$ should remain constant. The millivolt readings after shutdown $(\Delta mv_1 - \Delta mv_2)_s$ at any particular time, T_s, are then divided by the average $(\Delta mv_1 - \Delta mv_2)_o$ to obtain the ratio P_s/P_o. Thus

$$\frac{P_s}{P_o} = \frac{(\Delta mv_1 - \Delta mv_o)_s}{(\Delta mv_1 - \Delta mv_2)_o}. \tag{7-35}$$

The values of P_s/P_o may then be plotted on Fig. 7-19 to compare with the Untermyer-Weills curves shown thereon. Fig. 7-19 is an enlargement of the central portion of Fig. 7-11 and covers values of P_s/P_o and the time intervals of interest in the experiment described here.

B. Errors. There are several obvious sources of error in the experiment. The first of these, which has already been mentioned, is the assumption that the heat generation is proportional to temperature drop. This is not expected to result in serious error except in very short times after shutdown.

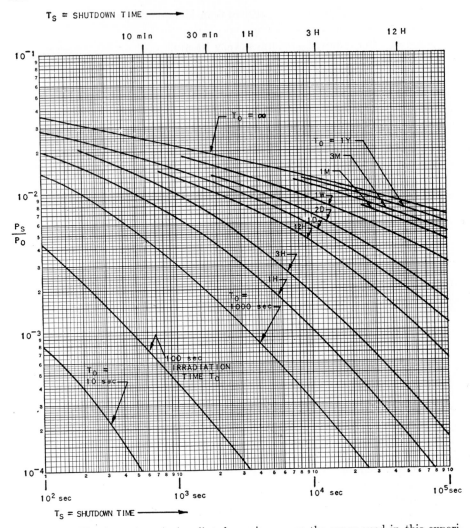

FIG. 7-19. The decay heat in irradiated uranium, over the range used in this experiment. (This is part of FIG. 7-11.)

The largest error will probably be due to gamma escape from the sample. In a similar experiment,* the losses were estimated at approximately 10 per cent of the total beta and gamma decay energy.

Other errors, which are expected to be minor in nature, are those due to thermal radiation loss, change of conductivity of aluminum with temperature, and thermal losses due to conduction along thermocouple wires. Calculation of thermal radiation losses indicates they will be less than 2 or 3 per cent.

* K. Way, *loc. cit.*

THE ARGONAUT AND ITS USES*

By B. I. SPINRAD, D. H. LENNOX, R. H. ARMSTRONG, and C. N. KELBER†

The Argonaut was designed for reactor physics research and instruction, to have convenience and sensitivity, relative safety, low cost, and flexibility. Its use as a subcritical assembly for measurement of the multiplication of neutrons as the fuel loading is increased toward criticality, and for the measurement of control-rod worth, has been described in Experiment 4-7, where many

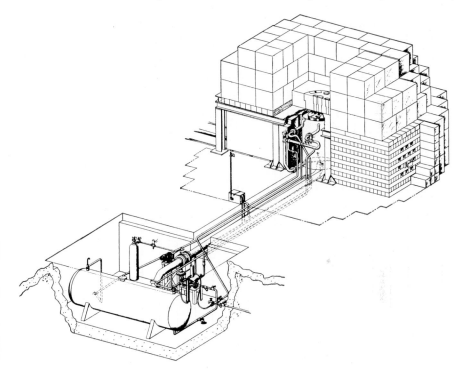

FIG. 7-20.   Isometric view of the Argonaut.

* See R. H. Armstrong and C. N. Kelber, Nucleonics, 15, No. 3, 62 (March 1957); H. B. Stewart, F. G. La Violette, C. L. McClelland, G. B. Gavin, and T. M. Snyder, "A Low-Power Thermal Test Reactor Adaptable to Nuclear Physics Research," KAPL-832 (November 3, 1952); L. Tonks, "The Thermal Test Reactor of the Knolls Atomic Power Laboratory," AECD-3530 (1953); "Research Reactors," prepared by the United States Atomic Energy Commission, McGraw-Hill Book Co., Inc., New York (1955); R. H. Armstrong, W. L. Kolb, and D. H. Lennox, "Argonaut, Engineering Construction and Costs," ANL-5704 (March 1957); D. H. Lennox and C. N. Kelber, "Summary Report on the Hazards of the Argonaut Reactor," ANL-5647 (December 1956); D. H. Lennox and B. I. Spinrad, "Interim Report on 'Argonaut'," ANL-5552 (March 1956); "Annual Report, Argonne National Laboratory," ANL-5680 (1956), p. 56.

† The Argonaut group consisted of D. H. Lennox, Project Engineer, R. H. Armstrong, F. Bewersdorf, C. N. Kelber, W. H. Kolb, A. Selep, and B. I. Spinrad.

of the details of the central lattice structure will be found. This should be studied before proceeding further.

This reactor is of the thermal, heterogeneous type with an annular core and with external and internal graphite reflectors; it uses water as a coolant and moderator. It is in the category of "inherently safe" reactors such as MTR, LITR, BSTF, and Borax. Tests on Borax have shown that in reactors of this type, it is a difficult job to achieve a nuclear runaway that will damage the reactor even when the safety circuits are inoperative. While the Argonaut system is as safe as any reactor can be, it is nevertheless no safer than the men who

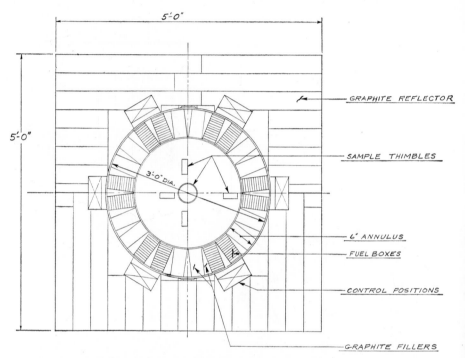

FIG. 7-21. Top view of the core region of the Argonaut.

make and use it. Continued emphasis on good safety practices is as essential as any industrial research or control program. Respect for possibly dangerous conditions must be instilled in the student's mind. Re-study the safety features outlined in the multiplication experiment of Chapter 4.

The maximum flux of the Argonaut is approximately 1×10^{11} neutrons/(cm^2) (sec), at a power level of 10 kw. An over-all view of the reactor is shown in Fig. 7-20, and a top view is shown in Fig. 7-21. In the latter, the fuel loading arrangement is shown. The critical loading is less than 4 kg of U^{235}. There are 190 fuel plates arranged in 12 clusters of a maximum of 17 plates per cluster.

The top of the reactor is kept free of control mechanisms so as to be accessible for loading the fuel assemblies, for the insertion of experiments such as a pile oscillator or danger coefficient equipment in the central hole, or in the four holes around the periphery of the internal reflector, or for placement of an external exponential assembly to use the thermal flux rising from the top of the internal reflector.

A graphite thermal column 5 ft wide, 5 ft long and 4 ft high is mounted on one side of the core region and contains 15 horizontal ports. On the opposite side of the core, there are various units such as a water tank 4 ft wide, 6 ft long and 3½ ft high, for bulk shielding measurements. These are moved into place

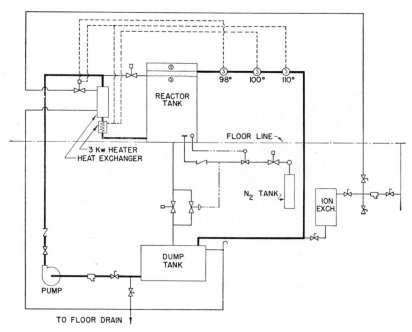

FIG. 7-22.   Argonaut flow diagram.

on a flat-bed truck. Ordinary concrete blocks (150 lb/ft³, 18 × 18 × 30 in.) are stacked against the two remaining lattice faces. This is a cheaper arrangement and more flexible than a monolithic shield. Each of these faces has an experimental port. The over-all dimensions of the assembly are, approximately 15 ft wide, 17 ft long, and 8 ft high.

Directly over the lattice or core region there is a shield made of dense concrete (250 lb/ft³) in a steel box 1 ft thick and 5 ft square, which contains a large removable plug directly over the internal reflector. The top shield also contains removable plugs, each of which is filled with heavy concrete, to provide apertures for the insertion of fuel elements. For higher-power operation, additional, ordinary concrete blocks are to be used to supplement the heavy concrete shield. A jib crane of 3-ton capacity, with a boom arc of 15 ft, is used for removal of these shields. The floor loading required under the reactor is 1500 to 2000 lb/ft². ·

The Flow Diagram. The heat-removal system is rudimentary. For a short time of operation at the higher power of 10 kw, the heat generated is about 49 watts or 168 Btu per hr per plate. Hence, the circulation rate of the coolant water should be approximately 2-3 gal/min, the pump having a maximum capacity of 10 gal/min. The heat-removal and safety system is shown in Fig. 7-22. Tap water is introduced into a 5-gal/hr, 3-liter, laboratory mixed-bed ion exchanger. The water then passes into a 275-gal aluminum storage tank. In ordinary use only 125 gal of water are needed. The extra capacity is made available in case an entirely different lattice is to be used inside the 3-ft aluminum tank in the reactor. From the storage tank, the water feeds through a strainer into the suction side of a ¼-hp stainless-steel centrifugal pump rated

at 20 gal/min against a 14-ft head. The discharge from the pump passes through a flow control valve and a check valve to the tube side of a 34,000-Btu/hr (10-kw) single-pass, stainless-steel shell-and-tube heat exchanger having 4.3 ft² of surface.

From the heat exchanger, the water goes through a 3-kw heater and to the inlet of the reactor tank. The heater is used for temperature control of the moderator. It is energized by a thermo-switch and a snap action controller in the reactor coolant outlet line. The coolant passes up the reactor tank, over a weir, and back to the storage or dump tank. Two safety float switches are used to monitor the water level in the reactor—one to indicate when the water has reached the operating level, the other to stop the pump should the water go higher than this level.

It is possible to cool the reactor by natural circulation when operating at low power levels. For this, a solenoid valve is opened to allow the coolant to bypass the regular pump circuit, but to circulate through the heat exchanger.

FIG. 7-23. Water pump, dump valve, clutch, counterweight, and drive assembly, in the utility pit.

A 6-in. aluminum dump line is welded to the bottom of the main reactor tank and runs to the storage tank in the utility pit, as shown in Fig. 7-20. Here a 6-in.

rubber-lined, electrically operated butterfly valve can be held closed by a magnetic clutch. When de-energized, a weighted lever arm opens the valve to empty the reactor promptly. Fig 7-23 shows some of the units just discussed.

A supplementary safety system consists of the introduction into the water of bubbles of nitrogen gas through a series (4 to 6) of 35-micron porosity spargers, at the same time that the dump system operates (see Fig. 7-22). This causes a rapid decrease in the bulk density of the moderator (10 to 20 per cent voids). This injection system is made to "fail safe" by using the nitrogen pressure to close a normally open mercuroid pressure switch. Additional control is obtained by the use of conventional absorbing materials next to the core in the outer reflector, as in Figs. 4-24 and 4-28.

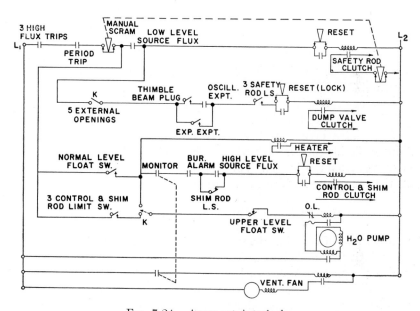

Fig. 7-24.   Argonaut interlocks.

Safety Features. As shown in Fig. 7-24, a sequential system of interlocks is used such that if any step is omitted from the proper startup procedure, or if an interlock is not satisfied, the operator cannot go on to the next step. Also, a burglar alarm is used to keep personnel from working on the top of the reactor when it is critical.

Even if all six safety rods, four independent instrument trip circuits, the manual scram, the water dump, and the nitrogen injection system should fail, an excursion would be terminated automatically by the reactor's negative temperature and void coefficients, without the release of any of the fission products to the environment.

If a large mass of fissile material were dropped into the inner tank (internal

graphite reflector removed) while fuel and water are in the annulus, a dangerous situation could result. Interlocks are provided so that the annulus must be
unloaded and the water dumped before changes can be made in this region.

Despite the comparative safety of the nuclear system of the Argonaut, a
competent instructor, with four to six months' training, must be on hand during
the operation. This individual (supervisor, operator, or professor) has the following responsibilities: (1) The trips, safety devices, and monitors must be
checked periodically for proper operation. If they are not working correctly
the operator has the responsibility of shutting down the reactor until they are
repaired. (2) All experimental proposals must be reviewed with regard to their
safety. (3) All experimenters must be taught safe operating conditions and
procedures. (4) All experiments must be checked before and during operation
for safety of performance. (5) The introduction of appreciable amounts of fuel
into the internal column, as for an internal exponential experiment, or in the
tank on the side converts the Argonaut into a very different reactor. A separate
safeguard review is required, involving a series of multiplication tests as in
Experiment 4-7, additional interlocks, etc. (6) The fuel is to be under the control of only one responsible person. (7) The safety precautions stated in Experiment 4-7 should be reviewed.

The fuel plates become radioactively hot after a few tests, through the
formation of fission products. Provision must then be made, whenever they are
to be removed from the Argonaut, of a "coffin" or lead shield suitable to protect
against the gamma rays which the waste products emit.

EXPERIMENTS WITH THE ARGONAUT (7-6)

A wide variety of experiments can be performed with the Argonaut, ranging
from the relatively simple irradiation of materials to provide short-lived radioisotopes to complex programs such as the investigation of lattices of various
types, containing, say, heavy water and depleted uranium.

Some of the experiments possible with the standard Argonaut are:

1. Measure the neutron temperatures and distributions in the reflector and
thermal columns. Measure the cadmium ratio (see Chapter 1) in the thermal
column to determine the degree of thermalization of the neutrons.

2. Irradiate materials with neutrons to produce short-lived radioisotopes to
be used in studies of decay rates or in chemical, biological, medical, agricul-
tural or industrial studies. See Experiments 2-1 and 2-2.

3. Intercalibrate foils to be used in making a flux traverse. For this, a
graphite stringer is removed from the side of the external thermal column,
and the foils are inserted on a wheel which is rapidly rotated. Thus the foils
are irradiated simultaneously, and later counted against each other. See Experiment 3-1.

4. External exponential experiments can be performed, as in Experiments 4-1

and 4-2, by assembling an exponential pile on top of the internal thermal column of the Argonaut, or on the side of the system where the tank was located. Approximately 10^7 thermal neutrons/(cm^2) (sec) are available.

5. Control-rod studies can be made such as flux perturbations, as in Experiment 4-4; and control-rod worth as in Experiment 4-5.

6. Critical mass determinations can be carried out using various geometries and uranium enrichments, as detailed in Experiment 4-7.

7. Pile oscillator measurements and danger coefficient studies can be made in the central thermal column. The samples should have cross sections (ΣV) of the order of 0.01–0.001 cm^2. The Argonaut, like its precursor the TTR, was designed to be particularly sensitive to these tests. The sensitivity of this reactor to lumped nuclear parameters of materials, such as the effective resonance integrals of fuel assemblies, is an important asset of this facility for both research and reactor design problems. Studies of boiling water reactors with a heterogeneous core of thoria or urania elements would be facilitated by accurate measurements of the resonance absorption of various lattices of these fuels. Samples of U^{233}, U^{235}, and Pu^{239} can be compared to determine some of the characteristics of reactivity change on irradiation.

8. Internal flux distributions in fuel-moderator assemblies can be measured by irradiating them in the thermal columns, top or side. Hence, values can be determined of disadvantage factors and thermal-utilization factors, as in Experiment 6-1.

9. Fuel standardization, with and without cladding, and instrument calibrations can be performed in the irradiation holes in the thermal column and in the shielding facility area.

10. Bulk shielding and removal cross-section measurements, of the type detailed in Experiment 6-2, can be made in the shielding tank.

11. Leakage studies with stepped plugs and offset ducts can be made as in Experiment 6-3.

12. Macroscopic flux distribution in a reactor can be made, as detailed in Experiment 7-1.

13. Reactor power measurement, as in Experiment 7-2.

14. Startup and shutdown. See Experiment 7-3.

15. Temperature coefficient of reactivity. See Experiment 7-4.

The design of the Argonaut is such that major changes can be made in its internal structure with relative ease. The following experiments then become possible. However, a new and careful safeguard analysis and procedure must be made in each case.

1. Graphite-reflected critical experiments can be undertaken on partially or fully enriched heterogeneous lattices of various geometries, of 3-ft diameter, by removing the fuel, interfuel, inner tank, and internal reflector and insertion of the new lattices in this space.

2. The microscopic flux distribution in lattice cells can be determined in considerable detail, as well as reactivity changes due to lattice perturbations, using the danger coefficient method, by removing the inner tank and introducing the new lattice.

3. Exponential measurements can be carried out by loading the shield test facility with various lattices.

4. Thermal migration studies (see Experiments 3-2 and 3-3) can be made by suitable loading of the shield test facility.

The Argonaut, because of its long neutron lifetime (approximately 200 microsec), is advantageous in design problems met in reactor control and operation, i.e., in the whole field of reactor kinetics, since it permits transfer function measurements over a reasonable range of frequencies.

Exact theory in reactor design is complicated; hence semi-empirical formulae are the rule today. The Argonaut may be used to determine both the parameters of useful formulae and their ranges of validity. Thus, theory and experiment complement each other.

There are many more uses of a nuclear assembly such as the Argonaut for research and training purposes than those listed above. Studies of flux monitors and of automatic reactor controls should offer stimulating programs.

Chapter 8

HEAT REMOVAL FROM A REACTOR *

INTRODUCTION

By A. L. LONDON, ANL, Reactor Engineering Division

The International School of Nuclear Science and Engineering has a forced-circulation loop for water flow (up to 300 psig pressure) and a second loop for liquid-metal flow. Test loops such as these are useful for providing engineering answers to the many problems associated with the heat transfer and pressure-drop performance of reactor fuel elements and the performance of materials under dynamic conditions of corrosion and erosion. This type of equipment is also useful for research work leading to basic-design data.

The objectives of the experiments to be performed on these loops are (1) the determination of the convective heat-transfer and pressure-drop behavior for flow in circular and rectangular tubes under nonboiling and boiling conditions, (2) to introduce the student to the usual nondimensional methods of correlating basic heat transfer information, and (3) to introduce the student to instrumentation, pumps, controls, and piping circuits used in reactor engineering test loops.†

---

* This chapter has been reviewed by A. L. London.
† The conventional treatment of heat-transfer analysis can be found in the following references. A simple résumé is offered in Faires' volume, Chapter 23. Names of authors in the present chapter refer to this list. V. M. Faires, "Applied Thermodynamics," The Macmillan Co., New York (1947). W. H. McAdams, "Heat Transmission" 3rd ed., McGraw-Hill Book Co., Inc., New York (1954). W. M. Kays and A. L. London, "Compact Heat Exchangers," National Press, Palo Alto, California (1955). B. Lubarsky and S. J. Kaufman, "Review of Experimental Investigations of Liquid-Metal Heat Transfer," National Advisory Committee of Aeronautics, Tech. Note 3336 (March 1955). W. H. Jens and P. A. Lottes, "Analysis of Heat Transfer Burnout, Pressure Drop and Density Data for High Pressure Water," ANL-4627 (1951). R. N. Lyon (Ed.), "Liquid-Metals Handbook," Government Printing Office NAVEXOS P-733 (Rev.) (1952). C. B. Jackson (Ed.), "Liquid-Metals Handbook" (Supplement), Government Printing Office, TID-5227 (1955). H. D. Monson, "Comments on Liquid Metals as Coolants in High Power Density Power Reactors," TID-7506, Part I (July 1956). J. F. Mumm, "Heat Transfer and Boiling Water Forced Through a Uniformly Heated Tube," ANL-5276 (1954). H. P. Grace and C. E. Lapple, "Discharge Coefficients of Small Diameter Orifices and Flow Nozzles," Transac-

Forced Convection Heat Transfer. For the case of single-phase flow of a colder fluid past a hotter surface, *the rate equation* (also known as Newton's law of cooling) for heat transfer from the surface to the fluid is

$$\frac{dq}{dA} \ (= q'') = h\Delta t_f, \tag{8-1}$$

where $dq/dA = q'' = $ heat transfer rate per unit of surface area, Btu/(hr) (ft^2) ; $A = $ surface transfer area, ft^2; $\Delta t_f = $ temperature difference from the surface to the bulk fluid temperature, °F; $h = $ the convective heat-transfer coefficient or film coefficient, Btu/(hr) (ft^2) (°F). In effect, Equation 8-1 states that the thermal current per unit of transfer area q'' is proportional to a temperature potential Δt_f; and h is the experimentally established proportionality factor which makes Equation 8-1 correct.

When the bulk of the liquid flow is at the saturation temperature, corresponding to the local fluid pressure, the heat transfer from the wall results in vapor bubble formation at the surface and these bubbles are swept by the fluid motion into the main stream. This type of evaporation will be termed *bulk boiling* and is one form of forced-convection two-phase flow. In contrast, if the surface temperature is above the liquid saturation temperature but the bulk of the liquid is subcooled, the vapor bubbles forming at the surface are collapsed by the subcooled liquid, and this intense action results in a high localized stirring. This type of forced convection heat transfer is qualified as *local boiling*.

The potential difference for bulk boiling is Δt_f, as in Equation 8-1; but for local boiling it is $(t_{\text{surface}} - t_{\text{saturation}})$, which is less than Δt_f because the fluid bulk temperature is subcooled. For local boiling then, it is necessary to modify Equation 8-1 to the form

$$q'' = h_{l.b.} \ (\Delta t_{\text{sat}}), \tag{8-2}$$

where $\Delta t_{\text{sat}} = t_{\text{surface}} - t_{\text{saturation}}$ and $h_{l.b.} = $ coefficient for local boiling heat transfer.

The coefficient h in Equation 8-1 is most useful for design purpose when it is essentially independent of the temperature difference Δt_f and depends primarily on the flow geometry, the flow mass velocity (velocity $\times$ density), and the so-called transport properties of the fluid—viscosity μ, thermal conductivity k, and specific heat at constant pressure c_p. This is the case for single-phase flow; and a great deal of information, established by experiment, is available for the ordinary gases and liquids.* For purposes of generalization and to reduce the tremendous amount of information to a usable form, these results have been correlated using nondimensional parameters such as Reynolds number and

---

tions of the American Society of Mechanical Engineers, **73**, 639 (1951). W. M. Rohsenow, "Heat Transfer with Evaporation," Heat Transfer Symposium, University of Michigan (1952) section. S. Glasstone, "Principles of Nuclear Reactor Engineering," D. Van Nostrand Co., Princeton, N. J. (1955).

* McAdams, *op. cit.*; Kays and London, *op. cit.*

others, as is customary in model experiment investigations. Unfortunately much less is known for liquid metals; and for boiling, h and $h_{l.b.}$ become functions of Δt_{sat}, as well as for some additional fluid properties such as latent heat of vaporization, interfacial surface tension, and vapor density and for adsorbed gas fraction, character of the solid surface, etc. Because of these additional complications there is not sufficient basic information available.* Hence, test loops are extensively employed to get "engineering answers" for liquid-metal and boiling heat-transfer problems.

The difficulty of obtaining basic heat-transfer information of the desired accuracy for liquid metals lies in the fact that the convective heat-transfer coefficient is so large that it is difficult to measure the small Δt_f in Equation 8-1 with a great enough precision, still using reasonable magnitudes for the thermal current per unit area q''. The accurate measurement of wall surface temperature provides the major difficulty in this respect. Moreover, any slight scaling of the heat-transfer surface introduces an additional thermal resistance to the current q'', and this fouling or scaling resistance is erroneously included in h (the reciprocal thermal resistance). Consequently, if h is large, then $1/h$ is small, and even a small amount of fouling of the surface results in a substantial error. The same difficulties exist for bulk and local boiling research investigations, though to a lesser extent.

In the case of single-phase flow friction in tubes, the results of many experiments can be correlated in the form of a friction factor f vs. a flow Reynolds number N_R, for a variety of liquids and gases, and the correlation will apply to any geometrically similar flow situation. In effect

$$f = \text{Function of } (N_R). \tag{8-3}$$

The particular functional relationship, determined by experiment, depends on the flow geometry under consideration.

In a similar manner, the theory of models and experience have confirmed that for forced-convection single-phase heat transfer at high Reynolds number, experimental results may be correlated as

$$N_{Nu} \text{ (or } N_{St}) = \text{Function of } (N_R, N_{Pr}), \tag{8-4}$$

where the nondimensional groupings are defined as:

$$N_{Nu} = \text{Nusselt No.} = hD/k \ (= N_{St}N_RN_{Pr}),$$
$$N_{St} = \text{Stanton No.} = h/Gc_p \ (= N_{Nu}/N_RN_{Pr}),$$
$$N_R = \text{Reynolds No.} = DG/\mu,$$
$$N_{Pr} = \text{Prandtl No.} = \mu c_p/k.$$

The meaning of these symbols is given in the Nomenclature on page **247**. It is recognized that the N_{Nu} or N_{St} numbers are characterized by the heat-transfer

---

* McAdams, *op. cit.;* Jens and Lottes, *op. cit.*

coefficient h; the Reynolds number characterizes the flow; while the Prandtl number includes the transport properties μ, k, and c_p only. Empirically, it is found that for a particular flow geometry, if $0.6 < N_{Pr} < 100$ (the range of ordinary gases and liquids),

$$N_{Nu} \cdot N_{Pr}{}^n = \text{Function } (N_R) \left.\right\}$$

or

$$N_{St} \cdot N_{Pr}{}^m = \text{Function } (N_R). \left.\right\}$$

(8-5)

For liquid metals, on the other hand, $N_{Pr} < 0.05$, and it is found that

$$N_{Nu} = \text{Function } (N_R \cdot N_{Pr}).$$

(8-6)

The product $(N_R \cdot N_{Pr})$ is termed the Peclet number.

$$N_{Pe} = \frac{DG c_p}{k}.$$

For the single-phase turbulent flow $(N_R > 6000)$ of ordinary liquids in circular tubes McAdams recommends the following equation as representative of the experimental results

$$N_{St} \cdot N_{Pr}{}^{2/3} \left(\frac{\mu_w}{\mu}\right)^{0.14} = 0.023 \, N_R{}^{-0.2} \, [1 + (D/L)^{0.7}],$$

(8-7a)

or, using the Nusselt number form

$$N_{Nu} \cdot N_{Pr}{}^{-1/3} \left(\frac{\mu_w}{\mu}\right)^{0.14} = 0.023 \, N_R{}^{0.8} \, [1 + (D/L)^{0.7}].$$

(8-7b)

Except for the viscosity evaluated at the wall temperature μ_w, all fluid properties are evaluated at the bulk average fluid temperature.

The $(\mu_w/\mu)^{0.14}$ ratio is used to account for the variation of the fluid properties in the boundary layer due to their temperature dependency. The term $[1 + (D/L)^{0.7}]$ accounts for the fact that in the entrance section of a tube, the boundary layer is forming and, as a consequence, is less thick on the average than for the fully developed flow boundary layer which would eventually be established in a very long tube.

The above equations can also be extended to tubes of rectangular or triangular cross section by using $4r_h$ in place of the diameter D, where r_h is the so-called hydraulic radius, i.e., flow cross section divided by wetted perimeter.

For liquid metals, Lubarsky and Kaufman and the "Liquid-Metals Handbook" summarize the available information on convective heat transfer. For the flow in circular tubes, an equation due to Monson is

$$N_{Nu} = 2.3 + 0.23 \, (N_R \cdot N_{Pr})^{0.5}.$$

(8-8)

This equation, fitting the greater bulk of experimental evidence, is about 30 to 40 per cent below the semitheoretical predictions of Lyon and Martinelli. As in the case of Equations 8-7a and 8-7b, it is also limited to turbulent flow $(N_R > 6000)$. For flow inside of an annulus or between parallel plates, with heat transfer through one side only, the heat transfer coefficient can be expected to be only about 80 per cent of that given by Equation 8-8.

For bulk boiling with water in circular tubes, a correlation due to Mumm is

$$N_{Nu} = \left[4.3 + 5 \times 10^{-4}\left(\frac{v_{fg}}{v_f}\right)^{1.64} X\right]\left[\frac{q''}{Gh_{fg}}\right]^{0.464}\left[\frac{GD}{\mu}\right]^{0.808}, \qquad (8\text{-}9)$$

where x denotes the quality or steam fraction.

No similar equation is available for local boiling, but a correlation due to Jens and Lottes relates the degree of wall superheat, Δt_{sat}, to the heat-transfer current per unit wall area q'' and the pressure p, as follows

$$\Delta t_{sat} = \frac{60\ [q''/10^6]^{1/4}}{e^{p/900}}, \qquad (8\text{-}10)$$

where the units are °F for temperature, Btu/(hr)(ft²) for q'', and psia for pressure p, the letter e denotes the base of natural logarithms.

One of the main objectives of the experiments to follow will be the comparison of the test results with predictions based on Equations 8-7 to 8-10.

NOMENCLATURE

A	Inside surface area of tube, ft²
A_0	Orifice flow area
C	Orifice coefficient, dimensionless
c_p	Average specific heat, Btu/(lb)(F°)
D	Inside diameter of tube, ft
E	Voltage drop, volts
g_c	Reciprocal proportionality factor in Newton's second law when pounds mass (lbm) and pound force (lbf) units are employed: $g_c = 32.2$ (lbm/lbf) (ft/sec²)
G	Mass flow rate, lb/(hr)(ft²)
h	Film coefficient for heat transfer for single-phase forced-convection and bulk boiling, Btu/(hr)(ft²)(F°)
$h_{l.b.}$	Film coefficient for local boiling, Btu/(hr)(ft²)(F°)
h_n	Specific enthalpy, Btu/lb
$h_{n.fg}$	Change in enthalpy from saturated liquid to saturated vapor, the latent heat of vaporization, Btu/lb
J	Conversion factor, 778 ft lbf/Btu
k	Thermal conductivity, Btu/(hr)(ft²)(F°/ft)
l	Length, in.
L_0	Length measured from power terminal to point where local boiling begins, in.
L_x	Length measured from power terminal to point where net steam generation begins, in.
$l_{1.b.}$	Length of tube in local boiling from inception to a point, in.
l_{LB}	Total length of local boiling region, in.
LB	Length of tube undergoing net steam generation, in.
l_b	Length from zero quality to a point in the net steam generation region, in.
m,n	Unspecified exponents
N	Wattmeter reading, watts
N_{Nu}	Nusselt number, hD/k, dimensionless
N_{Pe}	Peclet number, $N_{Pr}N_R = DGc_p/k$, dimensionless
N_{Pr}	Prandtl number, $\mu c_p/k$, dimensionless

N_R Reynolds number, DG/μ, dimensionless
N_{St} Stanton number, $h/Gc_p = N_{Nu}/N_R \cdot N_{Pr}$, dimensionless
p_s Static pressure at a point psia, lb/in.², absolute
q Power input, watts or Btu/hr
q_T Total rate of electrical input to tube, Btu/hr
q_B Rate of heat input to steam, Btu/hr
q_l Rate of heat input to liquid, Btu/hr
q' Heat flux per unit of tube length, Btu/(hr)(ft of length)
q'' Heat flux, Btu/(hr)(ft²)
q''' Volume heat generation rate, Btu/(hr)(ft³)
R Manometer reading, in.
r_h Hydraulic radius of a flow channel, ft
r_i Inside radius of tube, in.
r_o Outside radius of tube, in.
t_b Bulk fluid temperature, °F
t_s Inside surface temperature, °F
U Over-all heat-transfer coefficient, Btu/(hr)(ft²)(°F)
u Internal energy of fluid, Btu/lb
v Specific volume of fluid, ft³/lb
v_s Velocity of steam, ft/sec
W Actual flow rate, lb/min, lb/hr, lb/sec
W_c Flow rate from curves for water at 140°F, lb/min
z Height from some datum level, ft
x Steam quality at a point, lb vapor phase/lb mixture
X_0 Weight quality at the exit

Δp_{pt} Pressure drop from tap at inlet to a point, lb/in.²
δT Total temperature rise of fluid, F°
δt_b Temperature rise of fluid up to a point, F°
Δt_m Log mean temperature difference of heat exchanger, F°
Δt_f Temperature difference from wall to bulk fluid, F°
Δt_t Temperature drop of fluid through side of heat exchanger, F°
Δt_{sat} The temperature difference between the inside wall and the fluid which causes local boiling, F°
Δt_w Temperature drop through wall, F°
ρ_a Density of liquid flowing through orifice, lb/ft³
ρ_c Density of water at 140°F, lb/ft³
μ Dynamic viscosity of water, lb/(hr)(ft)

EXPERIMENT 8-1

METHODS AND APPARATUS USED IN THE EXPERIMENTAL DETERMINATION OF WATER FILM COEFFICIENTS FOR SINGLE AND TWO PHASE FLOW

By RAYMOND R. RHODE, ANL, Reactor Engineering Division

I. APPARATUS *

* Original design, construction, and use by G. Leppert for his Ph.D. thesis. Modifications for student use by R. R. Rhode.

A. General Flow Description. The apparatus and instrumentation that will be used to regulate and measure the variables of flow rate, heat flux, and pressure and to determine the temperatures of the surface and the fluid at various points will now be described.

The low-pressure, water heat-transfer loop shown in Fig. 8-1 is for the purpose of circulating high-resistivity water through the inside of a horizontal, tubular test section wherein heat is generated electrically and the water absorbs the heat from the tube. The pressurization of the system is accomplished by

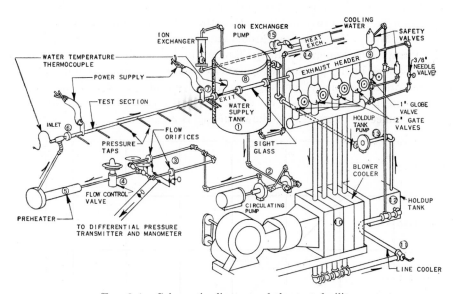

FIG. 8-1.   Schematic diagram of the test facility.

throttling the flow at the discharge end of the loop through the exhaust header valves.

The flow diagram (Fig. 8-1) shows that the flow of water originates from the supply tank, point (1), when the circulating pump, point (2), is started up and the water is pressurized in the pump according to its characteristic curve of flow versus head. The water is forced in the direction of the arrows through one orifice in the flow-measuring arrangement, point (3). The flow-control throttle valve, point (4), which is air-operated, sets the flow at its desired rate and allows the water to enter the preheater, point (5), which is capable of putting up to 40 kw into the water. A set of two variable autotransformers, with three banks each, provides a stepless control over the power input to the water and regulates the water temperature. The water enters the test section, point (6), where the temperature of the fluid is measured, and flows through the electrically heated test section, where the water is heated because of the transfer of heat from the test section to the water; it leaves at point (7), where its temperature is measured again. A sight glass is provided to study the type of flow that leaves the test section at point (8).

The fluid is then delivered to the exhaust header, point (9), and throttled down to about atmospheric pressure in the blower cooler at point (10). The water drains through another cooler located in the drain line at point (11) and drains into a holdup tank, point (12), for further cooling if desired.

From the holdup tank, the water is transferred back into the water-supply tank. An auxiliary ion-exchange system takes a portion of the water, cools it to about 100°F between points (14) and (15), forces it through the vertical ion exchanger, point (16), and then sends the water back into the water-supply tank. This flow pattern goes on throughout the test.

B. Pump. It is imperative in the flow of fluid through the test section that any variations in the pressure drop experienced by the fluid should not affect the flow rate. "Periphery" or "regenerative" type pumps were chosen because of their steep curve of head vs. capacity. The characteristics of these two pumps, connected in series, are shown in Fig. **8-2**.

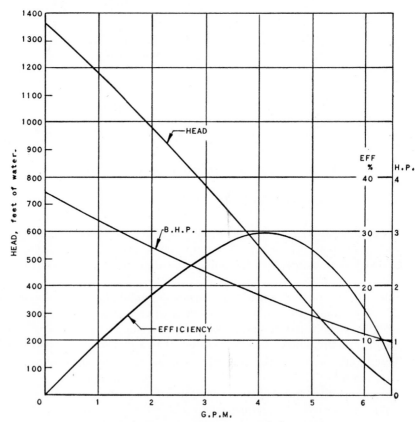

Fig. 8-2. Characteristic curves of the pumps.

C. Flow Measurement. Three calibrated, sharp-edged orifices—0.174 in., 0.2765 in. and 0.429 in.—are available for the measurement of flow. The loop is equipped to handle two of the orifices in the parallel pipe arrangement shown in Fig. 8-1. Two 2-in. gate valves permit the selection of one of the two orifices in the system. The machining and positioning of the orifice in the 1 inch pipe is

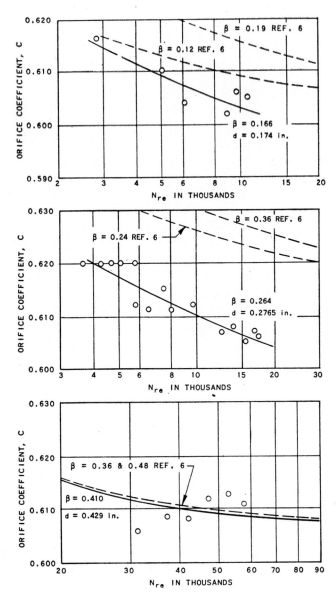

Fig. 8-3.   Coefficient of discharge vs. Reynolds number.

according to the Grace and Lapple method except for the dimension of the
land, which they advised be less than or equal to 0.001 in. The land which was
machined on the three orifices is less than or equal to 0.005 in. Slightly lower
orifice coefficients resulted because of this when compared with the Grace and
Lapple coefficients as shown in Fig. 8-3. The calibration curves are given in
Fig. 8-4.

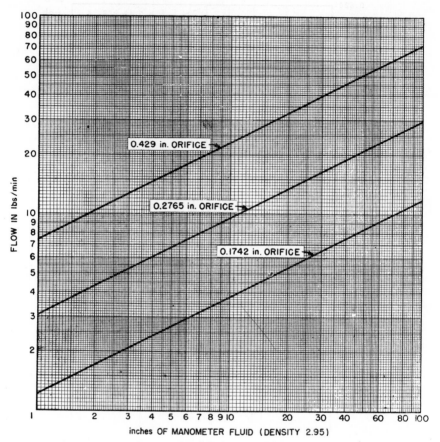

FIG. 8-4. Water heat-transfer experiment: flow rate vs. manometer reading. Flow
of 140°F water through thin-plate orifices in 1-in. pipe.

D. Flow Control. The pressure drop across the orifice is transmitted to a
differential pressure transmitter (Fig. 8-5) which is connected to an air-
operated flow-control throttle valve as shown schematically in Fig. 8-5. A
U-type manometer is connected in parallel with the pressure transmitter and
across the orifice. The manometer is capable of high accuracy and for this
reason was chosen to measure the flow. The flow-control system is of the type
that employs the standard 3-to-15-psi pressure differential. The air is fed to

the set-point pressure regulator (Fig. 8-5) and the differential from the pressure regulator operates the flow throttle valve. The pressure differential from the orifice is transmitted to the differential pressure transmitter and a balance is made in the flow controller.

E. Preheater. Three calrod immersion heaters are inserted into a pressure vessel which is shown at point (5) in Fig. 8-1, and connected through two variable autotransformers to a 440-volt, 3-phase power source to provide a maximum of 40 kw to the water as it flows to the test section. The autotransformers are provided to permit continuous variation of the power to the preheater and thereby accurately control the inlet water temperature to the test section.

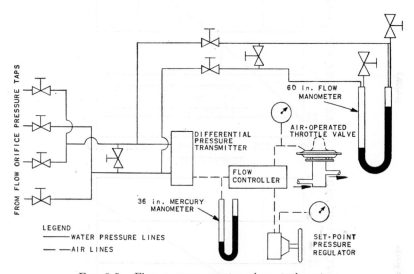

Fig. 8-5.   Flow measurement and control system.

F. Test Section. A round, type 347, stainless-steel tube, of 0.465-in. inside diameter × 0.020-in. wall and 6 ft long, was chosen because the thin wall will have a small temperature drop from the outside to the inside surface and also because its electrical resistivity changes very slightly with temperature as shown in Fig. 8-6. The test section dimensions and other particulars appear in Fig. 8-7 and are shown pictorially in Fig. 8-8.

Electrical power is supplied to the tube by applying a voltage across the silver-soldered terminals and passing a current through the tube. The thermal energy produced by the electrical heating is transferred as heat to the water flowing through the tube. Teflon insulators isolate the test section from the piping and thereby prevent the passage of current through the external piping in the system.

Ten pressure taps are attached to the surface of the tube by silver-soldering type 347, stainless-steel tubes, 1/8 in. o.d. × 1/16 in. i.d. and 3/4 in. long, radially to the tube and then drilling a $\frac{1}{32}$-in.-diameter hole concentric to the tubing through the wall of the test section. All burrs are removed from both sides of the hole. A typical pressure tap is shown in Fig. 8-8.

G. Power Measurements. Single-phase alternating current is supplied to the test section through three parallel-connected 20-kw welding transformers. The power may be changed in a stepless manner by using a motor-driven

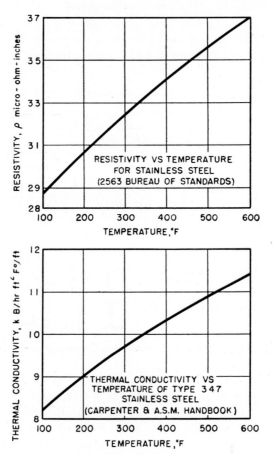

Fig. 8-6. Resistivity and thermal conductivity vs. temperature of stainless steel.

chain drive. Measurements of the current, voltage, and power will be made and voltage drop readings will also be made along the length of the tube to check the uniformity of heat flux (dq/dl).

H. Temperature Measurements. The orifice, inlet, and exit temperatures of the coolant are measured using #30 gauge (0.010-in. diameter) select iron-constantan thermocouples as shown in Figs. 8-9 and 8-10. The outside surface temperature of the tube is measured in 37 places, as in Data Sheet 8-1, by attaching the thermocouples directly to the tube by using glass tape as shown in Fig. 8-11. The outside surface temperature will also be measured on a quadrant at the designated points to check for temperature gradients around the tube. A set of nine thermocouples are also placed in the insulation, as shown in the sketch on Data Sheet 8-1, to check the heat loss from the tube.

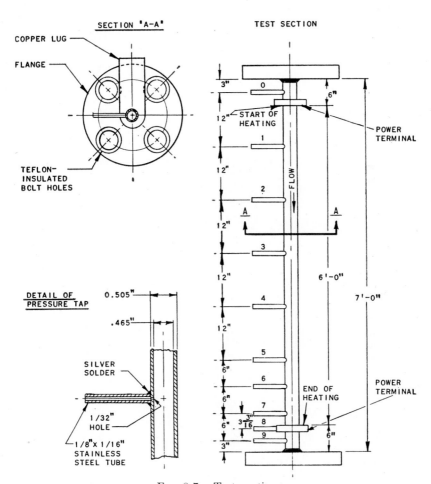

FIG. 8-7.   Test section.

Fig. 8-12 shows the position of the 48-point temperature indicator at point (1) which will be used to measure directly in °F the surface, insulation, orifice, and holdup-tank coolant temperatures. The inlet and exit temperatures will be measured in terms of millivolts by a potentiometer, point (2). Plots of the calibration tables for iron-constantan thermocouples appear in Appendix 7 for the range of temperatures covered. In addition the inlet, exit, orifice and

holdup tank coolant temperatures will be recorded by a chart recorder at point
(4).

I. Pressure Measurements. The ten pressure taps are connected as shown
in Fig. 8-7, and insulated electrically by hydraulic hose from the four U-type
manometers which have been converted to a well-type manometer. The wells
are shown in Fig. 8-13. The piping arrangement for the manometers is such

FIG. 8-8.   Test section and pressure tap.

that all pressure drops may be measured in relation to the first pressure tap or
the pressure drops after tap No. 4 may be measured in relation to tap No. 4.
This is done if pressure drops greater than the range of the manometer occur
in the later part of the tubes. A pressure tap is located in the exit power terminal to check bubble collapse phenomena during local boiling. A 500 psi precision pressure gauge, point (3) Fig. 8-12, is located at tap No. 7 to measure the
static pressure in the loop.

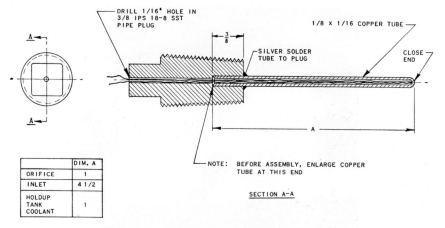

	DIM. A
ORIFICE	1
INLET	4 1/2
HOLDUP TANK COOLANT	1

Fig. 8-9. Thermocouple well construction.

J. Sight Glass. A glass tube, Fig. 8-1, with the same inside diameter as the test section has been installed in the system to furnish a visualization of different flow phenomena. This tube will furnish information relative to the velocities of the fluid flowing in the system.

K. Exhaust Header. The exhaust header shown in Fig. 8-1, is composed of two horizontal, 4-in. stainless-steel pipes separated by four 2-in. gate valves, a 1-in. globe valve, and a 3/8-in. needle valve. The gate valves are used to handle large steam rates, and the smaller valves are used for the coarse and fine adjustment of the system pressure. After the fluid has been throttled in the valves, it is delivered to the blower cooler.

L. Cooling. The blower cooler or condenser, shown in Fig. 8-1, is an air-to-

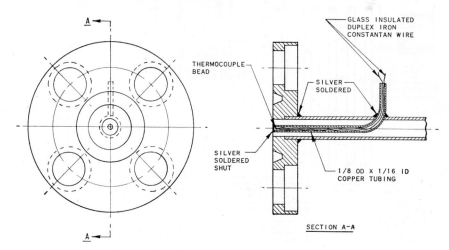

Fig. 8-10. Exit thermocouple installation.

FIG. 8-11. Thermocouple installation.

water or -steam heat exchanger which incorporates vertical copper tubes with aluminum fins attached to the tube in its design. A set of four banks constitutes the heat exchanger. The fluid from the system is forced downward through the tubes and is cooled by the passage of air forced over the fins. The

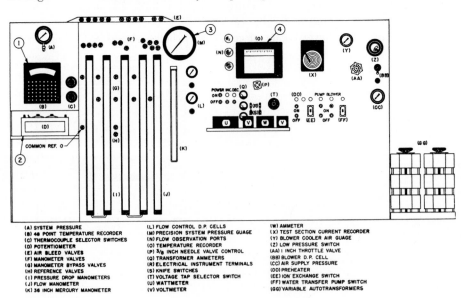

(A) SYSTEM PRESSURE	(L) FLOW CONTROL D.P. CELLS
(B) 48 POINT TEMPERATURE RECORDER	(M) PRECISION SYSTEM PRESSURE GUAGE
(C) THERMOCOUPLE SELECTOR SWITCHES	(N) FLOW OBSERVATION PORTS
(D) POTENTIOMETER	(O) TEMPERATURE RECORDER
(E) AIR BLEED VALVES	(P) 3/8 INCH NEEDLE VALVE CONTROL
(F) MANOMETER VALVES	(Q) TRANSFORMER AMMETERS
(G) MANOMETER BYPASS VALVES	(R) ELECTRICAL INSTRUMENT TERMINALS
(H) REFERENCE VALVES	(S) KNIFE SWITCHES
(I) PRESSURE DROP MANOMETERS	(T) VOLTAGE TAP SELECTOR SWITCH
(J) FLOW MANOMETER	(U) WATTMETER
(K) 36 INCH MERCURY MANOMETER	(V) VOLTMETER

(W) AMMETER	
(X) TEST SECTION CURRENT RECORDER	
(Y) BLOWER COOLER AIR GUAGE	
(Z) LOW PRESSURE SWITCH	
(AA) I INCH THROTTLE VALVE	
(BB) BLOWER D.P. CELL	
(CC) AIR SUPPLY PRESSURE	
(DD) PREHEATER	
(EE) ION EXCHANGE SWITCH	
(FF) WATER TRANSFER PUMP SWITCH	
(GG) VARIABLE AUTOTRANSFORMERS	

FIG. 8-12. Panel board.

temperature of the fluid as it leaves the cooler is controlled by an air-operated louver which limits the air supplied to the fins. After being cooled, the fluid is discharged through the bottom of the heat exchanger into the drain line.

A line cooler is positioned in the drain line to provide further cooling before sending the water to the holdup tank. It consists of 45 ft of $\frac{1}{4}$-in. o.d. $\times$ $\frac{3}{16}$-in. i.d. copper tubing. Tap water is sent through the inside of the tube and then discharged to a drain.

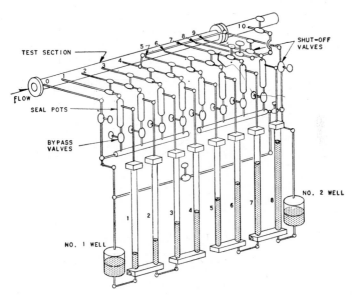

Fig. 8-13.   Pressure measurement apparatus.

The final cooling stage occurs in the holdup tank shown in Fig. 8-1. The tank measures 24 in. wide, 20 in. high, and 37 in. long. The cooling coils consist of a header with two separate coils 40 ft long, and made of $\frac{3}{8}$-in. o.d. $\times$ $\frac{5}{16}$-in. i.d. copper tubing. The upper coil may be shut off if desired. Tap water does the cooling as it passes through the inside of the tubing and out to the drain. The fluid is allowed to stand in the tank for a period of time which depends upon the setting of the level control switch. The holdup tank pump, shown in Fig. 8-1, transfers the fluid from the holdup tank to the supply tank.

M. Ion Exchange. Fig. 8-14 shows the components of the ion-exchange system. The ion column has a capsule design which permits easy recharging of the resin (which is the ion-exchange medium). A coil, which consists of 40 ft of $\frac{1}{2}$-in. o.d. $\times$ $\frac{3}{8}$-in. i.d. aluminum tubing, is connected to a small pump which forces about 0.1 gal/min through the ion exchanger after the fluid is taken from the supply tank and cooled below 100°F. The coil is situated

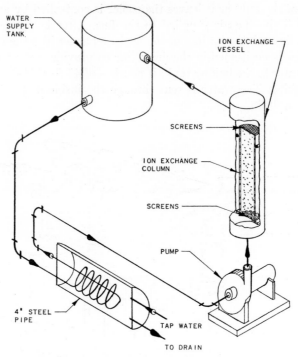

FIG. 8-14. Ion-exchange apparatus.

horizontally inside a 4-in. steel pipe 2 ft long which has tap water supplied to it.
The system water is pumped into the ion-exchange vessel and flows through
the vertical ion column and then returns to the supply tank.

II. OPERATION OF LOOP

A. Safety Features. The water heat-transfer loop has several safety
features. These devices or interlocks are required because of the danger of
applying electrical power to a system that under certain conditions will force
excessive temperatures on the test section and components.

Before any power can be applied to the loop, the circulating pump must be
running and developing at least 20 psi. This is required because the supply
tank may be empty or blocked in some manner. In addition to running the
pump with at least 20 psi, it is also necessary to have the blower cooler in
operation. With the pump and blower cooler operating satisfactorily, it is
permissible to put power into the loop through the preheater and test section.
As power is absorbed by the water, the pressure increases. "Overpressure" is
prevented by a maximum steam pressure switch which automatically shuts off

the preheater and test-section power. A panic button is also attached to the loop, in case of an emergency, to shut off all power to the test section and preheater.

Before the test is conducted, and also before anything is put into operation, a general check list is used to prevent delays.

B. Check List for Startup of Loop

1. Check water supply in the holdup tank and supply tank.
2. Check which orifice valve is open.
3. Be sure that ice junction has been filled with crushed ice.
4. Turn on the air supply.
5. Close all throttle valves at the discharge end of the loop.
6. Open flow-control throttle valve for maximum flow.
7. Shut off all pressure gauges except those over 400 psi.
8. Close all valves on manometers, except bypass lines.
9. Turn on coolant water for pump.
10. Open blower damper.
11. Move both preheater controls to minimum position on powerstats.
12. Open ion-exchange coolant valves.

C. Startup of Loop and Selection of Conditions

First determine the operating conditions. Then:

1. Turn all power switches to ON position.
2. Move transformer settings to minimum position.
3. Start ion exchange.
4. Adjust ion coolant water so that water in the ion exchanger is less than 100°F.
5. Start pump.
6. Start blower.
7. Allow flow to circulate.
8. Control pressure at 105 psig.
9. Bleed off air from loop and manometers
10. Turn on preheater.
11. Put power to the test section.
12. Cool discharge water in the holdup tank to correspond with conditions desired, but keep below 180°F.
13. Readjust water temperature out of ion-exchange cooler.
14. Set flow through orifice.
15. Control inlet temperature.
16. Let the loop settle out to equilibrium.
17. Adjust inlet temperature and control discharge temperature.
18. Settle conditions and make adjustments with flow rate and power.
19. Take data as required on data sheets.

III. Test Procedure

A. Data Required. Once the conditions of equilibrium have been reached, as indicated by the temperature recorder, the following data are to be recorded on Data Sheets 8-1 and 8-2.

1. Power in watts.
2. Current and voltage.
3. Voltage drops along the test length.
4. Flow manometer reading.
5. Static pressure at position No. 7.
6. Surface temperature versus length of tube.
7. Insulation temperatures.
8. Orifice, inlet, and exit temperatures.
9. Pressure drop at ten positions.

In addition to these measurements, the following should be noted:
1. Run number.
2. Date.
3. Orifice dimensions.

B. The Data Sheets, Graphs and Tables. With the information obtained for conditions of forced convection, local boiling, and bulk boiling, it will be possible to obtain the film coefficients for these three types of heat transfer by convection. The pressure-drop data which are required for a part of the analysis of the data can also be investigated by interested students if they desire, but it is not necessary for this report. The following data sheets and graphs, together with the tables and graphs in Appendix 5, will help in the analysis of the data.

IV. Calculations

The calculations for the film coefficients will be outlined. Assumptions will be made in the analysis which will be left to the student to verify.

A. Assumptions

1. Steady state.
2. Uniform heat flux along length; i.e., $dq/dl = q'$ is constant with l.
3. Change in kinetic energy is negligible.
4. Unity power factor.
5. Heat leak to the surroundings through the test section insulation is negligible.

B. Power. The instrument factor for the wattmeter measuring the power input to the test section is 300. This factor is the result of a reduction by the

DATA SHEET 8-1

RUN NO. _____   DATE _____

MEASURE-MENT	POSITION in. FROM INLET	THERMO COUPLE	POINT	TEMP-ERATURE
SURFACE THERMOCOUPLES	7 1	1	A	
	6 8	2		
	6 6	3		
	6 4	4		
	6 2	5		
	6 0	6		
	5 8	7		
	5 4	8		
	5 2	9		
	5 0	1 0		
	4 8	1 1		
	4 6	1 2		
	4 2	1 3		
	4 0	1 4		
	3 8	1 5		
	3 6	1 6		
	3 4	1 7		
	3 0	1 8		
	2 8	1 9		
	2 6	2 0		
	2 4	2 1		
	2 2	2 2		
	1 8	2 3		
	1 6	2 4		
	1 4	2 5		
	1 2	2 6		
	1 0	2 7		
	6	2 8		
	4	2 9		
	2	3 0	A	
INSULATION THERMOCOUPLES	6 8	3 1	E	
	6 0	3 2		
	5 2	3 3		
	4 4	3 4		
	3 6	3 5		
	2 8	3 6		
	2 0	3 7		
	1 2	3 8		
	4	3 9	E	
SURFACE THERMO-COUPLES	6 6	4 0	B	
	6 0	4 1	C	
	5 0	4 2	D	
	3 8	4 3	B	
	2 6	4 4	C	
	1 4	4 5	D	
	4	4 6	B	
ORIFICE	———	4 7	—	
CONDENSATE	———	4 8	—	

POSITION in. FROM INLET	VOLTAGE TAP	VOLTAGE DROP
9	1	
2 0	2	
3 2	3	
4 4	4	
5 6	5	
6 4	6	
7 2	7	

CURRENT_____ amperes

TOTAL VOLTAGE_____ volts

*Wattmeter*_____ watts/300

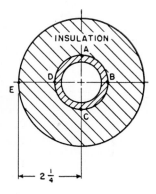

INSULATION

VIEW LOOKING AT
INLET OF TUBE

DATA SHEET 8-2

DATE _____

OBSERVERS _____   _____   _____

_____   _____   _____

RUN NO. _____

BAROMETRIC PRESSURE _____

AMBIENT TEMPERATURE _____ °F

TEST SECTION. *Horizontal, type 347 stainless steel tube 0.465" I.D. x 0.020" wall x 72" long*

ORIFICE _____ in.

RUN NO.	TIME		FLOW MANOME-TER READ in.		WATT METER READ	psig		INLET TEMP. MV	EXIT TEMP. MV	PRESSURE TAPS										
										RED FLUID UNDER WATER (inch)					MERCURY UNDER WATER (inch)					
	START	FINISH	DOWN	UP		EXIT	INLET	MV	MV	1	2	3	4	5	6	7	8	9	10	

PH = _____

RESISTIVITY = _____ ohm⁻cm.

MANOMETER ZERO [   ]

DATA SHEET 8-3

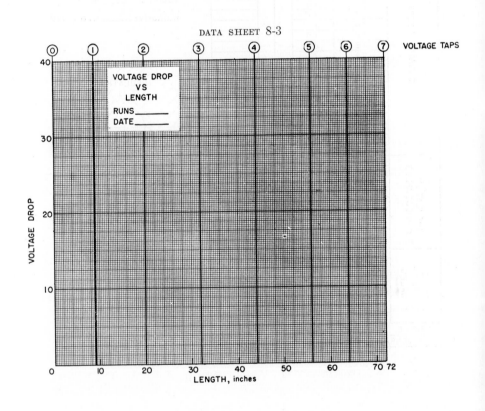

VOLTAGE DROP
VS
LENGTH

RUNS _____
DATE _____

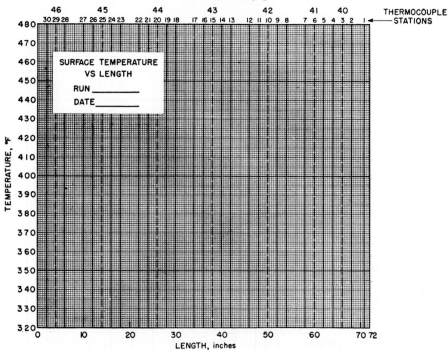

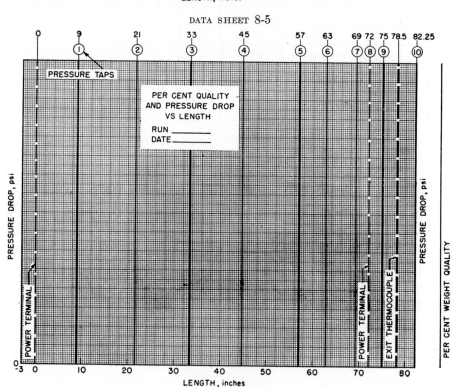

DATA SHEET 8-6

RUN NO.		PRESSURE TAPS										
		RED FLUID				MERCURY					EXIT THERMO-COUPLE	IO
		1	2	3	4	5	6	7	8	9		
	ΔP inches MANOMETER FLUID											
	ΔP, psi											
	PRESSURE, psia											
	T_{SAT} °F											
	ΔP inches MANOMETER FLUID											
	ΔP, psi											
	PRESSURE, psia											
	T_{SAT} °F											
	ΔP inches MANOMETER FLUID											
	ΔP, psi											
	PRESSURE, psia											
	T_{SAT} °F											
	ΔP inches MANOMETER FLUID											
	ΔP, psi											
	PRESSURE, psia											
	T_{SAT} °F											

current transformer of 300 to 1. The power input q, in watts, is

$$q_T = 300 \times \text{wattmeter reading.} \qquad (8\text{-}11)$$

C. Variation of Power with Length. Since the voltage is measured and plotted on Data Sheet 8-3 and the current is also measured, the relation of $dq/dl = q'$ versus length can be found. The power input is related to the voltage and current according to: Power = (Voltage drop) (current), or, in symbols,

$$q = EI \text{ watts.} \qquad (8\text{-}12)$$

Since the current I, must be constant with length, $dq/dl \, \alpha \, dE/dl$. Thus, if the E-l curve is linear, $dq/dl = q'$ is constant.

D. Heat Flux. If the power input is found to be uniform along the length of the tube, the calculation of the heat flux q'' is simply

$$q'' = \frac{EI \times 3.413}{A}, \qquad (\text{Btu/hr})(\text{ft}^2), \qquad (8\text{-}13a)$$

$$q'' = \frac{EI \times 3.413}{l_{\text{total}}} = \frac{q_T}{l_{\text{total}}} \quad \text{(Btu/hr)(ft}^2\text{)}. \tag{8-13b}$$

If the power input varies with the length, then the variation of the heat flux should be plotted vs. length. Experience has shown that this will not be necessary, but the student should verify it.

E. **Flow Rate.** The flow curves of three calibrated orifices are shown in Fig. 8-4, relating the manometer reading in inches and the flow rate in pounds per minute for a water temperature of 140°F. If the water flowing through the orifice is other than 140°F, a correction must be applied for the density of the water. The corrected flow is

$$W = W_c \left[\frac{\rho_a}{\rho_c} \right]^{1/2}, \quad \left(\frac{\text{lbs}}{\text{min}} \right) \tag{8-14}$$

F. **Pressure Drop.** The pressure-drop piping has been arranged to measure the pressure drop from the first pressure tap to any of the remaining taps downstream. The first four manometer legs contain a red fluid with a specific gravity of 2.95 and the last four contain mercury, which has a specific gravity of 13.56. The last manometer leg is valved to permit the reading of the last three pressure tap positions separately.

The conversion of the manometer reading R into the pressure drop in psi is

$$\Delta p = 0.0705R \text{ psi}, \tag{8-15}$$

for the pressure taps from No. 1 to No. 4, and

$$\Delta p = 0.454R \text{ psi}, \tag{8-16}$$

for the pressure taps from No. 5 to No. 10.

G. **Pressure.** For the conditions of local boiling and two-phase flow, it will be necessary to know the relation of the pressure to the length of the tube. Since the pressure drop is obtainable and also the static pressure is known at pressure tap No. 7, the pressure vs. length variation can be plotted on Data Sheet 8-5. The relation to the pressure p is psia and the pressure difference Δp in psi to the pressure at a point is simply

$$p_{pt} = p_7 + \Delta p_{(0 \text{ to } pt)} \text{ psi}, \tag{8-17}$$

for pressure taps Nos. 1 to 7, and

$$p_{pt} = p_7 - \Delta p_{(7 \text{ to } pt)} \text{ psi}, \tag{8-18}$$

for pressure taps Nos. 7 to 10.

These quantities are to be tabulated in Data Sheet 8-6.

H. **Saturation Temperature.** Once the pressure is known at a point, the saturation temperature of the fluid at that point can be obtained by using the steam tables of Keenan and Keyes which have been used in the preparation of Figs. A5-11 and A5-12 of Appendix 5. The saturation temperature for the range of pressures that will be encountered in this experiment is given in

Appendix 5. For the conditions of local boiling and two-phase flow, the saturation temperatures are to be plotted on Data Sheet 8-4.

I. Temperature Drop Through Wall. The equation for the tube-wall temperature drop is from McAdams, *op. cit.*, p. 19.

$$\Delta t_w = \frac{-r_1 q''}{24(r_o{}^2 - r_i{}^2)k}\left[(r_o{}^2 - r_i{}^2) - 2r_o{}^2 \ln \frac{r_o}{r_i}\right] \qquad (8\text{-}19a)$$

where r_o = outside radius of tube in inches, r_i = inside radius of tube in inches, k = thermal conductivity of tube in Btu/(hr)(ft)(F°), q'' = heat flux in Btu/(hr)(ft²).
Substituting: $r_o = 0.2525$ in. and $r_i = 0.2325$ in. gives

$$\Delta t_w = 826 \times 10^{-6} \, q''/k \; F°. \qquad (8\text{-}19b)$$

J. Energy Balance. *1. In General.* One very important check on the validity of the test data is provided by an energy balance, comparing the electrical power input to the test section against the energy gain of the water stream. For steady-state flow the conservation of energy principle yields:[*]

$$q_{T, \text{ electrical}} = W (h_{n, \text{ out}} - h_{n, \text{ in}}) + q_{\text{leak}}. \qquad (8\text{-}20)$$

The heat leak through the test section insulation can be demonstrated to be less than 1000 Btu/hr (= 0.3 kw, or less than 1 per cent of the electrical input). If the test data indicates an unbalance in the above equation which exceeds 5 per cent of the electrical input, the test results should be considered invalid.

2. Subcooled Liquid. As long as the bulk temperature of the fluid is below the saturation temperature, the temperature rise of the fluid can be determined from

$$\frac{dt_b}{dl} = \frac{1}{Wc_p} \frac{dq}{dl} = \frac{q'}{Wc_p}, \qquad (8\text{-}21)$$

assuming that dq/dl is constant with length.

3. Two-Phase Flow. The two-phase flow calculations of the temperature rise and the determination of the point where net steam generation begins involve a reiteration process because of the pressure drop which occurs in the tube. The profiles of surface temperature and pressure drop will be similar to Figs. 8-15 and 8-16.

The equation which is used to determine the point at which boiling begins is

$$q'l_b = W(h_{n, \text{ sat. liq.}} - h_{n, \text{ in}}), \qquad (8\text{-}22)$$

where $q'l_b$ denotes the heat input up to the point where boiling begins; $h_{n,\text{sat.liq.}}$ is a function of an unknown temperature at point b; and $h_{n,\text{in}}$ is the enthalpy of the water. A reiteration process must be used to determine l_b. Fortunately, the curves of surface temperature vs. length and pressure drop vs. length will aid in the first trial.

---

[*] The subscript n is used so as not to confuse the film coefficient, h, with the term enthalpy, h_n.

As a noticeable change in the wall temperature will occur at point b, Fig. 8-15, a departure of the pressure-drop curve from an essentially straight line to a power function will occur at b in Fig. 8-16. The bulk temperature at b can then be approximated. A few trials and the location of the start of boiling can be determined.

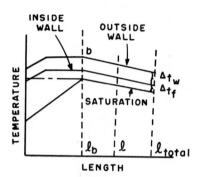

FIG. 8-15.   Profile of surface temperature drop.

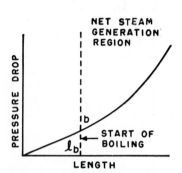

FIG. 8-16.   Profile of pressure drop.

To determine the quality of the steam, the relation of enthalpy and quality will be used, once point b is found. The quality at a point $l > l_b$ is

$$x = \frac{(l - l_b)q'}{Wh_{n,fg}}. \tag{8-23}$$

Information is now available for the preparation of a graph of temperature and pressure conditions vs. flow length, duplicating quantitatively the schematic representation of Figs. 8-15 and 8-16.

V. ANALYSIS OF DATA

A. Forced Convection:
Required Work

1. Determine the heat fluxes, q'' and q'.
2. Find the flow rate, W.
3. Calculate the temperature gradient of the fluid from Equation 8-21; calculate the total temperature rise of the fluid; and check this result against the measured rise.

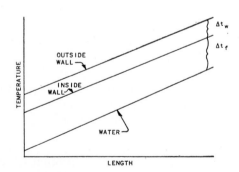

FIG. 8-17.   Temperature conditions.

4. Determine the temperature drop through the tube wall. (Equation 8-19b).
5. Determine the mean film drop, Δt_f, and calculate the film coefficient.

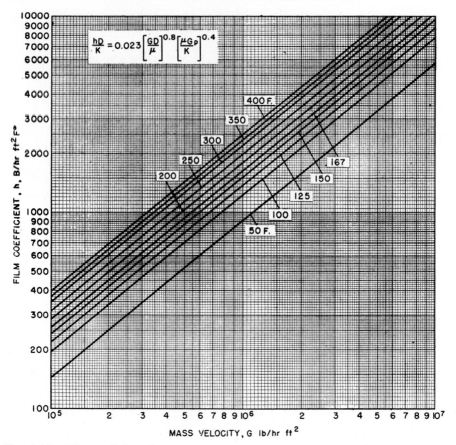

FIG. 8-18. Film coefficient h vs. mass flow rate G, for heating water at various temperatures inside a tube with a 0.465-in. i.d.

Preparation of a graph of temperature conditions, corresponding to Fig. 8-17, will be useful in this respect.

6. Use Equation 8-7a or 8-7b to evaluate a film coefficient to compare to your test results. Fig. 8-18, calculated from an equation approximating 8-7b, may be used as a rough check.

7. Discussion of experiment.

8. Conclusions.

B. Forced Convection: Optional Work

1. Determine the influence of L/D.

2. Determine the effect of introducing a viscosity correction into the correlation for the film coefficient.

3. Outline a method of using the film coefficient equation to determine if scaling is occurring in the tube.

4. Make an error analysis on the experiment.
5. Compare the pressure-drop data with the Moody friction factor which is given in ANL-5424.

C. Local Boiling: Required Work

1. Repeat steps 1 to 4 in the forced-convection analysis.
2. Calculate the pressure drop from the data for each pressure tap and tabulate in Data Sheet 8-6.
3. Determine the pressure at each tap and tabulate in Data Sheet 8-6.
4. Use Figs. A5-11 and A5-12 of Appendix 5 to determine the saturation temperature at the pressure tap positions, tabulate in Data Sheet 8-6, and then plot the data on Data Sheet 8-5.
5. Determine the point of local boiling by drawing a straight line fitting the data between A-B and B-C as in Fig. 8-19. The point of local boiling is then considered to be at point B.

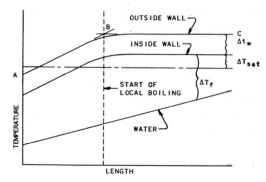

FIG. 8-19.   To determine the point of local boiling.

6. The amount of superheat should be found from Data Sheet 8-4 at point B and about three other points.
7. Calculate the $h_{l.b.}$ film coefficients as defined by Equation 8-2.
8. Calculate the single-phase film coefficient h before the start of local boiling.
9. Compare the measured Δt_{sat} with the correlation of Jens and Lottes, Equation 8-10.
10. Discussion of results.
11. Conclusion.

D. Local Boiling: Optional Work

1. Compare Δt_{sat} with the following correlations:

(a) $\dfrac{Cl\Delta t_{sat}}{h_{fg}} = C_{SF} \left[\dfrac{q''B}{\mu l h_{fg}} \sqrt{\dfrac{g_0\sigma}{g(\rho_l - \rho_v)}} \right]^{0.33} Pr_l^{1.7}$, Rohsenow.   (8-24)

(b) Others.

2. Outline a more detailed experiment.
3. Analyze the pressure-drop data.
4. Review the literature starting with McAdams and compare the experimental results with other investigator's data.
5. Make a complete error analysis.

E. Two-Phase Flow: Required Work

1. Determine the heat fluxes, q'', q'.
2. Find the corrected flow rate, W.
3. Calculate the pressure drop along the tube, tabulate in Data Sheet 8-6 and plot it on Data Sheet 8-5.
4. Determine the pressure along the tube and list in Data Sheet 8-6.
5. From Figs. A5-11 and A5-12 of Appendix 5, determine the saturation temperature of the fluid and plot on Data Sheet 8-4.
6. Calculate the point where boiling begins.
7. Determine and plot the quality on Data Sheets 8-4 and 8-5.
8. Find the average film-temperature drop and the coefficient h from Equation 8-1.
9. Compare the results with the correlation of Mumm, Equation 8-9.
10. Discussion of results.
11. Conclusion.

F. Two-Phase Flow: Optional Work

1. Check equations and assumptions used in analysis.
2. Discuss variables.
3. Compare the data with other investigators.
4. Outline a more detailed experiment.
5. Investigate the pressure-drop data and compare with the Martinelli-Nelson method given in ANL-5424.
6. Discuss and outline a method of correlating two-phase flow film coefficients.
7. Make an error analysis on the experiment.

D-C ELECTROMAGNETIC PUMPS*

By A. H. BARNES, Late Director of Reactor Engineering Division, ANL

The d-c conduction pump is the most direct approach to the problem of pumping liquid metals by electromagnetic means. The elements of this type of electromagnetic pump are illustrated in Figs. 8-20 and 8-21. A thin-walled duct,

* D. A. Wall, "Direct-Current Pumping of Liquid Metals," AERE CE/R 757 (1951); A. H. Barnes, "Direct Current Electromagnetic Pump," Nucleonics, 2, No. 1, 16 (1953); J. F Cage, Jr., "Electromagnetic Pumps for High Temperature Liquid Metal," Machine Design, 25, No. 3, 178 (1953); E. F. Brill, "Development of Special Pumps for Liquid Metals," Mechanical Engineering, 75, No. 5, 369 (1953).

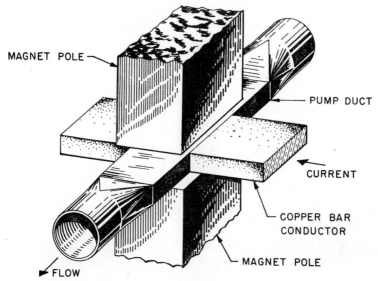

FIG. 8-20. Direct-current electromagnetic pump.

Fig. 8-22, with copper conductors attached to opposite sides is located between the poles of an electromagnet. Current entering through the duct wall traverses the liquid which fills the duct and develops in it a longitudinal thrust of magnitude

$$F = \frac{BI_c r}{10} \text{ dynes,} \tag{8-25}$$

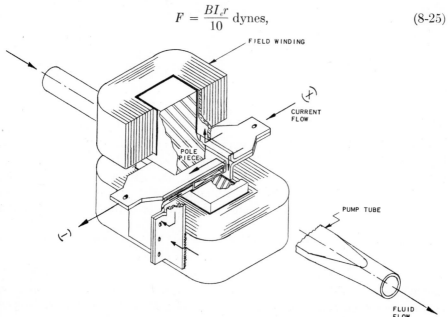

FIG. 8-21. Construction of a d-c electromagnetic pump.

where B is the magnetic flux density (in gausses) in the liquid between the magnetic poles, I_e is the current (in amperes) traversing the liquid which lies in the magnetic field and r is the width (in centimeters) of the pump duct parallel to the direction of current flow. If s is the height of the duct in the

FIG. 8-22. Electromagnetic pump tube.

magnetic-field direction, then rs is the cross-sectional area of the duct and the pressure developed will be

$$p = \frac{BI_e r}{10rs} = \frac{BI_e}{10s} \text{ dynes/cm}^2. \qquad (8\text{-}26)$$

The total current traversing the duct will be the sum of the currents in the liquid and in the duct wall. The current in the liquid will consist of that portion which passes through the region of strong magnetic field and is therefore effective in developing the thrust in the liquid, and that portion which bypasses the region of strong field and so contributes little or nothing to the pumping action.

Fig. 8-23 shows the equivalent circuit, where I is the total current, I_w is the current which bypasses through the duct wall of resistance R_w, I_e is the current traversing the liquid in the region of strong magnetic field along a path of effective resistance R_e, and I_b is the current traversing the liquid beyond the field at the entrance and exit sections of the duct. R_b is the effective resistance

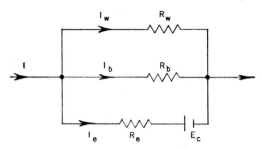

FIG. 8-23. Equivalent circuit of pump.

of the bypass paths through the liquid. E_c represents the counter emf developed in the liquid as it moves through the magnetic field. Since $E_c = Brv/10^8$ where v is the velocity of the liquid in cm/sec and $v = q/rs$ where q is the liquid flow in the duct in cm³/sec, then

$$E_c = \frac{Brq}{10^s rs} = \frac{Bq}{10^8 s} \text{ volts.} \tag{8-27}$$

Solution of the network equations, together with the expression for I_e obtained from Equation 8-26, leads to the expression

$$q = \frac{10^8 s}{B}\left[I\left(\frac{R_w R_b}{R_w + R_b}\right) - \frac{10 ps}{B}\left(\frac{R_w R_b}{R_w + R_b} + R_e\right)\right] \text{cm}^3/\text{sec.} \tag{8-28}$$

Replacing $R_w R_b/(R_w + R_b)$ by R_B, which represents the combined resistance of the bypass paths through both duct wall and liquid at entrance and exit sections of the tube and converting to engineering units give

$$Q = \frac{4 \times 10^6 S}{B}\left[IR_B - \frac{1.75 \times 10^6 PS}{B}(R_B + R_e)\right] \text{gal/min,} \tag{8-29}$$

where P is in psi, S is in inches, and Q is in gal/min. This relation indicates that the capacity is a linear function of the current input to the pump duct. Rearranging Equation 8-29 gives

$$P = \frac{5.7 \times 10^{-7} BI}{S}\left(\frac{R_B}{R_B + R_e}\right) - \frac{B^2 Q}{7 \times 10^{22} S^2 (R_B + R_e)} \text{ psi.} \tag{8-30}$$

From this we see that the pressure-capacity characteristic (neglecting hydraulic losses) is linear for a constant-current input.

The expression for the static (zero flow) pressure developed by the pump is obtained by setting $Q = 0$ in Equation 8-30. Thus

$$P = \frac{5.7 \times 10^{-7} BI}{S}\left(\frac{R_B}{R_B + R_e}\right) \text{ psi.} \tag{8-31}$$

The potential difference across the pump duct is $V = E_c + I_e R_e$ volts. From

Equations 8-26 and 8-27 we obtain

$$V = \frac{Bq}{10^8 s} + \frac{10ps}{B} R_e,$$

or

$$V = 2.5 \times 10^{-7} \frac{BQ}{S} + 1.75 \times 10^6 \frac{PSR_e}{B} \text{ volts.}$$ (8-32)

The electrical power input to the duct is therefore

$$W = VI = 2.5 \times 10^{-7} \frac{BQI}{S} + 1.75 \times 10^5 \frac{PSI \, R_e}{B} \text{ watts.}$$ (8-33)

The mechanical power developed in the liquid is $0.435PQ$ watts, so the efficiency of power conversion in the duct is

$$\text{Eff.} = \frac{0.435PQ}{2.5 \times 10^{-7} \frac{BQI}{S} + 1.75 \times 10^6 \frac{PSI \, R_e}{B}}.$$

Substituting the value of Q from Equation 8-29, we obtain

$$\text{Eff.} = \frac{1.74 \times 10^5 \, PS \left[R_B - 1.75 \times 10^5 \frac{PS}{BI} (R_B + R_e) \right]}{R_B (BI - 1.75 \times 10^6 \, PS)}.$$ (8-34)

It should be noted that the pressure P in Equations 8-32, 8-33, and 8-34 is the pressure which would be developed if there were no hydraulic loss in the pump duct. The actual pressure will be less by the pressure drop due to the duct impedance. The magnitudes of R_w and R_e may be calculated from the dimensions and resistivities of the duct and liquid respectively. R_b is a complicated function of the duct geometry, field distribution, and liquid velocity profile; its magnitude can best be determined on the basis of experimental tests. The expression for the efficiency given in Equation 8-34 is for the pump duct only and does not involve the power requirements for maintaining the magnetic field, nor does it take into account the I^2R losses in the bus work connecting the pump to the source of current supply.

The magnetic field due to the flow of current across the pump duct distorts the field between the magnet poles by introducing a component which increases the resultant field intensity on the entrance end and lowers it on the exit end. This variation in field intensity along the length of the duct produces a corresponding nonuniformity in the current distribution, with the result that the pumping action may be seriously impaired. For small pumps operating with high magnetic-field intensities and relatively small currents, the decrease in pump capacity is not important, but for high-capacity pumps operating with large currents in an extended field region, magnetic-field compensation should be provided. This may be achieved in two ways. In the first method the current, after traversing the liquid in the duct, is brought back across the main

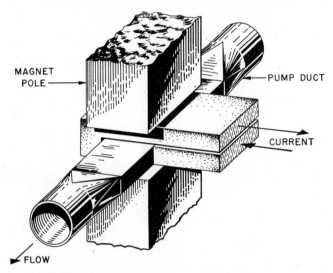

Fig. 8-24.   A d-c electromagnetic pump.

field through a conductor which is located adjacent to the duct in the region in which pumping occurs. The arrangement is illustrated in Fig. 8-24. The second method is to taper the poles so that the magnetic gap is wider toward the entrance end (see Fig. 8-25). In addition, the duct cross section is tapered so that the velocity of the liquid increases at a rate such that the counter emf, and hence the current density, remains constant as the liquid traverses the region between the poles. This method has the disadvantage that field compensation is complete for only one condition of current and field intensity.

The magnitude of the current which bypasses the region of strong field in the liquid increases as the voltage drop across the duct increases. Increasing the length of the magnetic poles beyond the area where the copper conductors are attached to the duct wall extends the paths which current must follow in the liquid beyond the field region. However, too great a field overhang will

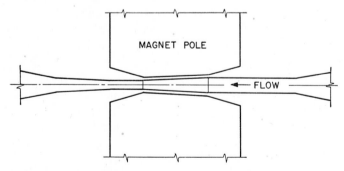

Fig. 8-25.   Electromagnetic pump with tapered tube.

introduce serious eddy current losses. Ideally, the falling off of field intensity should coincide with the falling off of current density due to the fringing of current. This distribution in field intensity may be approached by proper tapering of the pole ends as in Fig. 8-25. Bypassing of current in the end regions may also be reduced by introducing longitudinal insulating vanes into the duct in the entrance and exit regions. By this means a series of barriers is introduced into the fringing current paths.

The type of field winding employed is dictated mainly by the operating requirements of the pump. Separately excited windings are usually of the many-turn, high-voltage type which present an insulation problem when high-temperature operation is required. The series-type winding, on the other hand, may

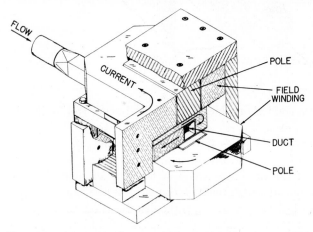

FIG. 8-26. A series-connected d-c electromagnetic pump.

consist of only a few turns (perhaps only a single turn for large pumps) of large-cross-section copper. Since the voltage drop through the winding will ordinarily be less than 1 volt, the insulation problem is very simple and no auxiliary cooling is required even for operation at high temperatures. Fig. 8-26 shows a series connected pump with a two-turn magnet winding.

The pump duct may be fabricated from sheet or may be formed by pressing seamless thin-wall tubing into the desired cross section. Wall thicknesses of 0.025 to 0.0625 in. are normally used. Since high electrical resistivity as well as compatibility with sodium and sodium-potassium alloy is necessary, the materials most frequently used are type 300 series stainless steels, nichrome (80 per cent nickel, 20 per cent chromium), and inconel-X. The heavy copper bars may be attached to the duct walls by either silver or nickel alloy brazing. A welded, box-type attachment employing a liquid bond has also been used successfully for pumps which are to operate at high temperature.

Pump performance is affected adversely by entrained gas in the liquid. The effect is due to the increased resistance which results from the presence of gas bubbles in the liquid stream. Consequently, it is important that adequate provision be made for venting gas from the pumping system and that situations do not exist which permit gas to be fed into the liquid because of turbulence in tanks, etc.

The current requirements of d-c pumps range from the order of 1000 amps for small pumps (5-10 gal/min) to many thousands of amperes for high-capacity pumps. The voltage drop across the pumps is in the vicinity of 1 to 2 volts. The large direct current required may be supplied by either rectifiers or

FIG. 8-27.   A d-c electromagnetic pump.

generators. Since the voltage required is about the same as the forward voltage drop of rectifier elements, the efficiency of this source of current supply is rather low (20-40 per cent).

The advantages of d-c electromagnetic pumps stem from their inherent simplicity of construction together with the practical absence of insulation problems. Reliable operation at high temperatures ($\sim$800°C) for long periods, with only natural convection and radiation cooling, has been achieved. Moreover, because of the simple insulation requirements operation in the presence of intense radiation presents no difficulty. The efficiencies obtainable vary from around 15-20 per cent for small pumps to 40-50 per cent for large pumps. Overall efficiencies, including current-supply source and bus losses are in the range of 10 per cent for small pumps to 40 per cent for large systems in which homopolar generators are used.

A photograph of a d-c electromagnetic pump is shown in Fig. 8-27.

EXPERIMENT 8-2

METHODS AND APPARATUS USED IN THE EXPERIMENTAL DETERMINATION OF LIQUID-METAL FILM COEFFICIENTS*

By K. D. Kuczen, Reactor Engineering Division, ANL

I. Apparatus

A. General Flow Description. An isometric drawing of the loop is shown in Fig. 8-28, and a flow diagram is given in Fig. 8-29. Starting from the discharge side of the pump, NaK flows through an electromagnetic flowmeter (Fig 8-30,

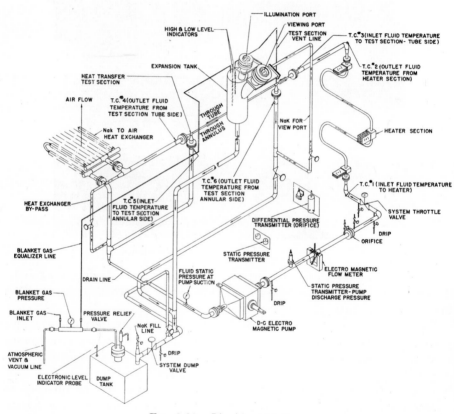

Fig. 8-28.   Liquid-metal loop.

* The author expresses his thanks to Mr. Florian Simanonis for his efforts in the preparation of the construction drawings for the test facility; also to Mr. Vincent Shoemaker for help given in the construction and instrumentation. The author is particularly grateful to Dr. A. H. Barnes for his counsel on the design of the test facility.

discussed in detail below). The voltage developed by the flowmeter is indicated and recorded on an electronic circular chart recorder 0-2.5 mv (Fig. 8-31). The NaK then passes through a 0.4-in.-diameter circular, sharp-edged orifice. The pressure drop across the orifice is fed into a differential pressure transmitter (Fig. 8-32). The differential pressure transmitter consists of a differential stain-

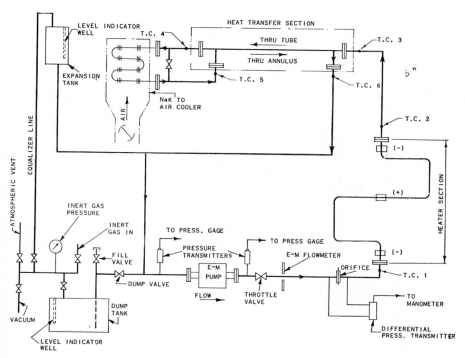

FIG. 8-29.   A typical liquid-metal system.

less-steel bellows which transmits an air pressure which is proportional to the pressure drop across the orifice. The air pressure is indicated on a mercury manometer (right side of Fig. 8-31).

Flow continues through a stainless-steel, bellows-sealed, 2-in. globe valve (Fig. 8-33) into an electrical heater section (Fig. 8-34). Heating takes place by passing alternating current through a 1-in. stainless-steel (347) schedule-40 pipe filled with flowing NaK. Most of the current flows through the NaK, and it is heated directly by resistance heating. The power supply for the heater section is a 50-kw, 220-volt, single-phase, water-cooled transformer. The secondary voltage can be varied from 2.2 volts to 5.8 volts by means of the selector switch on top of the transformer. It should be noted that both ends of the heater section are at the same potential at any instant. This method of feeding the current prevents the loop from short-circuiting the heater section. From the heater section the NaK flows through a mixing chamber into the tube side of the heat exchanger (Fig. 8-35).

FIG. 8-30.   An electromagnetic flowmeter.

The mixer consists of two baffles followed by a block of copper through which the NaK flows. This arrangement insures an accurate measurement of the NaK bulk average temperature. Four mixing chambers are provided for the heat exchanger—inlet and outlet of the tube side and inlet and outlet of the annular side of the heat exchanger.

Coming from the tube side of the heat exchanger, the NaK flows through a finned-tube air cooler. The cooling capacity is approximately 50 kw. The capacity can be varied by opening the cooler bypass valve or by throttling the air with dampers on the discharge side of the blower.

From the air cooler, flow is through the annular side of the heat exchanger, and back to the suction side of the pump.

NaK can be made to flow through the expansion tank (Fig. 8-36) so that visual inspection of the fluid can be made. However, this should be done only when the NaK is at room temperature. Vapors from hot NaK will condense on the viewing and illuminating ports and will prevent further inspection.

The static pressure on the suction side of the pump is measured by an ordinary bourdon tube pressure gauge. The discharge pressure is measured by means of a static pressure transmitter (Fig. 8-37). The static pressure transmitter contains a stainless-steel bellows which positions an air nozzle with respect to its seat, so that the air signal transmitted is proportional to the static pressure of the NaK system. The transmitted air pressure is fed into a bourdon gauge on the instrument panel (Fig. 8-31).

Thermocouple wells are located at the following places: inlet and outlet of heater section, inlet and outlet of the tube side of the heat exchanger, and inlet and outlet of the annular side of the heat exchanger. These thermocouples (TC) are #28-gauge, chromel-alumel wire and are connected to the thermocouple selector switch and designated in the following way:

FIG. 8-31. Control and instrument panel.

T.C. #1—fluid inlet to heater section.

T.C. #2—fluid outlet from heater section.

T.C. #3—fluid inlet to heat exchanger on tube side.

T.C. #4—fluid outlet from heat exchanger on tube side.

T.C. #5—fluid inlet to heat exchanger on annular side.

T.C. #6—fluid outlet from heat exchanger on annular side.

The emf's of these thermocouples are read with a portable precision potentiometer. The cold junction used is an ice bath. Calibration data for chromel-alumel thermocouples is given in Appendix 7, Table A7-1.

To facilitate the operation of the loop, the inlet and outlet fluid temperatures of the heater section are also indicated on two indicating pyrometers. These instruments are located on the instrument panel (Fig. 8-31).

The temperature rise of the fluid through the heater should be limited to 40 C°. If the temperature rise is greater, excessive thermal stresses are present in the heat-transfer wall of the heat exchanger.

Three interlocks are incorporated in the loop. Each one is arranged to open the circuit which supplies power to the 220-volt transformer. The outlet fluid temperature from the heater is not permitted to rise above 350°C. The heater-wall temperature is not permitted to rise above 450°C. These temperatures are limited by means of the electronic indicating pyrometers. The third interlock prevents heater power from being turned on until flow is indicated by the flow meter.

Two methods are used to indicate liquid level. One is by means of an electronic level indicator whose circuit is shown in Figs. 8-38 and 8-39. Essentially,

Fig. 8-32. Orifice metering system.   Fig. 8-33. Cut-away of bellows-sealed globe valve.

it consists of a bridge circuit which is thrown out of balance when the impedance of a searching coil is changed by the liquid-metal level. The searching coil is raised and lowered in a dry well built into both the dump tank and the expansion tank (Fig. 8-36).

The second method of level indication is by means of electrodes. Electrodes in the form of spark plugs are placed at the level to be indicated. When the liquid metal reaches this level, an electrical circuit is completed and either a light is energized or an alarm is sounded. Two such electrodes are installed in the expansion tank, Fig. 8-36. The low-level electrode is used to indicate, by means of a light, that the loop is filled. The high-level electrode sounds an alarm if the loop is overfilled or excessive thermal expansion of the NaK has taken place.

Any NaK or sodium system must include a method for maintaining an inert atmosphere and also for purging the system of air on initial startup. This is accomplished through the system of valves shown in Fig. 8-28. The dump tank and loop can be evacuated or pressurized independently. The blanket gas used in the experiment is helium; however, argon can also be used. Filling a system under a vacuum is a good method for reducing gas entrainment. However, it should be noted that the flat design of a pump tube offers very little strength against external pressure. In this experiment, to prevent collapsing of the pump tube, the casing around the

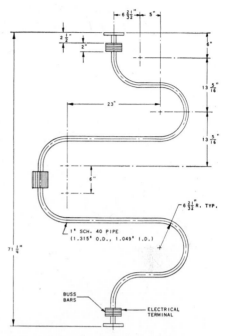

Fig. 8-34.   Heater section.

pump tube is evacuated along with the loop. Because of the glass viewing ports in the expansion tank, the blanket-gas pressure should not exceed 30 psig.

The power to the electromagnetic pump is supplied by an air-cooled rectifier unit. The input is 440 volts, 3-phase, 60-cycle; the output can be varied by

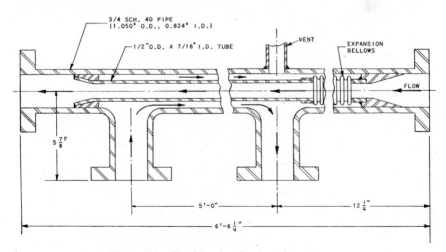

Fig. 8-35.   Double-pipe heat exchange.

means of the selector switch on the front of the rectifier. The output is 3000 amps at 0–3 volts. The power into the pump is measured with the voltmeter and ammeter on the front panel of the rectifier.

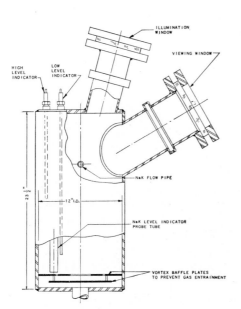

Fig. 8-36. Expansion tank.

Fig. 8-37. Static pressure transmitter.

All piping and valves in the loop are stainless steel 347. All valves, except the valves in the drip legs, are bellow sealed. The drip valves are gate-type and are always closed except when the loop must be completely drained; a close gate valve prevents any fluid from reaching the packing. All flange faces are grooved for a ring joint (Fig. 8-40). The ring is octagonal in cross section and made of stainless steel 347. The flanges are also made of the same material.

B. Electromagnetic Flowmeter. The electromagnetic flowmeter is simple in both construction and operation. A permanent magnet is clamped to the pipe in which flow is to be measured. The magnet is placed in such a manner as to permit the magnetic flux to be at a right angle to the direction of flow. Two

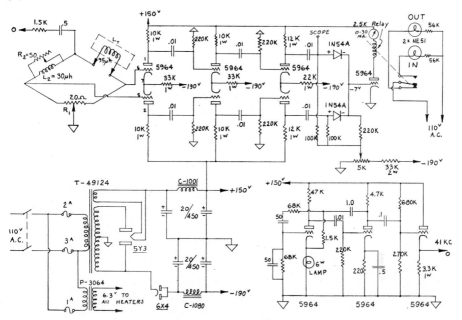

Fig. 8-38. NaK level indicator.

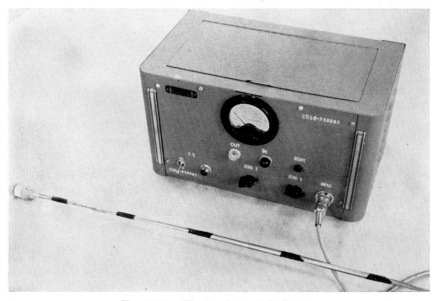

Fig. 8-39. Electronic level indicator.

electrodes are brazed or welded to the pipe 180° apart, and at right angles to both the direction of flow and the magnetic field (Fig. 8-30). A voltage is developed by the flowing liquid metal which is proportional to the rate at which the magnetic flux is interrupted. This voltage is then a measure of the rate of flow of the fluid.

A distinct advantage of this type of flow measuring device is that it offers very little resistance to fluid flow. Also, since the meter is completely external to the piping, maintenance is no problem.

In this experiment the electromagnetic flowmeter is to be calibrated using a

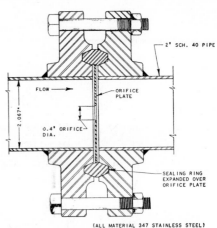

FIG. 8-40. All stainless-steel ring-joint flange.   FIG. 8-41. Method of mounting orifice plate.

sharp-edged, circular orifice having a 0.4-in.-diameter hole (Figs. 8-32 and 8-41). The pressure drop across the orifice is piped to a differential bellows-type instrument which in turn transmits an air pressure to a mercury manometer. The transmitted air pressure is proportional to the pressure drop across the orifice.

The differential pressure transmitter not only completely contains the liquid metal but amplifies the incoming pressure signal. The amplification is shown in Fig. 8-42. The calculation for flow through the orifice can be made using the equation

$$W = \rho_a C A_o \sqrt{2g_c\, h}, \tag{8-35}$$

where the coefficient of discharge, C, has the value of 0.61. The above equation neglects the velocity of approach, since it is small in comparison with the velocity through the orifice. The orifice head, in ft-lb force per lb mass of flow, can be evaluated from the pressure drop measurements.

Simultaneous readings of the voltage output of the electromagnetic flowmeter and pressure drop across the orifice enable one, with the use of the above equation, to plot a calibration curve for the electromagnetic flowmeter.

It is important to note that the range of the differential pressure transmitter will reach its upper limit when the transmitted air pressure is approximately 45 in. Hg. Therefore, readings of the manometer above 45 in. Hg are meaningless.

The flow is varied by varying the power input to the electromagnetic pump,

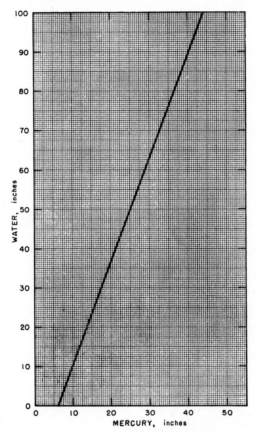

FIG. 8-42.   Calibration curve for Moore Nullmatic differential-pressure transmitter, model #10 C 100.

and not by throttling. The throttle valve will remain in the wide-open position throughout the calibration.

C. Electromagnetic Pump. The d-c electromagnetic pump used in this experiment is similar in construction to the one shown in Fig. 8-27. The field winding is a series type; therefore the magnetizing current is the same as that which flows through the liquid metal. Consequently the pumping force produced will vary approximately as the square of the current. The power input to the pump is calculated from

$$P_{in} = EI \text{ watts,} \tag{8-36}$$

where E is the emf in volts and I is the current in amperes. Both the current and voltage are read from the front panel of the rectifier supplying power to the pump.

The head developed by the pump is the difference in the readings between the discharge and the suction-pressure gauges. The discharge pressure is read on the large gauge located in the control panel. The suction pressure is read on the bourdon gauge mounted on the suction side of the pump.

The power output of the pump is calculated from the equation

$$P_o = WH, \text{ ft-lb/hr,} \tag{8-37}$$

where W is the mass rate of NaK flow in lb_m/hr and H is the head developed by the pump, in $ft\text{-}lb_F/lb_m$. The efficiency of the pump, of course, is the ratio of power output to the power input. Both must be expressed in the same units.

II. TEST PROCEDURE AND DATA

All data and calculations can be recorded on Data Sheets 8-7, 8-8 and 8-9.

A. Calibration of the Electromagnetic Flowmeter. No heat input shall be supplied to the loop, so calibration will take place at room temperature.

1. Set the throttle valve to the wide-open position.
2. Take zero flow readings of the manometer and the millivolt meter.
3. Turn on the rectifier supplying power to the E-M pump. The selector switch should be in position #1. Take readings.
4. Continue increasing the power into the pump by means of the selector switch, taking readings for each position.
5. When the mercury column in the manometer is approximately 45 in., the upper limit of the differential pressure transmitter has been reached. Further readings are meaningless.

B. D-C Electromagnetic Pump

1. Turn the selector switch to position 1 on the rectifier supplying power to the pump.
2. With the throttle valve wide open, take the readings indicated on the data sheet.
3. Begin to throttle the flow, taking readings at each throttled position. About four different throttle-valve positions, including shutoff, should be sufficient.

NOTE: LEAVE THE THROTTLE VALVE IN SHUTOFF POSITION FOR ONLY A SHORT TIME BY TAKING READINGS QUICKLY. WITH NO FLOW, EXCESSIVE HEATING CAN TAKE PLACE IN THE PUMP TUBE.

4. Return the throttle valve to the wide-open position.
5. Switch the selector on the rectifier to position 2 and repeat steps 3 and 4.
6. Switch the selector on the rectifier to position 3 & 4 and repeat steps 3 and 4.

C. Measuring the Over-all Heat-Transfer Coefficient

1. Set the throttle valve to the wide-open position.
2. The selector switch on the rectifier supplying power to the E-M pump should be on position 4 (approximately 2500 amps).
3. Turn on the cooling water supply to the power transformer (at the transformer).
4. Turn on the blower which supplies cooling air to the finned cooler (at the control panel).
5. Adjust the air-throttling damper, located on the discharge side of the blower, to its halfway position.
6. The heat-exchanger bypass valve should be in the closed position (see the flow sheet for its location).

DATA SHEET 8-7
Electromagnetic Flowmeter Calibration

	SELECTOR SWITCH POSITION (POWER INPUT TO PUMP)	I	2	3	4	5	6
DATA	E_f -VOLTAGE GENERATED, IN MILLIVOLTS						
	h_{Hg}-PRESSURE TRANSMITTED TO MANOMETER, inches OF Hg						
CALCULATION	h_{H_2O}-ACTUAL PRESSURE DROP ACROSS ORIFICE inches OF H_2O						
	h_{NaK}-PRESSURE DROP ACROSS ORIFICE EXPRESSED IN ft OF NaK						
	Q – FLOW ft ^{3}/sec						
	W-WEIGHT RATE OF FLOW #/ hr						

DATA SHEET 8-8
D-C Electromagnetic Pump

	SELECTOR SWITCH POSITION	1	2	3	4	5
DATA	E - VOLTAGE ACROSS PUMP TUBE, volts					
	I - CURRENT INTO PUMP, amps					
	E_f - VOLTAGE FROM FLOW-METER, millivolts					
	p_1 - SUCTION PRESSURE lb/in^2					
	p_2 - DISCHARGE PRESSURE lb/in^2					
CALCULATIONS	H - HEAD DEVELOPED BY PUMP ft of NaK					
	Q - VOLUME FLOW RATE gal/min					
	W - WEIGHT FLOW RATE lbs/hr					
	P_{in} - POWER INPUT TO PUMP watts					
	P_0 - POWER OUTPUT OF PUMP watts					
	EFFICIENCY OF PUMP					

DATA SHEET 8-9

Measurement of Overall Heat Transfer Coefficient in a Double Pipe Heat Exchanger

			POWER LEVEL		1	2	3	4	5
DATA	t_1 – FLUID TEMP. INLET TO HEATER	mv							
		t °C							
	t_2 – FLUID TEMP. OUTLET FROM HEATER	mv							
		t °C							
	t_3 – FLUID TEMP. INLET TUBE SIDE	mv							
		t °C							
	t_4 – FLUID TEMP. OUTLET TUBE SIDE	mv							
		t °C							
	t_5 – FLUID TEMP. INLET ANNULAR SIDE	mv							
		t °C							
	t_6 – FLUID TEMP OUTLET ANNULAR SIDE	mv							
		t °C							
	E_f – VOLTAGE FROM E-M FLOWMETER IN millivolts	mv							
		t °C							

		POWER LEVEL		1	2	3	4	5
CALCULATION	W – FLOW RATE lbs / hr							
	Δt_f – TEMP. DROP OF FLUID THROUGH TUBE SIDE OF HEAT EXCHANGER , °F							
	Q – HEAT TRANSFERRED IN HEAT EXCHANGER Btu / hr							
	Δt_m – LOG MEAN TEMP. DIFFERENCE OF HEAT EXCHANGER °F							
	U – OVERALL HEAT TRANSFER COEF. Btu / hr-ft^2-F							

7. Turn on the power to the power transformer (on the control panel).
8. Set the power-transformer selector switch to position 6 (on the power transformer).
9. After the steady state has been reached, take the data indicated on the data sheet. Thermocouples shall be read with the portable precision potentiometer.
10. Reduce the NaK flow by means of the d-c rectifier, taking data for each flow until the temperature rise through the heater section is approximately 40 C°.

NOTE: THIS TEMPERATURE RISE OF 40 C° SHOULD NOT BE EXCEEDED AT ANY TIME DURING THIS EXPERIMENT.

11. Shut off the power to the heater section.
12. Maintain maximum flow with maximum cooling until the loop is at room temperature.
13. Secure the equipment by turning off the pump and the blower.

III. CALCULATIONS AND ANALYSIS

1. Plot a calibration curve for the electromagnetic flowmeter. Since this curve must be used for other parts of the experiments, two different units should be used as the ordinates. In one case, millivolts are to be plotted against flow rate in lb/hr; in the other case, flow rate in gal/min.
2. Note the relation between flow rate and the voltage generated in the electromagnetic flowmeter.
3. Plot the characteristics of the electromagnetic pump, using the head in lb/in.^{2} as ordinate, the capacity in gals/min as the abscissa, and the power input as a parameter.
4. Plot an efficiency curve, using efficiency as ordinate, capacity as abscissa, and power input as a parameter.
5. Using the film coefficient relations provided in the discussion in this chapter, calculate the over-all heat-transfer coefficient U for a particular run. Compare the calculated value of U with the measured value.
6. For a particular run, calculate the over-all coefficient one could expect if water were used. Compare this with the value found for NaK.

Chapter 9

FUEL PREPARATION FOR A HETEROGENEOUS REACTOR

By J. E. Baird, assisted by R. J. Friddle and T. H. Chiesna,
Metallurgy Department, International School of Nuclear Science and Engineering

INTRODUCTION

The hazards from radioactivity are slight in the following experiments, but you should wear a dosimeter and/or a film badge and also clean laboratory coats to prevent your clothes from being contaminated. When handling uranium tetrafluoride, wear rubber gloves. It is important to wash your hands frequently. This is one of the best methods for preventing personal contamination. There are two reasons for these protective measures; the more important one is to avoid contaminating your shoes and clothes. The other is to prevent contamination from being spread into "clean" areas. There are often many delicate experiments in progress in other laboratories that cannot tolerate any extra background of radioactivity. The filtering system on the fume hoods should be adequate to remove all of the uranium dust (UF_4 and UO_2) from the air that enters.

Do not dump any solutions that contain uranium down the drain. If any UF_4 or UO_2 is spilled on the floor, get it cleaned up before it is tracked around. The coolant water of the abrasive cutoff wheel is contaminated since it is recirculated, and since the uranium burns to oxide during the cutting process.

On the polishing benches, there is a slight pickup of contamination; but if the hands are washed, it will come off. The waste water from the polishing benches goes into a filter to remove the uranium oxide particles before it is discharged into the sewer. No food or cokes are permitted in the laboratory. Smoking is possible without radioactive hazard. The following are some safety regulations:

1. Whenever carrying heavy objects which might fall on your toes, wear steel safety toe clips that fit over ordinary shoes and prevent injuries to your toes.

2. For eye and face protection, wear face shields.

3. Wear the heavy asbestos gloves when handling hot material. Wear canvas gloves when handling warm things.

4. The rolling mill should be equipped with a magnetic brake so that it may be stopped instantly if necessary.

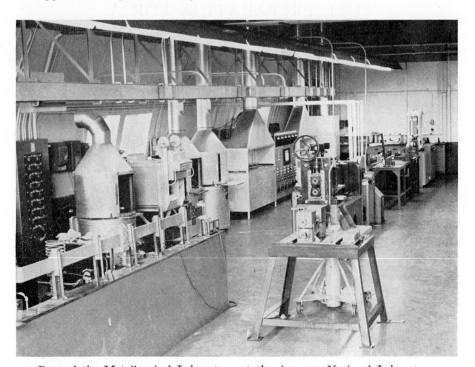

Part of the Metallurgical Laboratory at the Argonne National Laboratory

Note the extensive use of ventilation hoods essential in the handling of radioactive materials and in metallurgical studies of them.

5. The abrasive cutoff wheel should be shielded with a Plexiglass hood which is to be down and in place before starting to cut. Also be sure the exhaust fans are on.

6. When working in the fume hoods, be sure the exhaust fans are on.

It is suggested that the student now re-read the section on radiation protection on pages 15 and 16 in Chapter 1.

A storage drawer should be provided in which each experimenter may keep his samples. Do not take uranium away from the laboratory, since all of it must be accounted for. Work with the uranium, even burn it, but always recover the oxides and residues.

EXPERIMENT 9-1

HEAT TREATMENT AND METALLOGRAPHY OF UNALLOYED URANIUM

Introduction and Purpose of the Experiment. In this experiment uranium is to be heated to several different temperatures, the samples are to be cooled to room temperature, and the changes that take place inside the uranium as a result of the heat treatment are to be studied. Metallography includes the method of preparing samples for the examination of the internal structure of metals and determination of what happens inside a piece of metal during rolling, heat treating, extrusion, or cold-working. The metallographic examination of metals will be used in several of the following experiments, so it is well to understand the method.

Many people who work with metals see only the outside surface, but the metallurgist carries a picture in his mind of its internal structure during fabrication. He visualizes the crystal grains as being compressed during cold-working, or he "sees" the grains grow with heat treatment at elevated temperatures. These changes in the internal structure are to be studied in order to understand the reasons why fuel elements are fabricated the way they are.

The techniques of metallography now to be acquired are to be considered tools for the study of the internal structure of uranium. A number of short cuts will be used so that a complete knowledge of the art of metallography will not be necessary. Only the basic principles of metallography and instruction in sample preparation, so as to see the internal structure of the uranium samples, will be presented.

The Crystallographic Forms of Unalloyed Uranium. The alpha phase of uranium exists from room temperature up to 662°C and is of the orthorhombic crystalline form where all three dimensions of its unit cell are different.

The beta phase of uranium exists between 662°C and 772°C and has a tetragonal crystalline form. Two dimensions of the basic unit cell are the same and the other is different.

From 772°C to 1133°C, the melting point, uranium has a body centered cubic crystalline form where all three dimensions of the unit cell are the same. This is called the gamma phase.

These structures exist in uranium only at the temperatures mentioned, and only alpha uranium exists at room temperatures. On cooling a specimen from the gamma region, it undergoes phase transformation to beta and then to alpha. It is not possible to retain even the beta phase by quenching, because the transformations are so rapid. What will be seen under the microscope will be alpha grains. These are of the same size as the beta grains at 725°C, which is in the beta-phase region.

The orthorhombic crystalline structure of alpha uranium, with three different dimensions in the basic unit cell, gives rise to many problems in the stability of uranium when it is undergoing fission in a reactor. This peculiar nature of uranium has caused many difficulties for metallurgists and has made the development of "good" fuel elements a difficult problem in reactor technology. Better fuel elements at less cost is one of the goals for improving the life, stability of operation, and economy of the entire reactor. One of the present big questions in the study of power reactors is the degree of burnup that can take place in a fuel element. Large power reactors (100,000 kw or more) are needed in order to try out full-size fuel elements to see how they behave over a period of months and years. Then one may have greater confidence that the fuel elements will stand up for a long time. Fuel for a research reactor that is water-cooled and operated at 75°C can be made readily, but fuel for a power reactor operating at 250°C is a more serious problem involving both irradiation and corrosion effects.

The Internal Structure of Uranium. In the metallographic preparation of a sample, its surface is polished to a mirror-like finish. Then it is etched in an electrolytic bath to bring out the grain structure. This structure is examined under polarized light at about 100× magnification. The reflection of the polarized light from the specially prepared surface shows the grain structure of the uranium.

Each piece of uranium contains thousands of grains in every cubic inch. A section of these grains can be seen on the metallograph when a magnification of 100× or more is used.

In addition to the grains, there are numerous very small nonmetallic inclusions which get into the uranium when it is molten. Nothing can be done about these by heat treatment below the melting point. The inclusions are best seen after polishing with a 1-micron diamond paste and before electrolytic etching, because etching eats them out and leaves small pits. Inclusions can be seen under ordinary light with a binocular microscope at 500× magnification. They are usually bluish or pink in color and are of varying sizes and shapes. All uranium has some nonmetallic inclusions. However, if the inclusions are too numerous, it is possible that they will seriously affect the irradiation stability of the metal.

When looking at the internal structures of uranium under polarized light, the grain size can be seen, together with some lines within the grains such as twin lines or strain lines. Twin lines are found in a material which has been annealed, while strain lines are apparent in cold-worked uranium. All of the grains observed on a metallograph will be alpha grains. Under polarized light, many of these grains will be of different colors. This is due to the orientation of the individual grains and to the angle at which they reflect the polarized light. Some of the grains will appear much larger than other grains, especially after the sample has been subjected to heating, which causes considerable grain growth. One way to visualize the reason for the different-sized grains is to picture a bag of potatoes all of the same size. If one were to cut through the bag of potatoes, the cut would pass through large and small cross sections, depending on where one happened to cut each individual potato.

Lines or furrows running across several grains are scratches and are the result of improper polishing. Move the sample around so that they are not seen. Scratches are easily distinguished from twin lines because scratches run across grain boundaries while twin lines always stop at the grain boundaries. Scratches are not a part of the internal structure of uranium. Learn to look around them and to ignore them.

Metallographic examination cannot tell everything about the internal condition of uranium. It is not possible to tell whether uranium has any orientation effects as a result of fabrication other than severe strain lines from cold-working. If the strain lines are removed by annealing in the high alpha region, between 475°C and 662°C, the metal will appear to be free from these effects as far as metallographic examination is concerned. However, there are still preferred orientations left in the grains which will cause the uranium to grow abnormally when subjected to high-level irradiation. These preferred orientations can be detected only by X-ray diffraction studies. The preferred orientations are removed by heating into the beta region (662°C to 772°C) for a short time. This is called beta treating of uranium.

It is possible to obtain grains of the same size in a number of ways, such as changing the length of heat treatment or the temperature of heat treatment or both. To correctly interpret metallographic structures, it is necessary to know the history of the metal and its chemical composition.

The Heat Treatment of Unalloyed Uranium. Fig. 9-1 shows some photomicrographs of the internal structures of uranium resulting from heat treatment at different temperatures. These are in black and white, but would appear in color on the metallograph. Also, all of the grains seen are alpha grains on all of the photomicrographs.

Samples are to be heat-treated at three different temperatures: 475°C, 600°C, and 725°C.

Start with a sample of uranium with large grains. Notice that there are only a few grains in the cross section. Cold-work the sample by swaging at room temperatures to reduce it to about 20 per cent of its original cross-sectional area. The grains will be distorted and folded around each other so that the grain boundaries can hardly be seen; also, strain lines will appear in the grains. If the uranium is cold-worked too much, it will break up into little pieces along these strain lines. Twin lines will also be seen in the uranium sample. However, after it has been cold-worked, one cannot distinguish the twin lines from the strain lines.

A piece of uranium that has been cold-worked is heated to 475°C for 10 min. Then it will be found that the big grains with their strain lines are disappear-

Uranium, as cast

Uranium, cold worked by swaging

Uranium, cold worked and heated in lead
at 475°C for 10 minutes

Uranium, cold worked and heated in lead
at 525°C for 10 minutes

Uranium, cold worked and heated in salt
at 725°C for 10 minutes

Uranium, cold worked and heated in salt
at 825°C for 10 minutes

FIG. 9-1. Photomicrographs. Internal structure of uranium determined by polishing
and electro-etching. (Magnified 100×.)

ing, and that some new fine grains have appeared in clusters. This is called recrystallization. It is common to all metals that have been heavily cold-worked and heat-treated at the correct temperature. The uranium is now said to be fine-grained.

It is always necessary to do some work on unalloyed uranium in order to refine the grain size. A large-grained rod of uranium may be refined so as to reduce the grain size by either cold work and heat treatment or by hot work. Hot work is done by reducing the cross-sectional area at a temperature above the recrystallization temperature. It will require a larger reduction in cross-sectional area by hot work than it will by cold work and annealing. Deformation of the grains by cold work imparts energy to the crystal lattice and causes the realignment of grain boundaries. New grains are formed as the uranium is heated to the proper temperature.

If a cold-worked sample is heated to 500°C, recrystallization will become complete. If heated to 600°C, the grains will triple (or more than triple) in size as a result of grain growth. Since the volume of metal remains the same except for slight thermal expansion, the number of grains must decrease in proportion. The grains grow at the expense of one another. How they assimilate one another and where the grain boundaries move are questions of considerable interest to theoretical metallurgists.

If the heating is carried to still higher temperatures—say, 725°C—the grains continue to grow. The process of grain growth continues until melting at 1133°C. Grains will also grow larger if the uranium is held at one temperature for longer periods of time; but raising the temperature has much more effect on increasing the grain size.

Unalloyed uranium may be quenched from the heat-treating temperature without causing any appreciable change in the microstructure. Only the process of grain growth is interrupted.

Uranium will oxidize rapidly at elevated temperature. It must be protected from the oxygen in the atmosphere during fabrication and heat treatment. Melting and casting are done in vacuum. For rolling and heat treatment, the following general precautions for surface protection are to be observed:

> Up to 300°C—heat in heavy oil
> From 300 to 600°C—heat in lead
> Above 600°C—heat in a special salt bath of NaCl and KCl

At the higher temperatures, the molten salt acts as a protective blanket around the uranium while it is being rolled. Care must be taken that the uranium does not cool below the melting point of the salt during rolling, or the salt will no longer afford good protection.

Interpretation. In fabricating a cast-uranium ingot to a size usable in a reactor, the rolling is usually done with the uranium in the high alpha region, i.e., at about 600°C, which is above the recrystallization temperature. The uranium then fabricates with ease, but the process must be followed by a heat treatment in the beta region if maximum stability under irradiation is to be attained. Many of the uranium fuel slugs in the research reactors have been made in this manner. The final step in fabrication is usually a grinding or machining operation to remove the oxide surface layer.

A clue to the nature of the fabrication is given by the basic crystalline structure of the three phases of uranium:

ALPHA:	Orthorhombic	Contains 4 atoms per unit cell
BETA:	Tetragonal	Contains 30 atoms per unit cell
GAMMA:	Body-centered cubic	Contains 2 atoms per unit cell

From the large number of atoms per unit cell of the beta phase, the difficulty of fabrication in that temperature range can be appreciated. Uranium is not hot-worked in the beta phase. To extrude uranium, it is heated into the gamma region (above 772°C), where the crystal structure is body-centered cubic and the uranium is quite plastic. If an attempt is made to roll uranium in the gamma region, the uranium is found to be so plastic that it is difficult to control. There is excessive oxidation at these temperatures and the uranium must be canned to protect it during extrusion. Working in the gamma region results in very coarse grains; these are usually not desirable in a fuel element.

HEAT-TREATING

Four samples of uranium which have been cold-worked by swaging to produce a reduction in area are to be used. One of these will not be heat-treated. The other three are to be subjected to the following temperatures:

No. 1: 475°C in a lead bath for 10 min.
No. 2: 600°C in a lead bath for 10 min.
No. 3: 725°C in a salt bath for 10 min.

For this purpose small heat treat furnaces may be used. They are to have controllers, and thermocouples to record the actual bath temperature. Wrap each specimen tightly with steel wire and lower it into its proper bath for 10 min. Wear face shields and asbestos gloves when around the heat-treating baths, for it is possible that a small amount of moisture may be on a sample, which will blow out some salt. Remove the sample of uranium from the bath and quench it. This helps to remove salt or lead adhering to the specimen. It is suggested that the samples be marked by grinding flats on their round surface so that they can be identified when mounted in Bakelite. For example:

No flats	Cold-worked sample
One flat	475°C
Two flats	600°C
Three flats	725°C

Place the heat-treated specimens in separate envelopes and identify with the temperature and with your name.

Metallographic Preparation. The following are some of the general steps to follow: The specimens are mounted in Bakelite so that they may be held with the hands during the polishing stage. Polish one face of each piece of uranium to a *flat mirror finish*. A mirror finish is needed so that the electrolytic etching will bring out the internal structure of uranium. This can then be observed at 100× magnification on the metallograph.

To mount the specimens in Bakelite, place the bottom plug in the mold, with the hole side down, against the table top (see Fig. 9-2). Place the four

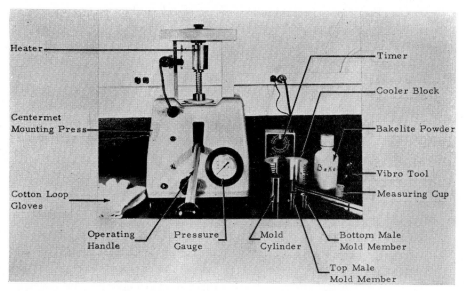

Fig. 9-2. Specimen-mounting equipment.

specimens inside the mold with forceps. Be sure that the surface to be examined is resting on the bottom plug. Pour in about 10 cm³ of black Bakelite powder and place the top plug in the mold. Set the assembled mold in the mounting press, close the valve, and bring up the pressure to the red dot. Place the heater around the mold, turn on the timer switch and set it for 10 min if the mold is hot, or 12 min if the mold is cold. As the pressure drops off, keep pumping it up. After the buzzer sounds, lower the heater from around the mold, loosen the valve, and let the mold drop down far enough so that the top bearing plate can be swung out of the way. Then close the valve and pump it up until the top plug, the Bakelite-mounted specimens, and the bottom plug have been ejected. Cool the Bakelite mount under water at the polishing benches and then scribe your name, date, and sample identification on it with the Vibra marking tool.

At the polishing benches follow these steps:

1. Remove sharp edges of the Bakelite on the 120-grit paper.
2. Place the sample inside the split steel ring.
3. Grind the surface on 120-grit paper until the uranium is shiny.
4. Rinse your hands and the Bakelite mount to remove grit.
5. Polish on 240-grit paper until all scratches from the 120-grit paper are removed.
6. Remove the split steel ring.
7. Grind off the sharp Bakelite edge that was under the steel ring. Use the 240-grit wheel.
8. Rinse your hands and the Bakelite mount under water to remove grit.
9. Polish on the 600-grit canvas-covered wheel. Shake on the 600-grit carborundum liberally.
10. Polish on the 600-grit wheel to remove the scratches from the 240-grit wheel. The surface should start to look like a mirror.
11. If scratches do not come out in a few minutes, go back to the 240-grit wheel for a few minutes.
12. After using the 600-grit wheel, wash your hands and the Bakelite mount thoroughly and proceed to the room where the final polishing wheels with diamond paste are located.
13. Spray Hypres oil on the specimen and on the blotter paper supplied to you. This blotter paper is already impregnated with 1-micron diamond paste. Polish for about 1 min on the wheel covered with blotter paper.
14. Wash your hands and the specimen with soap and water and dry with alcohol.
15. Apply Hypres oil to the specimen and to a billiard cloth which is already impregnated with 1-micron diamond paste. Rotate the specimen in the opposite direction to that of the polishing wheel to help prevent dragging out inclusions. This should take only a minute.
16. Wash the sample with soap and water and dry with alcohol.

To look at inclusions, place the specimen under the binocular microscope at about 500× magnification. The microscopes are equipped with three turret objectives to give 100×, 250×, or 500× magnification. Usually the inclusions are little blue spots or larger pink spots. Some have definite shapes, some are irregular. The number and distribution vary with each sample. They are mostly uranium carbides and uranium oxides. Grain boundaries will not be seen until the specimen has been etched.

The electro-etching panels are set up for use by the instructor (see Fig. 9-3). All that is required is that the specimen be placed in the solution. This is a mixture of 5 parts orthophosphoric acid, 5 parts ethylene glycol, and 8 parts ethyl alcohol. Lower the specimen into the solution with forceps and swish it around a little to remove air bubbles from the uranium surface that is to be etched. Loosen the clamp on the electrode and let it down so that the platinum tip rests on the specimen you want to etch. Do not tighten the electrode clamp. Turn on the current of the control panel and adjust it to approximately 30 milliamperes, d-c (low voltage—say, 12 volts). If the electro-etching is proceeding at the proper current density, the uranium takes on a gold color and bubbles arise from it. Allow the sample to electro-etch for 1 min. Shut off the current and move the electrode to the next specimen. It is best to have the

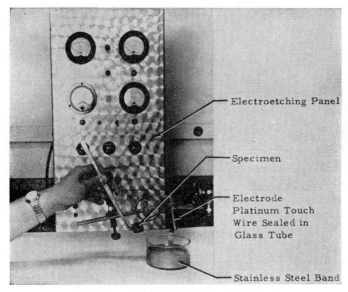

Fig. 9-3.   Electro-etching equipment.

electrode contact the specimen in a place other than the one to be examined. If there happen to be scratches on one portion of the specimen, place the electrode there. Immediately under the electrode, proper etching action for examination does not occur. After all of the samples have been etched, clamp the electrode back into the resting position and remove the specimen from the solution with forceps. Rinse under the faucet with water; also rinse with alcohol.

This etched surface will last only a day before it starts to tarnish from the moisture in the air. Take the specimen into the metallograph room and place it on the viewing stand of the metallograph (see Fig. 9-4). See the instructor for operating instructions concerning this instrument.

Make a sketch of what you see on each specimen.

FIG. 9-4. A TV camera and receiver, operating on a closed circuit, has been used on a metallograph for class discussion of the internal structure of uranium and its alloys.

EXPERIMENT 9-2

PRODUCTION OF METALLIC URANIUM FROM UF$_4$

Purpose of the Experiment. Metallic uranium is to be made by reduction of uranium tetrafluoride (UF$_4$, a green salt) with magnesium powder. The problems involved in making metallic uranium are to be studied, and a sample of metallic uranium is to be obtained which can be used for fabrication into usable shapes. This is the start of making a fuel element. The experiment to be described below is a laboratory-scale production of uranium which is the same as that on a commercial basis, except that graphite instead of a ceramic is used to contain the materials. Ceramic crucibles or rammed ceramic liners are not satisfactory for the small amount of uranium to be produced here.

The Chemical Reactions Involved. This experiment is based on the chemical reaction: UF$_4$ + 2Mg → U + 2MgF$_2$. It will take place between 600 and 700°C and is exothermic. There is sufficient heat evolved in the reaction to cause a rise in temperature of several hundred degrees so that the products of reaction, the uranium metal and the slag (MgF$_2$), are raised above their melting points.

The reaction is rapid. The melting points of materials are uranium, 1133°C;

slag (MgF_2), 1263°C; magnesium, 651°C. The boiling point of magnesium is 1110°C. The density of the products of reaction are uranium, 18.7 g/cm^3; slag (MgF_2), approximately 3 g/cm^3.

This difference in density results in a good separation of the uranium from the slag. The uranium collects in a pool in the bottom of the crucible.

Magnesium is used as a reducing material because it is commercially available in a fine-granular form and because it is cheap. The magnesium used here is −30 and +50 mesh. Magnesium can be stored and is not subject to rapid surface oxidation as is calcium. Its low melting point and low boiling point help to separate the excess magnesium from the molten uranium after the reaction has taken place. Furthermore, magnesium is helpful in the formation of the slag whose melting point is only 130° above the melting point of uranium.

Uranium tetrafluoride is used as a source of uranium because the reaction with magnesium is thermodynamically good and because it is safe to handle and store. Compounds such as the uranium chlorides are hygroscopic. The uranium tetrafluoride used here is depleted in U^{235} and is a by-product from the gaseous diffusion plant. At the present time it is very plentiful. The reaction with magnesium is the same whether the UF_4 is depleted or normal or enriched. For economical reasons, the UF_4 used contains 0.4 per cent U^{235}. Normal and enriched uranium are rather costly for research and educational purposes. The gaseous diffusion plant operates with UF_6, a gas. This gas is converted to the green salt UF_4 after it leaves the gaseous diffusion chambers.

Graphite is used as a crucible material because it is impossible, with the small samples used, to get a satisfactory reaction with a ceramic crucible. The graphite has some advantages over a ceramic, even though it is not used in commercial production. For example, the high thermoconductivity of the graphite crucible gives uniform heat distribution in heating the charge to its firing point. It requires approximately 30 min in the furnace for heat-up time until firing takes place. After the reaction has taken place, the thermal conductivity of the graphite helps to chill some of the slag so that it forms a coating on the inside of the graphite crucible. When uranium does collect in a molten pool at the bottom of the crucible, it is actually separated from the graphite crucible by this layer of slag. This prevents excessive pickup of carbon from the crucible by the molten uranium. The thermal-shock resistance of graphite is far superior to that of a preformed ceramic crucible. It has been found that the content of the uranium metal so produced is of the order of 100 to 200 ppm, which is satisfactory for reactor-grade uranium.

Prior to the reaction, the presence of the carbonaceous gases helps to slow down the oxidation of the magnesium and helps to keep it clean so that the reaction can occur.

The products of reaction are the white slag magnesium fluoride and the metallic uranium. About one-half of the slag will be coated around the inside surface of the graphite crucible. The rest of the slag will usually be found suspended in a little pocket above the metallic uranium. Molten uranium collects in the bottom of the crucible, where it solidifies. Occasionally, small prells of uranium are found dispersed in the slag, and occasionally some slag inclusions occur in the uranium. At the top of the crucible it is normal to find some of the excess magnesium which has been deposited there because this is the coldest part of the interior of the graphite crucible.

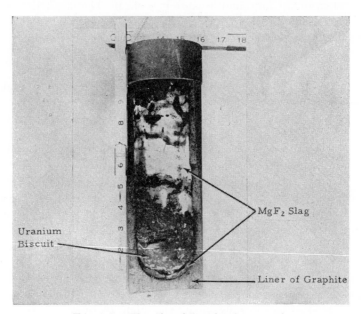

FIG. 9-5. The "bomb" reduction vessel.

General Outline of the Experiment. The amount of magnesium and uranium-tetrafluoride to be used are calculated for the stoichiometric ratio. Then, 3 per cent excess magnesium is added and the two materials are weighed in large amounts and thoroughly mixed in a bottle on power-driven rollers. The mixing is very important to insure the uniform distribution of magnesium throughout the UF_4.

After thorough mixing, the material is loaded into a graphite crucible and packed down with a tamping rod. The graphite crucible is then jogged to further pack the material and to remove as much air as possible. The crucible is slid into a stainless-steel housing, a graphite cap is placed on the crucible, and then a steel cap. The closed vessel is then taken to the furnace and heated. A few minutes after the reaction has taken place, this reduction vessel is removed from the furnace and cooled, and the uranium and slag removed from the graphite crucible.

The Commercial Production of Uranium. In the United States the commercial production of uranium is carried out on a large scale as a batch process by making pieces of uranium, called "derbys" or "biscuits," as large as 1 ft in diameter and weighing several hundred kilograms. This is done in a reduction vessel with a rammed dolomite liner and a mixture of magnesium and uranium-tetrafluoride. At the present time, this is the only process used in the production of uranium for use in reactors. The uranium so produced contains very little carbon and a few minor impurities of magnesium, iron, and silicon, each of which is usually less than 100 ppm.

In Europe the same type of production is used. In Belgium, calcium fluoride is used as a liner material, while magnesium or calcium is used as a reducing material on the uranium tetrafluoride.

There are other ways of making metallic uranium which are thermodynamically possible, although they are not of commercial importance. They reduce the oxide with magnesium or calcium to form powdered uranium.

Calculations for the Charge in the Production of Uranium:

DATA SHEET 9-1

$UF_4 + 2Mg = U + 2MgF_2$
Molecular weights are U 238, Mg 24.3, F 19
Add 3 per cent excess magnesium to insure complete reaction
The mixture will be _____ per cent Mg
_____ per cent UF_4
    and will contain _____ per cent U
Weight of graphite crucible and cap _____
Weight of crucible and charge _____
Weight of charge _____
Amount of uranium in charge _____
Amount of uranium produced _____
Per cent recovery of uranium from the UF_4 _____
Furnace temperature _____
Time of charging into furnace _____, time of firing _____
Heating time _____
Firing temperature, according to thermocouple in top of reduction vessel _____
Notes on the appearance of uranium and slag after contents have been removed
    from the reduction vessel _____
_____
_____

Details of the Experiment. Each experimenter is to wear a pair of short latex rubber gloves when working with UF_4 in the glove-box fume hoods (see Fig. 9-6). This makes it much easier to insert the hands into or remove them from the long rubber gloves in the hood. The fume hoods are equipped with prefilters in the back of each hood in addition to the extremely fine (AEC) filters on the balcony. This filtering system is expensive, but is absolutely necessary to keep UF_4 dust from blowing all over the neighborhood. For low-velocity ventilation, 100 ft³/min is adequate. Medium-velocity ventilation of 300 ft³/min permits opening the front of the hood during operation.

FIG. 9-6. A glovebox fume hood. Prefilters are at the rear. Additional fine filters (not shown) are a necessary part of these hoods. The front is equipped with sliding Plexiglas windows containing glove ports.

Wear the safety toe clips when walking around the laboratory while carrying the graphite crucible or the steel housing because your rubber gloves are slippery. The weight of the vessel can easily break toes if it falls on them. When working around the furnaces and opening the reduction vessel, *wear a face shield*. Also, wear asbestos gloves to prevent burns when working around the furnace and when handling the hot reduction vessels. Always wear a laboratory coat.

STEP 1. Put on the asbestos gloves. Remove a graphite crucible and graphite cap from the drying oven. Weigh the graphite crucible and cap to the closest gram. Scratch some identifying mark on the outside of the crucible with the Vibra marking tool. Place the crucible and cap in the hood. Remove the asbestos gloves and put on the short latex rubber gloves. Insert your hands into the long rubber gloves in the hood.

STEP 2. The mixture of UF_4 and magnesium containing 3 per cent excess magnesium is already prepared in a plastic bottle. Fill the crucible half-full of this charge and tamp it gently with a 1-in.-diameter aluminum rod. Do not scratch the walls of the crucible with the tamping rod. Fill the crucible and tamp gently; fill again and tamp until it is filled to within $\frac{1}{16}$ in. of the top. Brush off the loose charge from around the top of the crucible and move the crucible to the access door.

STEP 3. Remove your hands from the hood rubber gloves. Move the crucible to the hood in which the jogging machine is located. Be sure you are wearing toe clips, for the graphite crucible is quite slippery. Hold the crucible firmly on the jogger and turn the jogger up slowly to compact the charge. If the charge settles down so far that the cap would be completely down inside the crucible, then a small amount of additional charge must be added. The cap must protrude a small amount above the top of the crucible.

STEP 4. Weigh the crucible and cap with its charge. Calculate the amount of uranium in the charge.

STEP 5. Place the top plug in the top of the crucible. Examine a stainless steel housing to be sure that there is a ¼-in.-thick steel disc in its bottom. Slide the crucible into this housing. Place a ½-in.-thick graphite disc of the same diameter as the crucible on top of the crucible. Screw on the steel cap and hand-tighten only.

STEP 6. Drill a hole in the top graphite plug for a thermocouple.

STEP 7. Don a face shield and asbestos gloves. Insert a thermocouple into the top of the housing. See the instructor for assistance in charging the vessel into the furnace. Connect the thermocouple to the junction box of its recorder.

FIG. 9-7. A high-velocity exhaust system necessary for uranium work with an abrasive wheel and a lathe.

STEP 8. Note the time of charging and the temperature. Firing will take place in about 30 min, and is indicated by a sharp rise on the recorder chart. Allow the vessel to remain in the furnace for a few minutes more. Wearing protective clothing, remove the vessel from the furnace. Allow it to cool to a black color before cooling in the sink.

STEP 9. Remove the contents of the vessel and weigh the uranium. Calculate the yield. Note on the clipboard near the scale, your name, amount of charge, and amount of uranium you produced. This information is necessary for accountability records. Place the reduction button of uranium metal in a storage drawer. It is to be used during succeeding experiments.

STEP 10. If time permits, have the instructor section the uranium button on the abrasive cutoff wheel.

IMPORTANT. The abrasive cutoff wheel, as well as any lathe, drill, press, or grinder involved in uranium work requires a high-velocity exhaust system. Prefilters, followed by AEC filters, are used with "elephant trunks" over the machine-tool areas. These are necessary to remove the radioactive powder or toxic fumes from the area, as shown in Fig. 9-7.

EXPERIMENT 9-3

VACUUM MELTING AND CASTING OF UNALLOYED URANIUM

Introduction and Purpose. The first reason for melting uranium is to change its shape. It must be melted and cast into an ingot which can be rolled into a fuel element. The second reason for melting is to improve the quality of the metal. By heating uranium above its melting point, an opportunity is presented for the slag inclusions from the production process to float to the top. This makes it a much better metal for fabrication and for irradiation stability. The melt is poured from the bottom of the crucible. Thus slag and oxide that float to the surface of the melt remain in the crucible after pouring. Some of the dissolved magnesium that was in the uranium is also removed.

Uranium must be melted in a vacuum because it would burn up in the air at elevated temperatures. Uranium is precious and the extra expense and time for vacuum melting is well worthwhile. It is necessary to learn the techniques and requirements of vacuum systems for this purpose.

Since the uranium is to be melted in vacuum, a special means of heating the metal is needed. For this purpose, a high-frequency induction furnace operating at a frequency of 9600 cycles per second is used.

General Outline of the Experiment. Start with approximately one-half of the metal produced in Experiment 9-2. Weigh it. This will constitute the "charge." Assemble the furnace, "pull" a vacuum on it, heat it up, melt the metal, and cast it in vacuum; cool down the furnace, open it up, remove the casting, and check on the recovery.

Commercial Production of Uranium. Uranium is melted in induction furnaces on a large scale. Graphite crucibles and graphite molds are used. High-frequency induction melting is used, at 960 or 3000 cps. The main differences between the melting in this experiment and industrial melting are that the induction coil used here is on the outside of the furnace and that Vycor tubing is used in this laboratory work. Commercially, a large stainless-steel shell manifold is used and the induction coil is located inside the steel shell. This is a more rugged construction and will stand up under continual handling. The Vycor tubing used here is 6 in. in diameter and 21 in. long, with a $\frac{1}{8}$-in. wall thickness. Since it is transparent, one can see what is going on during the melting. The commercial production is a batch process and must follow the same steps as done here—charging a furnace, pumping down the vacuum system, heating the metal by induction heating and casting, followed by cooling down and removal of the ingot and crucible. The commercial ingots of uranium are 5 to 7 in. in diameter and several feet in length. These are rolled down to 1-in.-diameter rods on a large rolling mill. The principles employed in the laboratory are the same as used in production work. The only difference is in the scale of the operations.

DATA SHEET 9-2

Date _____
Weight of metal charged into crucible _____

Time	Vacuum	Temperature	Remarks

Weight of ingot produced _____
Length of ingot _____
Amount of scull left in crucible _____
Remarks on appearance of ingot _____
_____
_____

Experimental Procedure (Figs. 9-8 and 9-9): STEP 1. Weigh the metal for the charge. Select a mold, crucible, and stopper rod. Place a little dry lime in the bottom of the crucible. This aids in removal of the scull after the casting. Place spacers on the brass spider inside the manifold so that when the mold and crucible are in position, the crucible will be inside the induction coil. Place the mold on top of the spacers. Place a zirconia brick on top of the mold. The brick is approximately ½ in. thick by 3 in. o.d. and has a 1-in.-diameter hole in its center. Place the crucible containing the uranium to be melted on top of this zirconia brick. Be sure the crucible is inside the induction coil and that it is centered over the mold. Insert the stopper rod into the pouring hole of the crucible. Place two pieces of ½-in.-thick zirconia brick on top of the crucible. Keep them apart sufficiently so one can look in the crucible and observe the molten metal. Place a zirconia insulating tube down and around the crucible and mold. Attach the pull rod to the graphite stopper rod. Clean the red gasket on the cover and on the manifold with acetone and rags. Clean each end of the Vycor tube with acetone and a rag. Grease the ends (only) of the Vycor tube

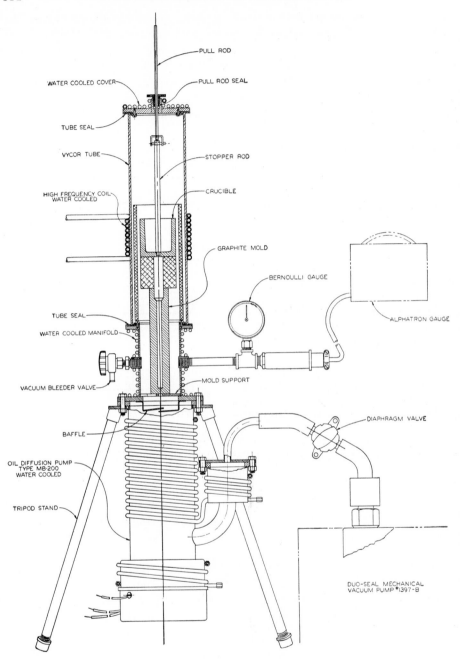

Fig. 9-8. Student vacuum furnace.

lightly with vacuum grease. Place the Vycor tubing down and over the insulation so that it comes to rest on the gasket on the manifold. Be careful not to chip the Vycor tubing. Place the cover on the furnace. Grease the two small packing gaskets and slip them over the pull rod and down into the packing gland. Insert the packing nut and hand-tighten. Your system should now be ready to "pull" a vacuum.

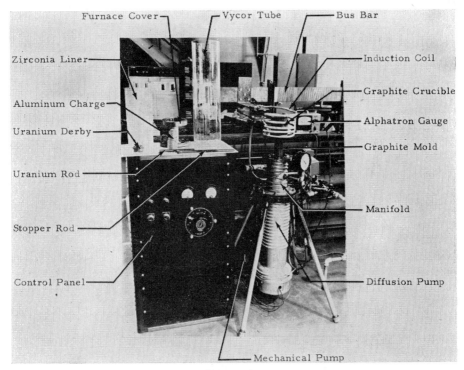

FIG. 9-9.   Vacuum furnace setup.

STEP 2. Turn on the mechanical vacuum pump with the switch on the control panel. After the pump has been up to speed for a few minutes, open the vacuum valve slowly. Smoke will come from the pump until a fairly good vacuum has been obtained. Turn on the alphatron vacuum gauge and watch it pump down. Switch from one scale to the next as pumpdown occurs. The mechanical pump should take the vacuum down to approximately 100 microns (0.1 mm Hg). If it does not pump down to this vacuum, there is a leak in the system. It will probably be necessary to disassemble and check the gaskets.

STEP 3. Connect the water cooling system. Turn on the water cooling to the diffusion pump. Connect the water cooling to the cover. Turn on the water cooling to the induction coil. The diffusion pump must be water-cooled in order to operate. The induction coil must be water-cooled or it will melt down from the high-frequency induction. The cover and manifold must be water-cooled to keep the flat gaskets from getting hot and thereby losing the vacuum. Turn on the diffusion pump and set to about 9½ amp. It is not necessary to run a large amount of water through the diffusion pump—just enough to keep the outside cold. After about 20 min, the diffusion pump should start to take hold and the vacuum should decrease below 1 micron. The furnace is now ready for melting.

STEP 4. Check with the instructor as to when to connect the induction coil to the bus bar. The instructor will turn on the power to the furnace. Keep hands off the bus bar. Note on your data sheet vacuum readings, temperatures, etc. After the crucible heats up to about 800°C, take temperatures with an optical pyrometer. See the instructor on how to use the optical pyrometer. The heat input into the crucible can be controlled by a variac on the motor generator control panel. Watch the meter for per cent of power. The generator set has a maximum power of 30 kw. The crucible will heat up rapidly. Notice that the vacuum becomes much poorer as the material in the furnace outgases. Two good reasons for using graphite crucibles are its resistance to thermal shock and its susceptibility to induction heating. The drawback to a graphite crucible is the carbon pickup during the melting operations. Take temperature readings and vacuum readings about every five minutes; note these on your data sheet. Note the melting point of the metal. This is a good time to check the optical pyrometer, because unalloyed uranium always melts at 1133°C. There are many errors possible in taking optical temperatures and in sighting through Vycor tubing. After the uranium has melted, the inside of the Vycor tube will darken. Then it is difficult to obtain an accurate reading. After the metal has been heated up to 1300°C, hold it there for a few minutes. Then pull the stopper rod. The ingot has now been cast.

STEP 5. Ask the instructor to shut off the power. Then shut off the diffusion pump. Keep the cooling water flowing in all parts. In about one-half hour you will notice on the alphatron gauge that the diffusion pump is no longer pumping. The system will have cooled down sufficiently that the furnace can now be taken apart. Disassemble the furnace by shutting off all the water, breaking all water connections to the cover. Hook up a hose to the bleeder valve of the argon tank and bleed the furnace with argon, watching the bourdon gauge to see the degree of vacuum. Prior to bleeding, be sure to close the vacuum valve to the mechanical pump. Wear asbestos gloves and a face shield when handling hot parts. When the bourdon vacuum gauge reads zero (atmospheric pressure), loosen the cover and lift off the cover with a pull rod and the stopper rod. Lay the cover down and pull off the pull rod. Lay the stopper rod in a white tray. Remove the Vycor tubing gently and place on a bench. Remove the insulation; place it in a tray. Pick out the crucible and mold and lay in the tray with the stopper rod. Take these over to the hood for emptying. Then weigh the ingot and the scull.

Metallurgical Foundry Terms

Crucible. The crucible is made of graphite and is the container in which the uranium is melted. Heat is induced in this graphite crucible by means of the induction coil. The crucible is called the susceptor of the induced current. The crucible has a hole in its bottom which is called the pouring hole. This is plugged with the graphite stopper rod.

Mold. This is made of graphite and is directly below the crucible. Molten uranium falls from the bottom of the crucible into the mold and solidifies. The metal takes the shape of the internal dimensions of the mold and is called an ingot.

Insulation. To prevent the loss of heat that has been induced in the crucible, a zirconia tube 12 in. long × 4-in. i.d. × $5\frac{1}{2}$ in. o.d. is placed around the mold crucible. There are also small pieces of zirconia placed on the top and bottom of the crucible to prevent heat losses.

Stopper rod. This is made of graphite and fits into a hole in the bottom of the crucible. The stopper rod extends several inches above the crucible. The melt is poured by pulling up the pull rod, which in turn lifts the stopper rod.

Induction coil. This is a coil of $\frac{3}{8}$ in. o.d. copper tubing about $6\frac{1}{2}$ in. i.d. containing five turns. The coil must be matched to the crucible to obtain good coupling. The number of turns in the induction coil varies with the diameter of the coil. Current passes through the coil at a frequency of 9600 cps. The rapid reversal of the electrical current induces a voltage in the graphite crucible which in turn drives a current through it. This induced current in the graphite crucible causes the heat which melts the metal. The induction coil is made of copper tubing so that it can be water-cooled.

Diffusion pump. This is a vacuum pump which is operated with a fore pressure of not over $\frac{1}{2}$ mm Hg (500 microns). It will produce a vacuum of 0.1 of a micron when the furnace is cold. The mechanical pump which produces the fore vacuum must always be used ahead of the diffusion pump to keep the fore pressure below 500 microns. The diffusion pump is heated with a 1200-watt electrical heater in its bottom. Diffusion pumps often use a butyl sebacate oil. When the pump is heated, oil vapors come up through the jets, entrap molecules of air, and carry them down to the place where they are pumped away by the mechanical pump. Do not open the system to air when the diffusion pump is working.

Mechanical pump. This is a rotary-type pump which sucks air in on one side, compresses it, and pushes it out the other. These pumps will produce a vacuum of about 35 microns when in good operating order.

Micron. This is 1×10^{-3} mm of mercury. More useful: 1000 microns are equal to 1 mm of mercury.

Alphatron gauge. This is a vacuum gauge. It has an alpha source in it. The gas molecules in the gauge are ionized by the alpha particles and are collected on a grid. The gauge is calibrated for air. Some alphatron gauges have seven scales, covering the range from atmospheric pressure down to $\frac{1}{10}$ of a micron. The instrument must be balanced for each scale.

Vycor tubing. This is an impure quartz, but it is transparent. It is 6 in. o.d. × 21 in. long with a $\frac{1}{8}$-in.-thick wall. It is very strong, but the ends can be chipped easily. The ends must be ground flat in order to achieve a vacuum seal on the flat gaskets.

Optical pyrometer. This is an instrument by which temperatures are measured up to 2800°C by comparison of the brightness of the melt with the brightness of the filament in the instrument. It is not as accurate as thermocouples but is a good control instrument.

Cold trap. This is a cooling and deflecting mechanism built into a vacuum system between the diffusion pump and the furnace manifold. Its purpose is to cut down the back diffusion of the oil from the diffusion pump into the vacuum system. A well-type cold trap made up of chevron-type fins which are filled with liquid air will improve a vacuum by a factor of 50 to 100.

Vacuum seal. The seals themselves are rubber gaskets which press against metal or ceramic surfaces. Vacuum grease is needed at the interface of the gasket and the metal to make a good seal. Notice that the vacuum seals on the Vycor tube are flat gaskets. To join two metal surfaces together, it is often feasible to machine a groove in one surface and place a gasket in the groove. This gasket is called an O ring from its shape. The other metal surface is ground flat. The two pieces of metal are bolted together and compress the O ring slightly. This is a very good type of vacuum seal.

Pull rod. This is a rod of stainless steel, $\frac{1}{4}$ in. in diameter × 10 in. long. It is attached to a molybdenum saddle which holds the top of the stopper rod. The pull rod extends through the top cover of the furnace and is made vacuum-tight by two small rubber gaskets and a packing-gland nut. By moving the pull rod, the stopper rod is pulled out of the pouring hole in the bottom of the crucible and the melt runs down into the mold.

Pump down. This is an expression signifying that a vacuum pump is taking the air out of the system. It takes only a few minutes to pump down with a mechanical pump to about 50 to 100 microns. It takes from 20 to 30 min to pump from 50 microns down to 1 micron because the oil diffusion pump has to heat up before it can start to work. The alphatron gauge will show the pumpdown.

Vacuum valve. This is a small valve between the mechanical pump and the diffusion pump. It permits the vacuum on a furnace to be held even though the mechanical pump is shut off.

Manifold housing. This is a small housing located just above the diffusion pump. The Vycor tubing rests on top of the manifold. The diffusion pump is hung from the bottom of the manifold. The vacuum gauges are connected to outlets in the manifold.

Furnace cover. This is a water-cooled cover which contains small gaskets and a nut for packing a seal around the pull rod. The gasket for the top seal on the Vycor tube is attached to the underside of the cover.

Bleeder valve. This is attached to the manifold housing and is used to break the vacuum after the furnace has cooled down following melting. Argon is bled into the furnace because there is finely divided magnesium on the cover and a chance of a small explosion if air is bled in.

EXPERIMENT 9-4

MAKING A URANIUM-ALUMINUM ALLOY

Purpose of the Experiment. This experiment is to demonstrate how to make an aluminum-rich uranium alloy that could be used as the fuel in an MTR type fuel element. The only difference between the laboratory practice described below and that used for making MTR (Materials Testing Reactor) fuel elements is that depleted uranium will be used, whereas the MTR fuel elements must be made with enriched uranium. From an equilibrium diagram of U-Al, it can be seen that much more aluminum than uranium is used. This makes the alloy behave like aluminum rather than uranium, which is a great help in fabrication and in handling throughout the process of making the fuel element.

Details of the Experiment: STEP 1. A graphite crucible of the same size will be used to make this alloy as was used to melt the unalloyed uranium. However, a much larger graphite mold will be used, i.e., one that will hold approximately 500 grams of charge. Decide on the percentage of uranium alloy to be made. Then weigh the uranium, using the small pieces that have been cut from the cast uranium ingot made in Experiment 9-3. To allow for melt losses, use 90 per cent of the weight of the uranium and calculate the weight of aluminum required. The total charge is to be less than 500 grams. The aluminum is in wire form and weighs 11 grams per running foot. Calculate the number of feet required and cut this footage. Wrap the wire on the mandrel at the lathe to form a spool of wire. When the mandrel has been removed there will be room for the stopper rod. This spool of wire is compact and should fit into the crucible.

STEP 2. Lime up the crucible with dry lime. Place the mold in position in the furnace so that the crucible which sits on top of the mold will be inside the induction coil. Place uranium uniformly around and on top of the aluminum. Proceed with the melting furnace as when making an unalloyed uranium ingot in Experiment 9-3.

STEP 3. *The melting of the charge.* Only the mechanical pump is required for obtaining a sufficient vacuum. Do not turn on the diffusion pump. The Vycor tubing should stay clean during the melting operation. During melting, read the temperatures with the optical pyrometer. Take the melt to about 200° above the liquidus point of your alloy. Allow about 10 min for the solution of the uranium in the aluminum. Hold the melt at this temperature by cutting back the power on the motor generator set. Then drop the temperature to between 75° and 100°C above the liquidus line. Then pull the stopper rod to pour the melt.

STEP 4. Allow the furnace to cool down for 20 min before opening. Bleed the furnace with air and open the furnace. Remove the crucible and its ingot. The ingot may have to be shaken out of the mold on the jogging machine in the hood.

STEP 5. Note the amount of shrinkage in the top of the ingot. This is due to the change in volume as the metal solidifies. If time permits, cut off the top part of the ingot which contains the pipe, and discard. Also cut a slice about ¾ in. thick from the bottom of the ingot as a metallographic sample. Grind and polish this sample and examine it under a bright field in a microscope or metallograph to see the internal structure of the ingot. Compare this internal structure with that expected from an equilibrium diagram.

DATA SHEET 9-3

Alloy: per cent uranium _____; per cent aluminum _____

Liquidus temperature of this alloy _____ °C

Actual weight of uranium _____ grams. 90 per cent of

wt. of uranium _____ grams

Weight of aluminum required _____ grams (based on 90 per cent of

uranium weight)

Total weight of charge in crucible _____ grams. Since the

aluminum wire weighs 11 grams per running foot, the number of feet of aluminum

wire _____

Appearance of ingot _____

Weight of ingot _____

Per cent of recovery of charge _____

Depth of pipe in top of ingot _____

MELTING DATA

Time	Vacuum	Power Setting on M.G. Set	Temperature	Remarks

ROLLING AND CAST-BONDING TO MAKE AN ALUMINUM-CLAD URANIUM-ALUMINUM ALLOY FUEL ELEMENT

Purpose of the Experiment. This experiment is to show some of the problems involved in making an MTR (Materials Testing Reactor) type fuel element. It is to be carried out with the material made in the preceding experiments. The cladding is to be cast around the core material of the aluminum-uranium alloy. This ingot will then be rolled out into a fuel element. For the present purposes, it is much easier to cast the aluminum than it is to use the machined plates which are necessary for the picture-frame type of bonding. The fuel plate that will be made will have some defects in it. The picture-frame method lends itself to closer quality control.

Rolling of the Aluminum-Uranium Ingot. Place the aluminum-uranium ingot made in the previous experiment in a muffle furnace near a rolling mill. The furnace should be set at 500°C. Allow the ingot to "heat-soak" for approximately 15 min before the start of rolling. One student feeds the roller, another catches the ingot as it comes out. Each pair of students rolls one ingot, taking turns on the two sides of the roller. As safety precautions around the rolling mill, each one must wear asbestos gloves and a face shield. Always use a rubber mallet to push the ingot into the rolls.

The first pass will be a sizing pass in the rolling mill, to remove approximately 0.025 in. The next pass will remove approximately 0.050 in. if the ingot will bite into the rolls. Only two passes should be made. Then put the ingot back into the muffle furnace for reheating because of the loss in heat during rolling. This alloy must be hot-rolled. If there are too many passes before reheating, the edges of the ingot will start to crack. If edge cracking is severe it may continue too far into the ingot and no usable material will result. Follow this alternate heating and rolling until the ingot has been taken down to approximately 0.250 in. thickness. This may be checked with a micrometer near the final passes.

Cast Cladding. Take the aluminum-uranium slab to the abrasive cutoff wheel where the instructor will trim it to a 2-in. × 2-in. × ¼-in.-thick piece. The excess material is to be placed in a storage drawer. Place the 2-in.-square piece of uranium-aluminum alloy in the mold (see Fig. 9-10). Place the piece which has the three projecting points on one side. Be sure it is centered with about ½ in. to spare on each side and the bottom, with respect to the mold walls. Place the other piece of the mold, which contains the one bearing point, on top. Clamp the mold with a C clamp and then insert the five bolts and tighten sufficiently to hold the aluminum-uranium alloy in place. Take the assembled mold to the pot furnace which contains molten 2-S aluminum. Be sure to wear asbestos gloves and a face shield. Insert a hot metal ladle into the molten aluminum. Bring up the ladle, skim off all the aluminum oxide, pour the molten aluminum into a corner of the mold. There should be sufficient metal to completely fill the space around and over the core material. Pour any excess aluminum back into the pot and remove the oxide from the ladle so that it will be ready for the next person to use. Open the mold and remove the ingot. You will

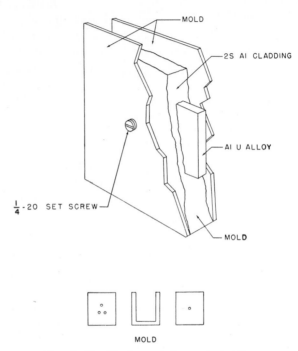

FIG. 9-10. Equipment for cast-cladding.

notice that this cast-bond ingot now has four small holes on the large faces. If the molten aluminum did not flow around the aluminum-uranium alloy core and cover it completely (except for these four places), repeat the cast-bonding with another piece of aluminum-uranium alloy.

Hot Pressing of Cast-Bonded Ingot. Place the ingot in a muffle furnace at 500°C. Allow it to "soak" for at least 10 min. Also place two stainless-steel plates, each $4 \times 4 \times \frac{1}{4}$ in., into the furnace to heat. Take the two pieces of stainless steel and the cast-clad ingot quickly to the tensile machine. Place the ingot between the two hot stainless-steel plates in the compression head of the testing machine. The instructor will compress the ingot to help close up the four small holes on the surfaces. This pressing, prior to rolling, is also helpful in breaking up the oxide layer that exists between the cladding and the core material. The pressing has been found to be of considerable help in obtaining good bonding between the core and its cladding. The clad ingot may be compressed as much as ⅛ in. in the testing machines. If it does not compress readily in the testing machine, the ingot has become too cold and must be reheated.

Rolling of Pressed Ingot. Heat the pressed ingot in a muffle furnace at 500°C for 10 min. Then proceed with the rolling operation, one man feeding and another man catching. A maximum of three passes is permissible between heatings. As the cross section reduces in thickness, larger bites may be taken on the rolling mill. When below 0.100-in. thickness, only one pass should be taken between heatings. The next to the last pass will take the slab to approximately 0.060 in. The final pass will roll it to approximately 0.050-in. thickness. The instructor will advise as to methods and procedures of feeding this slab through the rolling mill to obtain a straight plate. Should the fuel plate start to slide off to one side in the rolling mill and catch in the housing, let it go. Do not attempt to hold it by hand. There is a 15 hp motor on the rolling mill. Keep your hands out of the rolls. Many accordion plates have been made. It takes considerable care to obtain a good-looking, straight fuel plate. Take your time in the final passes if you wish to obtain one.

EXPERIMENT 9-6

INSPECTION OF FUEL ELEMENTS

INTRODUCTION

The purpose of this experiment is to detect flaws in fuel elements by nondestructive test methods, and also to study the defects after sectioning the elements. The fuel element prepared in the previous experiment (of the MTR type) is to be used. Both ultrasonics and X-rays will be used in the tests.

The ultrasonic test uses the through-transmission method, with the fuel elements immersed in water to prevent scattering of the sound waves. The sound waves, whose frequency is 5 megacycles/sec, are generated in a Sperry Ultrasonic Reflectroscope and travel through a cord to a quartz transducer which is immersed in water. The transducer surface normally used is 1 in. square, but for this experiment, is masked down so that the sound waves emerge from a hole approximately 1/16 in. in diameter. After traveling a short distance in water, the sound waves enter the fuel element. They pass through the element, if it has no defects, and then through a thin layer of water on the back side of the element and are picked up by a quartz receiver. The impulses from this receiver are transmitted back to the Reflectroscope where they are displayed on an oscilloscope.

Since it is very tiring to watch the screen of the oscilloscope continuously, it is more convenient to use an electrosensitive paper recorder in conjunction with the scanner. Thus a permanent record can be made of the condition of the fuel plate.

This paper records the entire scanning of the fuel plate. Where the sound waves are absorbed in the fuel plate owing to internal defects, a white spot will appear on the recorder paper. This is because the energy has been absorbed in a defect, such as a seam or blister or lack of bonding. The smaller the number and size of the white spots on the recorder paper, the better the fuel element.

In this type of testing, the sensitivity of the work is dependent on the diameter of the beam transmitted through the fuel plate. Since a beam $\frac{1}{16}$ in. in diameter is transmitted from the emitting quartz crystal, any defect larger than $\frac{1}{16}$ in. will be detected. In order to check the entire plate, the emitting and the receiving quartz crystals are connected to a yoke which fits over the fuel plate. The yoke moves vertically to scan the fuel plate from one side to the other; then it falls down to the bottom of the stroke and scans vertically again. The yoke is attached to a long screw feed which moves slowly in the horizontal direction, so that in the allotted time it is possible to scan the entire surface of the fuel plate. With plates of the size used here, it is possible to scan the entire surface in 10 to 15 min, with the recording on the electrosensitive paper completed, showing exactly where the sound waves were absorbed.

To locate the defect in the fuel plate, it is only necessary to lay the recorder paper on the fuel plate in the correct position and mark the spots where the sound was absorbed.

In order to prevent standing waves from being set up in the fuel plate, the sound wave is pulsed; it is applied to the fuel plate for only a very small percentage of the time. The sound waves are transmitted for a few microseconds. Then there is a delay of several hundred microseconds before a second pulse of sound waves is transmitted for a few microseconds.

Since the operation of this ultrasonic testing equipment is very delicate, it is to be done by highly trained personnel. The correct interpretation of the data and the correct operation of the equipment are a result of long experience. In order to make use of the ultrasonic test, it is necessary to carry out extensive tests on known flaws in order to determine the precise nature of the defect that is absorbing the sound waves. Every time a new type of fuel element is to be tested, many months of tedious metallographic work and a good knowledge of the factors that are detrimental to a fuel element are required in order to produce a standard for the Ultrasonic Reflectroscope. Once the standard has been decided upon, then it is quite easy for the Reflectroscope to be set so that it will pick up only the flaws which are felt to be detrimental in this fuel element. The range of the machine is so great, and the adjustments so complex, that it is possible to set it so that very bad defects could not be detected. On the other hand, it can be so sensitive that small, unimportant items such as a variation in grain size will absorb the sound waves and make the fuel element appear bad when there is really nothing wrong with it. The operation of this equipment requires much judgement on the part of the operator.

The fuel element is also to be X-rayed by a large commercial X-ray machine to show the exact location of the core inside of the cladding. This is done easily with X-rays because of the difference in density of the core and the cladding material. The uranium in the core alloy absorbs much more of the X-rays than does the aluminum. Thus the core will show on the negative as a light area inside the cladding. In general, the X-ray does not pick up the minute defects that the ultrasonic test shows because it can only show where there is a difference in density in two adjacent areas. Even though there is a blister on the surface of the fuel element, and it can be seen with the naked eye, and it is known that there is a void between the core and cladding, there still remains the same amount of cladding and core material for the X-ray to pass through. Hence the defect does not show. In ultrasonic testing, it will show because the sound waves are absorbed at the interface of the blister and never get through the fuel element at all.

Of particular interest in the X-ray pattern of a fuel element is the shape of the core near the end of the fuel element. It will be noted that when one started with a square piece of uranium-aluminum alloy in the clad billet, it became quite rounded at the ends after rolling, with the center of the fuel a few inches longer than its edge.

Ultrasonic Testing of a Fuel Element

First, it is necessary to trim the fuel element so that it has flat edges and can be supported in the tank of water for the test. This trimming is done on a shear.

The trimmed fuel element is then taken to the ultrasonic equipment. If the fuel element will not lie flat on a table, it is to be bent until it is flat. The instructor will place the fuel element in the tank of water and start the scanning mechanism in operation. This is the yoke which holds the emitting and receiving quartz crystals. The sound waves will be sent from the Reflectroscope to the emitting crystal, through the water in front of the fuel element, then through the fuel element itself, then through the water behind the fuel element and into the receiving quartz crystal, and back to the Reflectroscope. The amount of transmitted energy shows up on the oscilloscope, and is also transmitted to the recorder where it makes a mark on the electrosensitive paper.

Watch the electrosensitive paper. Whenever a white spot shows up, the sound is being absorbed in the fuel element. This may be due to one of the following defects in the fuel element: (1) Lack of bonding between core and clad. (2) A nonmetallic inclusion such as the slag or oxide from the aluminum poured around the core material. (3) A blister in the surface of the cladding. (4) A seam inside the core material itself, which may be from blow holes or "pipes" in the ingot of aluminum-uranium alloy. These ingot defects will some-times roll out as internal seams, or they may weld themselves together in rolling and never be found.

After the fuel element has been tested, lay the recorder paper on top of it in the correct location and mark the defects on the surface of the fuel elements with red marking crayon. Cut through these defects and examine them under a microscope.

X-Ray of a Fuel Element

After loading the cassettes with X-ray film, place the fuel element on top of the cassette so as to take an X-ray of about one-half of the fuel element. Be sure to X-ray one end of the element. Use lead letters on the cassette next to the fuel element so that the negative can be identified. Everyone must leave the X-ray chamber when the machine is in operation. The exposure is usually less than 1 min because the fuel elements are thin. After the exposure, develop the X-ray film, let it dry, and examine it.

Metallographic Examination of a Sectioned Fuel Element

The fuel elements are to be sectioned about 1 in. on both sides of the region to be examined. The defect is then sectioned on an abrasive cutoff wheel. This method is used to prevent tearing the cladding from the core, which can occur if the shearing method is used in the area of the defect.

The entire cross section of the fuel element can be polished, or a small portion can be mounted in Bakelite to facilitate holding while polishing.

Polishing is done on the 120-grit paper, 240-grit paper, 600-grit canvas wheel, and 1000-grit billiard cloth wheel, in succession. Then etch with warm concentrated sodium hydroxide solution. Dip it in the sodium hydroxide for a few seconds and then rinse under running water. Examination of the polished surface should show the dark core inside of the light cladding.

Examine under bright field illumination on a microscope or metallograph. The defect will usually show up as a black line either in the cladding or between core and cladding. Most of the defects will be due to stringers of aluminum oxide from the molten aluminum which was cast around the core material.

As seen under a microscope, the core will blend into the cladding and there will be no distinct line of bonding, provided there is a good metallurgical bond. Examine the edge cladding to see if it is tight to the core material. Since there is no force to bond the edges in the rolling process, there is frequently a small hole running the length of the fuel element, along the edge. This is not desirable, because if a break should occur in the cladding and water get into the hole, rapid corrosion could occur.

FUEL-ELEMENT QUALITY

It is relatively easy to make an MTR-type fuel element as described in the preceding experiment. However, it is much more difficult to produce one to rigid specifications, with close tolerances on thickness of core and cladding material and to the exact distribution of the core inside of the clad. In addition to these problems, the metallurgist must exercise judgment and much care in deciding whether the fuel element will stand up under irradiation.

ADDITIONAL EXPERIMENTS

Among the many metallurgical experiments possible for the student may be mentioned (1) studies with powder metallurgy, (2) studies of ceramic fuels, (3) the extrusion of aluminum-uranium alloys, (4) liquid metal corrosion, (5) radiation damage (see Chapter 10), (6) welding and brazing of fuel elements (a small Heliarc apparatus for welding of Zircaloy), (7) studies of uranium-zirconium alloys, (8) studies of uranium-chromium alloys, (9) the corrosion of cladding materials (see Chapter 10), (10) heat treating of uranium alloys, (11) techniques of machining uranium, (12) the melting, fabrication, and heat treatment of thorium, (13) solid-state studies of irradiated metals using "hot lab" facilities (see Chapter 11).

Chapter 10

CORROSION AND RADIATION EFFECTS

EXPERIMENT 10-1

HIGH-TEMPERATURE CORROSION TESTS

By J. E. DRALEY, ANL, Metallurgy Division

INTRODUCTION

The purpose of this experiment is to study the aqueous-corrosion behavior of materials which are of interest in the construction of water-cooled reactors. These materials are natural uranium, an aluminum alloy (prepared by the addition of 1 per cent nickel to commercially pure aluminum) Zircaloy-2, and

FIG. 10-1. A corrosion laboratory.

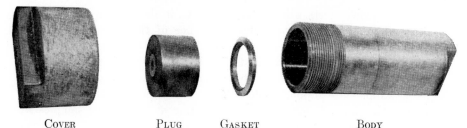

COVER   PLUG   GASKET   BODY

FIG. 10-2.   High-temperature corrosion test autoclave.

type 304 stainless steel. Chemical analysis of the metal supplied will be furnished by the instructor. In addition, the effect of a minor alloying constituent on the course of the corrosion reaction will be studied as an illustration of the theory of the corrosion process.

A corrosion laboratory setup is shown in Fig. 10-1. The high-temperature corrosion tests are performed in stainless-steel autoclaves (Fig. 10-2) which are heated in a forced-convection electric furnace (Fig. 10-3). To prevent galvanic action, samples are insulated from the autoclaves with synthetic-

FIG. 10-3.   High-temperature test furnace.

sapphire rods. These tests will be run at 315°C, in double-distilled water. To check water quality, pH and specific resistance of the water are measured before and after the test.

The corrosion of uranium will be studied in actively boiling distilled water. The short duration tests are run in Pyrex beakers with the heat supplied by a hot plate. Samples are supported on sections of Pyrex glass tubing.

In general it cannot be presumed that the rate of reaction of samples with the corroding environment will be the same at all times during the tests. Consequently the total amount of corrosion is determined after various exposure periods. These amounts of corrosion are plotted as a function of time. If the line best fitting the points is a straight line through the origin, then the corrosion rate of the material in the environment is the slope of that line. More characteristic of the corrosion of oxide-film–forming metals is a period of rather rapid reaction followed by a longer period of much slower reaction. When the period of slower reaction is characterized by a constant rate, then the slope of this straight-line portion of the corrosion curve can be called the corrosion rate. For any relatively long exposure of such material to the environment used in the test, the total amount of corrosion can be estimated from the corrosion rate and the intercept of the straight-line portion of the curve. In other cases, no part of the corrosion curve is a straight line. In these instances, it is generally not considered feasible to report a corrosion rate at all. Some other means of reporting the results of the test should be found. Sometimes in such cases the corrosion-vs.-time curve is given, and a person wishing to use the data must determine from the curve the amount of corrosion to be expected at the time of interest to him. It has been convenient to plot data of this sort on logarithmic coordinates, in cases where a straight line results.

Characteristic of the metals which are corrosion-resistant in water at high temperature is the formation of a tightly adherent thin protective film of oxide. Weights of samples after corrosion exposure do not thus give good indication of the amount of corrosion that has taken place. If the composition of the corrosion product is known, and if none of the product has been lost from the sample surface, and if no foreign material has deposited on the sample surface, then the gain in weight of the sample during corrosion test can be used to estimate the amount of metal which has corroded. These assumptions appear to be almost justified for Zircaloy II and for stainless steel. The resultant errors in the amount of corrosion calculated are not large. However, the exact nature of the corrosion curves cannot be determined with certainty, and they cannot safely be extrapolated to times much longer than the corrosion test period. After the initial period of reaction, the assumptions also appear to be nearly true for aluminum alloys. A more reliable method involves the chemical or electrochemical removal of the corrosion product after test without significant removal of the underlying metal. It is then possible to weigh the bare sample after test and determine directly the amount of metal which has corroded.

Experimentally, this procedure is usually quite difficult since the films which are protective to the metal in the corrosion environment are also quite resistant to attack during the film-stripping procedure. These considerations are generally not important for the cases of rapid corrosion, since corrosion products are generally lost to a considerable extent, and weighing errors caused by accidental amounts of adherent corrosion product are small compared to the total amount of reaction.

Since metals of interest as construction material corrode quite slowly, it is obvious that relatively long tests are necessary to determine valid corrosion rates. Long tests can only be run in a course of this nature by doing the work as a group effort. Consequently it will be necessary at the conclusion of the corrosion tests for students to have available data collected by all of the students in the class. To make this possible, data will be recorded, on sheets, in a notebook kept during the course by the instructor. This notebook will be available to all students at any time during the course, and will be provided for circulation among students at the conclusion of the corrosion tests.

The students at the first session will start the program by placing five samples in test. In all following sessions (except the last) some samples will be removed and others inserted to continue the program. In addition, autoclaves in test for long periods will be weighed at intervals to insure that no leakage is occurring. The assignments for each session are summarized in the program sheets, Table 10-1.

TABLE 10-1. HIGH-TEMPERATURE CORROSION TEST SCHEDULE

SESSION NO.	1	2	3	4	5	6	7	8	9	10
ELAPSED TIME, days	0	2	7	9	14	16	21	23	28	30
AUTOCLAVE	IN	OUT IN	OUT IN	OUT IN	OUT IN	OUT IN	OUT IN	OUT IN	OUT IN	OUT
1	A(30)									
2	S(30)									
3	Z(30)									
4	A(2)	A(21)						A(5)	2S(2)	
5	2S(2)	S(21)						S(5)	A(2)	
6		Z(21)						Z(5)		
7			A(5)	A(14)			Z(9)			
8				S(14)			2S(2)			
9				Z(14)						
10				2S(2)	S(5)	S(2)	A(12)			
11					Z(5)	2S(2)	S(7)			

NOTES: A – ALUMINUM–NICKEL ALLOY   2S – 2S TYPE ALUMINUM
S – TYPE 304 STAINLESS STEEL   ( ) – TEST TIME, days
Z – ZIRCALOY II

It is to be emphasized that corrosion tests in water at 315°C are hazardous both because of the temperature and the pressure involved. It is possible to receive severe burns from hot metal objects at this temperature, and the danger of equipment failure and explosion must be remembered. In order to minimize the hazard of explosion the autoclaves provided are safe to pressures considerably in excess of the vapor pressure of water at 315°C. The oven used has its temperature carefully controlled, with an additional safety-alarm control mechanism. If by accident the temperature rises somewhat above the primary control value, an auxiliary control simultaneously shuts off the main power lines and operates an audible alarm. In addition to the increase in the vapor pressure of water by accidental overheating, there is another possible source of internal pressure. One of the products of the corrosion reaction is hydrogen gas. If a sufficient amount of this gas is provided, dangerously high pressures will result inside the autoclaves.

Students are requested to calculate the maximum pressure which can be produced by the corrosion of one of each of the types of the samples provided in a typical autoclave as follows:

1. Determine the autoclave volume by weighing it empty, and again when filled with distilled water.
2. Determine the weight of water used in a typical loading by weighing an autoclave so loaded, ready for use except for the sample (which is omitted).
3. Determine the volume of the water at test temperature by using the weight of the water as in (2) and its specific volume (Table 10-2). Calculate the volume of the gas space in the autoclave.

TABLE 10-2. SPECIFIC VOLUME OF WATER[a]

Temp., °C	Sat. Pressure, psia	Specific Volume, ml/gram
4	0.1	1.00
100	14.7	1.04
150	69.1	1.09
200	225	1.16
250	577	1.25
300	1249	1.40
315	1543	1.47 (for steam, 16.7)
350	2400	1.75

[a] From J. H. Perry (Ed.), "Chemical Engineers' Handbook," 3rd ed., McGraw-Hill Book Co., Inc., New York (1950).

4. Compute the number of moles of hydrogen which would be produced by complete reaction of a sample of each of the three metals to be used. Assume the corrosion products are $Al_2O_3 \cdot H_2O$, ZrO_2, and Fe_3O_4 respectively.

5. Compute the pressure of the hydrogen in the gas phase, using the following two equations:

$$P_H = (N_T - N_L) RT/V, \tag{10-1}$$

$$N_L = 3.0 \times 10^{-7} P_H W_{H_2O}, * \tag{10-2}$$

where P_H is the pressure of the hydrogen in the gas phase, N_T is the total number of moles of hydrogen produced, N_L is the number of moles of hydrogen dissolved in the water, and W_{H_2O} is the weight of the liquid water (total water added minus the weight in the gas phase; use Table 10-2). R, T, and V are the gas constant, absolute temperature, and gas volume respectively. In the second equation, P_H is in psi and W_{H_2O} is in grams.

6. Add the vapor pressure of water at the test temperature to the hydrogen pressure computed in (5) to obtain the total pressure.

Experimental Procedure

At the beginning of the laboratory period, the beaker should be set up for the boiling-water tests of uranium corrosion. Clean and rinse the beaker carefully, and determine pH and resistivity of the water in the beaker prior to test. During the period that the water is heating in the beaker, samples can be prepared of uranium and of the materials to be tested at the higher temperature in autoclaves. All samples are received with an ordinary machine finish. They should be wet-ground. Keep abrasive paper thoroughly wetted with distilled water during hand-grinding. Use the coarser paper until machine marks are gone and then the finer paper for a clean finish. Avoid spreading uranium grindings; try to wipe it up as formed, using the tissues provided. All paper contaminated with uranium should be placed in the radioactive disposal can provided. In general, natural uranium should not be handled with the bare hands (even with no cuts or sore spots) for more than six hours in any one day.

After grinding, the sample length, width, and thickness are measured. Samples are then degreased by rinsing in methyl alcohol, blotted, and allowed to dry on Kleenex. They are then weighed on the analytical balance to 0.1 mg. Uranium samples are then placed in test on the glass holders provided, and the alloys for high-temperature test are placed in the special sample holders shown in Fig. 10-4.

For the uranium test, three samples are placed on test at the same time. These are removed after 1, 2.5, and 4 hours' exposure respectively. The exposure times are not important, although they should be spread out enough to give an idea of the type of corrosion curve which is being determined. At the end of test, samples are removed, and immersed in 25 per cent nitric acid

* Pray, Schweichert, and Minnick, "Solubility of Gases in Water at Elevated Temperatures," BMI-T-25 (May 1950).

(by weight) until clean of corrosion product. The acid treatment removes an insignificant amount of metal. They are then carefully rinsed with distilled water, dried, and weighed.

While the samples are being prepared, the high-pressure autoclaves in which tests are to be conducted may be prepared for test. The autoclave (Fig. 10-2) consists of a stainless-steel body, plug, and gasket and a carbon steel cap. All parts in contact with the corroding medium are stainless steel. The autoclave body, plug, and gasket are rinsed with distilled water and the body (with gasket in place) is filled to the level of the gasket with distilled water and

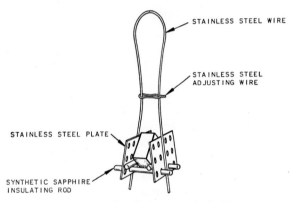

STAINLESS STEEL WIRE

STAINLESS STEEL ADJUSTING WIRE

STAINLESS STEEL PLATE

SYNTHETIC SAPPHIRE INSULATING ROD

Fig. 10-4.   Insulating sample holder.

placed on the vise table. The sample and holder are placed in the autoclave, which is then heated, using the hand torch provided, until the water has been boiling for a few minutes. A water sample is then withdrawn into the sample bottle, using the apparatus provided. (Beginning with the water-sampling operation it is advisable to wear asbestos gloves.) The autoclave is then closed with the water still boiling. After screwing on the cap hand-tight, it is to be well tightened while in one of the receptacles in the vise table, using the special wrench provided. The autoclaves are then weighed before placing on test in the oven.

After the autoclave has been in the oven for the prescribed length of time, it is removed and placed in the sink. After all autoclaves which are to be removed in the session are in the sink, the water is turned on for cooling. When the autoclaves have cooled, they are opened, using the wrench and extension handle. Samples are rinsed carefully in distilled water and dried prior to weighing. The water at the end of each test exposure is placed in a sample bottle and the pH and specific resistance are measured.

Since stripping procedures are difficult and time-consuming, corrosion product will not be removed from these samples during this course. However, the aluminum alloy samples will be stripped of corrosion product by the instructor and returned to the students for weighing at the next laboratory session. The procedure to be followed consists of two parts:

First, samples are cleaned of most of the corrosion product by an electro-chemical treatment in saturated boric acid solution, stirred at room temperature. With the temperature maintained at 20-25°C by a cooling coil, an alternating current of 0.02 amp/cm² of sample is passed between sample and auxiliary platinum electrodes. Up to 800 volts power supply is required. The sample is supported, completely immersed, by pointed holders which are carefully insulated from contact with the solution. To avoid overheating in the solution, it is necessary to restrict period of current passage to 1 min at a time. These periods are continued until the sample appears to be clean. It is then removed, brushed and rinsed in distilled water. Following this treatment the sample is similarly supported in a chromic–phosphoric acid bath at 85°C while it is made the cathode with a direct current of the order of 10 ma/cm². The bath contains 163 grams of CrO_3 + 200 ml of H_3PO_4, diluted to 2 liters with distilled water.

Finally, samples are examined microscopically for signs of local attack or other surface irregularities. The nature of the surfaces is recorded on the data sheets in the notebook. When finished data are available, they are plotted on graph paper to give the corrosion curve for each material in the corroding environment. These curves are then examined for shape, and where possible, corrosion rates and intercepts are determined and recorded directly on the graphs.

EXPERIMENT 10-2

THE CORROSION OF FUEL ELEMENTS

By J. BAIRD, International School of Nuclear Science and Engineering

PURPOSE OF THE EXPERIMENT

This is a qualitative test of uranium and its alloys to demonstrate the need for cladding the fuel elements when they are exposed to 300°C water for a short time. Although the test is conducted under conditions that are different from those encountered in a reactor, it will show not only the need for cladding but also the need for good bonding all around the metallic fuel elements.

GENERAL OUTLINE OF THE EXPERIMENT

The equipment used for the test, the autoclaves, and the oven are standard equipment for static-corrosion tests. Tests of this nature are the easiest to make, but give only relative information. Three different materials will be corrosion-tested: unalloyed uranium; aluminum–13%-uranium alloy clad with aluminum, with the aluminum–13%-uranium exposed; and uranium–5%-zirconium alloy clad with Zircaloy II, with the uranium–5%-zirconium alloy exposed. The samples will be cut on the abrasive cutoff wheel and then weighed to the closest three significant figures. They are to be placed in an autoclave, sealed up, and heated in an oven for approximately $1\frac{1}{2}$ hr at 300°C. They are then removed, cooled, weighed, and examined visually. The loss in weight per unit weight gives an idea of the amount of corrosion which occurred.

The EBWR-type fuel element contains a core of uranium-zirconium alloy approximately $\frac{1}{4}$ in. thick, with a cladding of Zircaloy only 20 mils thick. The MTR-type fuel element is approximately 50 mils thick. It contains a uranium-aluminum core alloy of approximately 13 per cent uranium, and is clad with aluminum. Its cladding is approximately 15 mils thick, and the core is approximately 20 mils thick.

SHORTCOMINGS OF STATIC CORROSION TESTS ON MATERIALS FOR USE IN REACTORS

The fuel in heterogeneous, water-cooled reactors must be clad in order to prevent its corrosion, with attendant radioactive contamination of the coolant, which could offer a serious biological hazard to workers in the area. After continued use there must be no break in the cladding material. Hence the following comments apply primarily to cladding materials. From the experiment on exposed core material, it will be seen that their resistance to water corrosion is very poor. It takes much longer to corrode the cladding materials.

Static-corrosion tests are easy to run but do not truly duplicate the conditions under which a fuel element is subjected in a reactor. A dynamic test with moving hot water would be far superior to the static test because circulation of water around the specimen has tremendous influence on the corrosion rate.

Static-corrosion tests may result in either a loss in weight or a gain in weight, depending upon the material. In the case of aluminum, there is a complete coating of aluminum oxide so that a gain in weight is a good indication that the material has a protective coat. Eventually, however, the oxide coating falls away and there is a loss in weight. Therefore, it is necessary to check quite closely on the loss in weight of this material. Assumptions must be made that a certain type of oxide forms on the surface. Once the protective oxide has started to break or fall away, the corrosion rates increase quite rapidly. It is possible to remove the oxide following a corrosion test and weigh the amount of sound metal. This requires considerable technique, and the results are not always reliable. If the test could be made in a reactor in which there is water flowing past the specimen, it is possible that one would find that some of the oxide had eroded away because of the moving water. This should speed the corrosion rate considerably. If the oxide adheres rather loosely, the rapid motion of the water certainly can rupture the surface. Aside from these con-

siderations, it is necessary to make a basic assumption in this type of experiment, namely, that the corrosion is uniform over the entire surface of the
sample. Then the corrosion rate, or loss in weight, in $mg/dm^2/day$, is uniform
over the entire sample. Thus it is assumed that there is a uniform attack over
the entire surface of the metal.

It has been found many times, however, that the observed corrosion is not
uniform. It is possible to have intergranular corrosion, where the corroding
medium seeps in between the grains of the metal and penetrates completely
through the material. In this case, no appreciable loss or gain in weight is
observed. Intergranular corrosion frequently occurs in a defect in the metal.
This is almost catastrophic as far as fuel elements are concerned. One must be
sure that good metal cladding, free from defects, is used in making up fuel
elements in order to overcome the possibility of intergranular corrosion, which
frequently is very rapid compared with the rather slow corrosion on the surface.
Fuel elements are generally tested in full section in autoclaves and are then
checked for surface defects and for possible corrosion effects prior to being
placed in a reactor. This is a necessary step. It is believed that the intergranular corrosion, if it is to occur at all, will have taken place in the relatively
short time of this test. The corrosion of areas which have been welded (in
making up the cladding around the fuel elements) is often critical.

In the case of picture-frame roll bonding, it is necessary that the metal bond
itself completely, one surface to the other, so that there is no interface for
corrosion to take place. The result of rolling should bond them perfectly and
without any possible leakage. Even a small pinhole through a weld area can
permit moisture to seep in and around the cladding material. When one is using
data from static-corrosion tests in fuel-element design, one must exercise judgment in determining the factors of safety that are required to insure a sound
fuel element. The static-corrosion test is only indicative.

Materials that are undergoing static-corrosion tests are not subject to a
neutron and gamma radiation. It is very possible that the adherence of the
oxide film to the base metal could be drastically changed as a result of irradiation if the material were in use. It is not feasible at the present time to subject
materials, on a small specimen scale, to neutron flux as well as corrosion conditions. Since the corrosion resistance of a material depends on the adherence
of the oxide film to the surface and to the base metal, anything that tends to
loosen it (and certainly a radiation effect could possibly do this) might increase
the corrosion tremendously. It is possible to make corrosion tests on irradiated
material, or the material may first be corroded and then subjected to radiation.
The combination of a radiation and dynamic corrosion test would be the best
for the determination of how well a material would stand up when put in use
as a cladding on a fuel element.

The temperature of the water in the autoclave of a static test is well controlled, but the temperature of material in the reactor is not as well controlled,

particularly since the source of heat is in the material itself. Anything that interferes with the heat transfer, such as the formation of a blister or the formation of dirt on the surface that slows up heat transfer, could lead to localized overheating. This could accelerate corrosion considerably. Frequently the failure in aluminum is by blistering combined with local overheating, which leads to rapid localized failure. The formation of the corrosion product on the surface of the fuel element can slow up heat transfer even though not appreciably affecting its corrosion rate.

The corrosion resistance of aluminum is affected by the condition of the water. A pH of approximately 5 to 6 is best for corrosion resistance in the case of aluminum. For completeness, the condition of the water must be stated in the corrosion data. If the solution becomes extremely acid or extremely alkaline, corrosion rates increase enormously. The optimum pH depends upon the hydroxide ion concentration. As the temperature increases, the optimum pH decreases. At 250°C the optimum pH is about 3.

CORROSION THEORIES

The most generally accepted theory is that aqueous corrosion is typically electrochemical in nature. Also, that the oxidation reaction of the metal atoms to metal ions need not occur at the same place as the electrically equivalent reduction reaction. The most common reduction reactions are the formation of hydrogen and hydroxide ions from the water and the formation of hydroxide and water. The corrosion resistance of most metals used in reactor components (such as the cladding material) is quite good in spite of the fact that they are active metals. The reasons for this are (a) the initial corrosion is quite rapid until a small protective layer of oxide is formed on the metal surface; (b) this oxide film is insoluble in the corroding solution; (c) this oxide film also adheres tenaciously to the base metal; (d) the oxide coating is impervious to the corroding solution; it keeps it away from the base metal; (e) this oxide layer is thought to be a continuous film rather than a small crystalline fragment; (f) whenever this film becomes so thick that it no longer adheres tenaciously it falls off and corrosion can again take place on the base metal.

Hydrogen has long been considered one of the bad actors in aqueous corrosion because it can form a metal hydride underneath the protective oxide and break away the protective oxide layer. It can also form as atomic hydrogen and diffuse into the metal through the metal atoms because of its small size. The atomic hydrogen will diffuse to an open spot in the metal and form molecular hydrogen. Since the molecular hydrogen cannot go back through the metal, a blister starts to form (as more atomic hydrogen comes to this location and forms molecular hydrogen). The accumulation of molecular hydrogen can cause the protective oxide layer to fall away or lead to intergranular corrosion or rupture of the specimen so that it may fall into several pieces.

In the corrosion of aluminum at ordinary temperatures, the corrosion rate, at the initial formation of the protective oxide, appears to be a function of the gaseous hydrogen forming under the oxide film. This causes a continuous rupturing of the oxide film in local spots. At elevated temperatures most aluminum will eventually form blisters under the metallic surface, which lead to rapid failure by exposing new metal surfaces for corrosion.

This undesired effect of hydrogen can be overcome by anodic protection. For this, the hydrogen liberated at the reacting surface is caused to form molecular hydrogen, and the formation of atomic hydrogen is prevented in its subsequent diffusion through the metal atoms to places where hydrogen can collect in pockets and form blisters. This anodic protection for the case of aluminum may be accomplished either by adding salts to the water or by alloying the aluminum with 1 per cent iron and 1 per cent nickel, approximately. Cobalt sulfate and nickel sulfate have also been effective in water solution.

The corrosion of zirconium and zirconium alloys proceeds at a much slower rate than that of aluminum and its alloys. Eventually there is a build-up of a heavy oxide layer on the zirconium. When this layer becomes relatively thick, it falls away from the base metal owing to strains in the lattice of the oxide structure or to the formation of molecular hydrogen just between the oxide layer and the base. The corrosion resistance of the zirconium is improved by adding 1½ per cent tin to make the alloy known as Zircaloy II.

The corrosion of uranium proceeds quite rapidly. The thin oxide films that form fall away rather quickly, possibly owing to the formation of uranium hydride beneath this film. Uranium alloys are also prone to intergranular corrosion or cracking after prolonged exposure. Corrosion of thorium is similar to that of uranium, although it occurs at a much slower rate.

EXPERIMENTAL PROCEDURE

Rinse out the stainless-steel autoclaves with distilled water, wipe off all sealing gasket surfaces with Kleenex, and fill about one-half full of water. Weigh each sample to three significant figures. In one autoclave place uranium-zirconium alloy clad with Zircaloy II, and a piece of unalloyed uranium. In another autoclave place a piece of aluminum-uranium alloy clad with aluminum. Insert the stainless-steel ring, which is a gasket, and the top plug. Seal the cap with a wrench, tightening it snugly in place with a 6-ft length of pipe on the tightening handle. It is necessary that the cap be very tight to prevent loss of moisture during the test.

Place the autoclaves in the oven at 300°C. The oven has a circulating fan which speeds up the heat transfer and keeps temperatures uniform throughout the furnace. Allow the autoclaves to remain in the oven approximately 1½ hr.

Approximately ½ hr is required for the autoclave to heat to the operating temperature.

After the required length of time in the oven, remove the autoclaves, place them in the sink and cool with water for about 10 min. Handle all autoclaves with asbestos gloves, open the autoclaves with a special wrench, and stand clear. There is considerable build up of hydrogen and it will "spit."

Remove samples from the autoclave, and rinse the autoclave with distilled water so that all oxide is washed into a tray. Rinse the specimens at the polishing benches, remove oxide from pits in the samples. The unalloyed uranium may be badly corroded; in fact, it may have disappeared in this length of time. Look at all of the specimens with the stereoscopic microscope to observe the attack of the core material. In general, the cladding will not have been affected at all.

This is only a qualitative test to show how rapidly corrosion can take place when core material is exposed. If corrosion does start to take place inside a clad fuel element, it will tend to expand, owing to the build up of hydrogen, and could rupture the entire fuel element. Even pinhole leaks cannot be tolerated. The rapid rate of corrosion of uranium, even under static conditions, points drastically to the need for careful cladding of the fuel material. The oxide that is formed is not adherent and continually falls away to form a mud in the bottom of the autoclave. If this were a dynamic test, the corrosion would undoubtedly proceed far more rapidly than in the case of bare uranium. The corrosion rate of unclad uranium metal would be intolerably fast in a reactor.

EXPERIMENT 10-3

IMPACT TESTS ON IRRADIATED CARBON STEEL

By W. F. MURPHY, Metallurgy Department,
International School of Nuclear Science and Engineering

INTRODUCTION

The purpose of this experiment is to determine the effect of neutron irradiation on the impact energy absorption at different temperatures.

Charpy impact specimens of C1018 steel are to be used. They should be irradiated to an integrated fast-neutron flux of at least 10^{18} nvt. The material is first annealed by holding it at 1575°F (857°C) for ½ hr, followed by air cooling. The nominal chemical composition of this steel is as follows: carbon 0.15/0.20 per cent; manganese 0.60/0.90 per cent; phosphorus 0.04 per cent max.; sulfur 0.050 per cent max. Control specimens, annealed but not irradiated, should be available. Temperatures during irradiation should not be greater than approximately 150°C.

The equipment consists of a pendulum-type impact machine (Fig. 10-5) a stop watch, Thermos bottles, tongs, a hardness tester, a potentiometer, a thermocouple, Dry Ice, and acetone.

The procedure is as follows: determine the time-temperature curve for a sample specimen which has been cooled to the temperature of a Dry Ice-acetone mixture and which was then removed from the cold bath, placed on the anvils of the impact machine, and allowed to come to room temperature. The curve obtained will be used to estimate temperatures of the impact specimens at the time of fracture. The test specimens will be cooled to the temperature of the

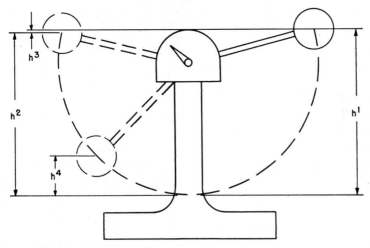

h¹ – PENDULUM HEIGHT AT STARTING POSITION
h² – MAXIMUM PENDULUM HEIGHT AFTER FREE SWING
h³ – PENDULUM HEIGHT LOST IN FREE SWING DUE TO WIND AND FRICTION
h⁴ – PENDULUM HEIGHT AFTER BREAKING SPECIMEN

FIG. 10-5.   Impact testing machine.

Dry Ice–acetone mixture, placed on the anvils of the impact machine, and broken by releasing the pendulum. The time on the anvil before releasing the pendulum will be governed by the temperature desired and will be determined from the time-temperature curve previously made.

Construct a curve of impact energy vs. temperature for both the irradiated and unirradiated specimens. Tabulate all data.

Irradiation. A group of twenty modified Charpy impact specimens are irradiated in a reactor such as CP-5. The nature of the specimen and its mounting are shown in Figs. 10-6 and 10-7. Two of the edges of the specimens have been beveled so that they can be arranged in a circle in the reactor hole.

Hardness. Hardnesses of both irradiated and unirradiated specimens are to be determined. Rockwell A or B scales may be used. The irradiated specimens are handled with tongs in all operations.

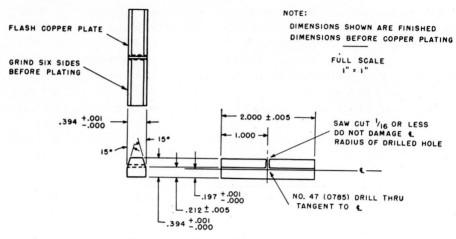

FIG. 10-6.   Keyhole Charpy specimen.

Impact Test: Time-Temperature Data. A hole about $\frac{1}{16}$ in. deep and $\frac{1}{16}$ in. in diameter is drilled in a sample specimen near the notch. The junction of a copper-constantan thermocouple is placed in the hole and lead shot is peened into the hole to hold the thermocouple in place. The specimen is then put into a handling fixture and immersed in a mixture of acetone and solid carbon dioxide. The temperature of the mixture is $-78°C$. The impact specimen generally has the same temperature as the cold bath after about 10 min, as indicated by the thermocouple voltage.

At temperatures above $0°C$, the copper wire of the thermocouple is $+$ and the constantan is $-$. Below $0°C$, the polarity reverses. For this experiment most temperatures are below $0°C$, so the thermocouple connections are reversed at the potentiometer. The millivolt measurements can be made with a Leeds & Northrup student-type potentiometer. A correction must be made for the reference junction temperature where the thermocouple is connected to the potentiometer. The temperature at the reference junction is determined with a thermometer. The millivolt equivalent for the reference junction temperature is obtained from a standard table for converting millivolts to C° for a copper-constantan thermocouple with a reference junction at $0°C$. This value is to be subtracted from the millivolt

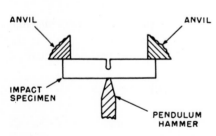

FIG. 10-7.   Charpy impact specimen and pendulum face.

readings indicated by the potentiometer. This millivolt difference is then converted to temperature by means of the standard table. As the temperature goes through $0°C$, the sign of the emf changes.

To obtain the required time-temperature data, the specimen, with the thermocouple attached, is removed from the cold bath and placed on the anvils of the impact machine. The holding fixture assists in properly positioning the specimen and is then removed. When the specimen is removed from the bath, a stop watch is started. At intervals of 15 sec thereafter, millivolt readings are taken until the specimen has returned almost to room temperature. This generally takes about 3 min. The time involved in the transfer from the bath to the anvil is important. The rate of heat absorption is slower during this period than when the specimen is on the anvils. For the purpose of this experiment, transfer times of 3 to 10 sec are acceptable. If the transfer takes more

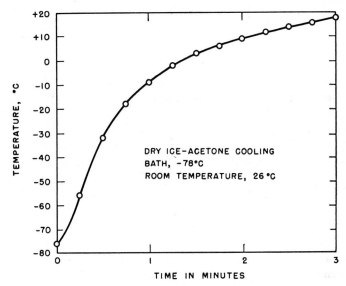

FIG. 10-8.   Time-temperature curve for impact specimens warming up on anvils.

than 10 sec, the specimen must be returned to the cold bath. A consistent operator can standardize this procedure at about 5 ± 1 sec.

The time-temperature data are shown in Fig. 10-8. The graph is typical of the acceptable data. This curve is used to determine the temperatures of the actual test specimens which have no thermocouple attached.

Impact Test Data. The general principle of the impact testing machine is shown in Fig. 10-5. Windage and friction loss corrections are indicated. This correction is small and may be neglected in this experiment. The manner in which the specimen is mounted in the machine and the place of impact of the pendulum hammer are shown in Fig. 10-7.

A specimen for testing is placed in the fixture and immersed in the cold bath for 10 min. It is then transferred to the anvils of the impact machine. The pendulum is released and the specimen broken. The temperatures at which

the specimens are broken range from -70 to $+26°C$. Temperatures are determined by reference to the time-temperature curve and measurement of the
elapsed time from the moment the specimen is removed from the cold bath to
the instant it is broken. The energy absorbed in breaking the specimens is read
directly from the indicator dial. The type of data obtained is susceptible to
relatively wide scatter, due primarily to variation in techniques.

EXPERIMENT 10-4

STRENGTH AND DUCTILITY OF IRRADIATED CARBON STEEL

By W. F. Murphy, Metallurgy Department,
International School of Nuclear Science and Engineering

INTRODUCTION

The purpose of this experiment is to measure hardness, strength and duc-
tility of tensile specimens of a low-carbon steel, both irradiated in a reactor
and not irradiated.

The material used is AISI-C1018 steel, annealed at 1575°F (857°C) for
½ hr and air-cooled. The nominal chemical composition of the steel is as
follows: carbon 0.15/0.20 per cent; manganese 0.60/0.90 per cent; phosphorus
0.040 per cent max.; sulfur 0.050 per cent max. The gauge section of the tensile
specimens is $0.10 \times 0.10 \times 1$ in. The irradiated specimens are left in a reactor
such as CP-5 for six weeks. Control specimens are available. The measured
irradiation temperature is approximately 135°C.

The equipment consists of a 1000-lb-capacity tensile machine, a 1-in. extensometer and recorder, a hardness tester, a ruler, and dividers.

The procedure is as follows: Measure the hardness of irradiated and unirradiated tensile specimens. Break the specimens in the tensile machine. Note
the highest load attained. Record elongation to just beyond the yield point on
the recorder, using the 1-in. extensometer. Measure elongation of broken
specimens.

Calculate the ultimate tensile strength, the yield point for 0.2 per cent offset,
and the per cent elongation. Tabulate the data for the controls and the irradiated specimens for comparison.

THE EXPERIMENT (10-4)

Irradiation. A suitable number (say, one for each student) of tensile specimens of the type shown in Fig. 10-9 are irradiated to an estimated integrated
fast-neutron flux of 5×10^{18} nvt, or, at the discretion of the instructor, to cover
a range of fluxes. Temperatures of the specimens while in the reactor should not
be such as would result in annealing; for this experiment 150°C is suggested as

a practical maximum. The specimens are placed in storage for one week after removal from the reactor. At the end of that time, the radioactivity is at a low level, so that the specimens can be handled with tongs.

Hardness. Hardness measurements may be made with a Rockwell hardness tester using either the A or B scale. Measurements are made on both irradiated and unirradiated specimens. The indentations are made on the flat end sections of the specimens. Averages of the hardness values for both the irradiated and unirradiated specimens are to be computed.

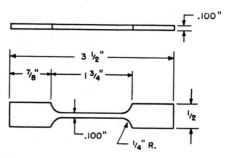

Fɪɢ. 10-9. Tensile specimen. Note: put a slight taper toward center on width of gauge section. Tolerances on gauge section ± 0.001 in.

The Tensile Test. A hydraulic tensile-testing machine with a capacity of 1000 lb may be used to load the specimens in tension. A microformer extensometer is employed to measure the stretch of the specimen to a little beyond the yield point. Some types of extensometers must be removed before the specimen is broken.

The yield point is obtained as indicated in Fig. 10-10. A line *A* is drawn tangent to the initial straight-line portion of the load-elongation curve. At a distance on the graph equivalent to 0.002 in. on the specimen (magnification 500×) a line *B* is drawn parallel to *A*. The intersection of line *B* with the load-elongation curve indicates the load necessary to stretch the 1-in.-gauge section of the specimen to 1.002 in. The load, in pounds, is converted to stress in psi

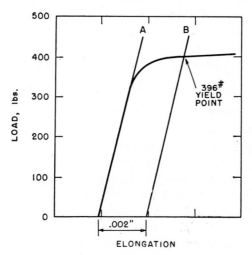

Fɪɢ. 10-10. Yield point by the offset method.

using the original cross-sectional area of the specimen. The stress thus obtained is the yield strength for an elongation of 0.2 per cent as determined by the offset method.

The ultimate tensile strength is the stress in psi obtained by dividing the maximum load, indicated on the machine before the specimen breaks, by the original cross-sectional area.

The elongation is obtained by measuring the length of the gauge section after the specimen is broken. The increase in length, divided by the original length × 100, gives the per cent elongation. Specimens with a longer gauge section would yield different values of per cent elongation. It is customary to state the original gauge length in reporting data of this type. Averages of the three types of data obtained—ultimate tensile strength, yield strength, and per cent elongation—are to be computed.

EXPERIMENT 10-5

GAS EVOLUTION FROM AQUEOUS SOLUTIONS EXPOSED TO NEUTRONS AND GAMMA RAYS IN CP-5

By Edwin J. Hart and Sheffield Gordon, ANL, Chemistry Division

Introduction

Pure water exposed to high gamma-ray and neutron fluxes in heavy-water-moderated reactors does not decompose. Low steady-state levels of deuterium and deuterium peroxide are established in the water during irradiation, but a continuous decomposition does not take place.

Organic compounds and impurity ions, however, when present in water in low concentrations do promote the decomposition of water. The decomposition is of a catalytic nature for some ions possessing two valence states. These remarks may be clarified by consideration of the basic reaction representing the decomposition of light water with ionizing radiations:

$$n\mathrm{H_2O} = a\mathrm{H_2} + b\mathrm{H_2O_2} + c\mathrm{H} + d\mathrm{OH}. \qquad (10\text{-}3)$$

In this reaction, hydrogen ($\mathrm{H_2}$) and hydrogen peroxide ($\mathrm{H_2O_2}$) are termed the molecular products. Atomic hydrogen ($\mathrm{H}\cdot$) and the hydroxyl radical ($\cdot\ddot{\mathrm{O}}\mathrm{:H}$), each containing an unpaired electron, are the free radical products.

The coefficients a, b, c, and d in Equation 10-3 are characteristic of each particular type of ionizing radiation. In general, a and b are relatively small for light-particle radiations such as electrons and gamma rays, whereas the free radical coefficients c and d are relatively large. This behavior is reversed for protons, deuteron and alpha-particle radiations. The yields of free radical and molecular products depend on the mass and velocity of the ionizing particle. A practical unit, used widely in radiation chemistry, is the number of molecules or radicals liberated per 100 ev of energy absorbed in the water. The symbol G is used to denote these yields. $G(H_2)$, $G(H_2O_2)$, $G(H)$, and $G(OH)$ designate respectively the yield of hydrogen, hydrogen peroxide, hydrogen atoms, and hydroxyl radicals per 100 ev of energy absorbed.

Owing to the complexity of the ionizing radiations in a reactor such as CP-5, it is difficult to measure the yield of molecular and free-radical products. In general, however, if the yield of free radicals exceeds the yield of molecular products, water in CP-5 will not decompose.

In the absence of impurities, the free radicals formed in Reaction 10-3 effect a recombination of hydrogen and hydrogen peroxide according to the reactions:

$$OH + H_2 = H + H_2O, \tag{10-4}$$

$$H + H_2O_2 = OH + H_2O. \tag{10-5}$$

The excess of hydrogen atoms and hydroxyl radicals react to form water:

$$H + OH = H_2O. \tag{10-6}$$

Impurities act to stabilize the molecular products by promoting Reaction 10-6. This behavior is explained by Reactions 10-7 and 10-8, for the iodide-iodine oxidation-reduction reactions:

$$I^- + OH = I + OH^-, \tag{10-7}$$

$$I + H = I^- + H^+, \tag{10-8}$$

$$H^+ + OH^- = H_2O. \tag{10-9}$$

Note that a catalytic combination of hydrogen and hydroxyl radicals takes place through the intermediate formation of hydrogen and hydroxyl ions. Experiments 1 and 2 described below will enable the student to test the stability of pure water and water containing 0.0001 M potassium iodide. These solutions will be exposed to a neutron flux of 2×10^{13} n/(cm^2)(sec) and to a gamma-ray flux of approximately 3×10^{19} ev/(min)(gram sol).

Organic impurities, frequently present in water, lead to the formation of carbon dioxide and hydrogen. Owing to the radiation stability of carbon dioxide in liquid water, a catalytic decomposition of water does not occur. After conversion of the organic impurities to carbon dioxide and hydrogen, water no longer decomposes.

Impurities undergoing reaction with neutrons may or may not lead to the decomposition of water. The two main classes of impurities of this type are (1) reactions producing heavy-particle recoils such as the B^{10} (n,α) Li^7 and U^{235} fission, and (2) (n,γ) reactions such as H (n,γ) H^2 and Cd^{113} (n,γ) Cd^{114}. The disintegration reactions decompose water, whereas the (n,γ) reactions stabilize water. The effects of these reactions are demonstrated in Experiment 3. The data taken in Experiments 2 and 3 may be used to measure the gamma-ray and neutron fluxes existing in CP-5.

GAMMA-RAY AND THERMAL NEUTRON DOSIMETRY

Gas-evolution dosimetry has been used to determine the gamma-ray and neutron fluxes in CP-3' by measuring the rate* of decomposition of aqueous solutions. Pure water does not show steady decomposition in the vertical thimbles of CP-5. This is demonstrated by Experiment 1. However, if potassium iodide is added to water, a catalytic recombination of the hydrogen and hydroxyl free radicals occurs. (Reactions 10-7, 8 and 9.) Consequently hydrogen and hydrogen peroxide accumulate in the irradiated solution. After the solubility of hydrogen is exceeded, hydrogen gas is expelled into the gas phase. Hydrogen peroxide also accumulates in concentrations of the order of 10^{-2} to 10^{-3} M. At these concentrations hydrogen peroxide competes with the iodide ion for the hydroxyl radical and oxygen is liberated according to the equations:

$$OH + H_2O_2 = H_2O + HO_2,$$

$$HO_2 + H_2O_2 = O_2 + H_2O + OH,$$

$$HO_2 + HO_2 = H_2O_2 + O_2.$$

Therefore, under steady-state conditions, hydrogen and oxygen are liberated in the molar ratio of 2 to 1. Usually 30 to 60 min of irradiation in CP-5 are allowed for the attainment of this equilibrium condition. The rate of molecular hydrogen and oxygen formation is then an index of the extent to which hydrogen and hydrogen peroxide are formed in Reaction 10-3.

The pure gamma-ray effect is assumed to be measured in CP-5 by irradiating 0.0001 M potassium iodide (Experiment 2). Under these conditions, gas evolution is given by

$$\left(\frac{dn}{dt}\right)_\gamma = \frac{G_\gamma}{100}\left(\frac{dE}{dt}\right)_\gamma, \tag{10-10}$$

where n = number of gas molecules liberated ($O_2 + H_2$), t = time in minutes, $G = 0.56$ molecules gas/100 ev,† E_γ = gamma-ray energy absorbed, in electron volts.

The sum of the gamma-ray and thermal neutron effect is measured by irradiating 0.0001 M potassium iodide plus 0.025 M boric acid (Experiment 3). The corresponding equation is:

$$\left(\frac{dn}{dt}\right)_B = \left(\frac{dn}{dt}\right)_\gamma + \frac{G_B}{100}\left(\frac{dE}{dt}\right)_B, \tag{10-11}$$

where $G_B = 1.94$ molecules gas/100 ev generated by the B^{10} (n,α) Li^7 reaction.

---

* E. J. Hart and S. Gordon, Nucleonics, **12** (4) 40-43 (1954).
† Hart and Gordon, *ibid.*

Equations 10-10 and 10-11, expressed in terms of energy absorption are

$$\frac{dE_\gamma}{dt} = 178 \left(\frac{dn}{dt}\right)_\gamma, \tag{10-10'}$$

$$\frac{dE_B}{dt} = 51.5 \left[\left(\frac{dn}{dt}\right)_B - \left(\frac{dn}{dt}\right)_\gamma\right]. \tag{10-11'}$$

Since $(dn/dt)_\gamma$ and $(dn/dt)_B$ are measured in Experiments (2) and (3), E_γ and E_B may be calculated from Equations 10-10' and 10-11'. (See the section Treatment of Results for equations used to convert rates of gas evolution to dn/dt and to convert $(dE/dt)_B$ into thermal neutron flux.)

APPARATUS

Fig. 10-11 shows a schematic drawing of the apparatus employed for studying the decomposition of aqueous solutions. The manometer system consists of: a 25 ml burette, A; a dibutyl phthalate manometer, G; a temperature equalizing bulb I; a $\frac{1}{16}$ inch i.d. 2S aluminum capillary tube J; a silica cell L of about 60 ml capacity; and a 2S aluminum can K. After the cell assembly, K and L is placed in the vertical thimble of CP-5. Gas evolution at constant pressure is measured by the manometer system. Three experiments will be run simultaneously to measure gas evolution from the following solutions:

Experiment 1: Pure triply distilled water ($3 \times H_2O$).
Experiment 2: $0.0001\ M$ potassium iodide in $3 \times H_2O$.
Experiment 3: $0.025\ M$ boric acid + $0.0001\ M$ potassium iodide in $3 \times H_2O$.

EXPERIMENTAL PROCEDURE

Since the amount of gas evolved will be proportional to the weight of solution irradiated, the weight of solutions added to the cells must be known. Two types of cells are employed (see Fig. 10-12). Type A cells will be used to demonstrate the stability of water in the vertical thimble and type B cells will be used in thimble 25 providing a flux of 2×10^{13} neutrons/(cm^2) (sec) in order to measure the gamma-ray and thermal neutron fluxes. The cells are weighed before and after addition of the solutions. The liquid should be added in sufficient quantity to minimize expansion of gas due to a temperature increase as the sample is inserted in the reactor. However, the liquid level should not be so high that a 25-C° expansion will force liquid into the narrow inlet tube of the cell. After filling, the cells are placed in 2S aluminum cans. These cans are used in order to safeguard against breakage of the silica cells and to prevent poisoning of the thimbles of the reactor.

The cells are next attached to the manometer system as shown in Fig. 10-11.

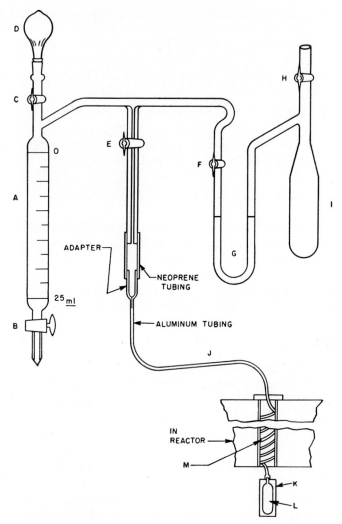

FIG. 10-11. Manometer system for measuring gas evolution in CP-5.

Capillary tube J is approximately 15 ft in length and is connected to cell L by means of a Neoprene rubber tube. The surface of Neoprene exposed to the gases evolved is minimized by making the connections as short as possible. Aluminum wire is then wrapped around the capillary tubing and fastened securely through the holes in the top of the can. Masking tape is also wrapped around the whole joint in order to minimize attack on the Neoprene by ozone. (See Cell A of Fig. 10-12 for details.)

The system is now ready to be tested for leaks. In case burette A is empty, fill with dibutyl phthalate in the following manner: place a beaker containing dibutyl phthalate under burette B so that the tip of the burette projects well below the surface of the liquid. Close all stopcocks on the system. Squeeze rubber bulb D, provided with a 10/30 standard taper joint, and place in standard taper joint above stopcock C. Release pressure on rubber bulb. Dibutyl phthalate is then drawn up to the 0.0 mark on this burette by opening C and carefully controlling the flow of fluid through B. Next open three-way stopcock E to bring the entire system to atmospheric pressure. Now open F and turn E

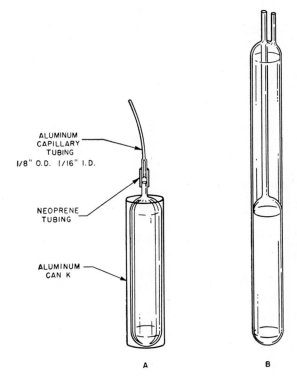

ALUMINUM
CAPILLARY
TUBING
1/8" O.D.   1/16" I.D.

NEOPRENE
TUBING

ALUMINUM
CAN K

A   B

Fig. 10-12.   Silica irradiation cells.

to connect burette A with cell L. Press bulb D until manometer G indicates a pressure of about 25 cm of liquid. Then close stopcock C and allow the system to stand under pressure 15 to 20 min or until a leak is detected by a change in the level of the manometer. Stopcock H should be closed during this operation.

The cells are ready for insertion in the reactor after assurance is obtained that each system is airtight. At this point, make a record of the number or code on the cells, burettes, and thimbles associated with each irradiation. The aluminum tubing J is threaded along the spiral groove in the thimble plug and lowered into the desired position in the reactor. Record the depth of the sample in the reactor by measuring the length of tubing lowered into the thimble. During this operation, stopcock E is opened to atmospheric pressure to release the slight pressure built up above the solution. After a second check for possible leaks in each system is made, stopcocks C, F, and H are opened. The reactor is then brought up to full power.

After the reactor has been operating at constant power for 15 to 60 min, connect burette A to cell L through E and close stopcocks C and H. Record the temperature and pressure at this time. The irradiations are now in progress and the pressure developed in each system is a measure of the gas evolved from the solution. Each solution must become saturated with hydrogen and oxygen before equilibrium amounts of gas are evolved. As gas is evolved, the pressure registers on manometer G. This pressure is equalized by opening stopcock B on the burette and draining out dibutyl phthalate until the original pressure is restored. By recording the time and volume of withdrawals of phthalate, the rate of gas evolution at constant pressure is measured.

Plot the volume of gas liberated as a function of time of irradiation while the irradiation is in progress. After the rate is constant, as is shown by a linear production of gas, the experiment is concluded. Stopcock E is then opened to atmospheric pressure and stopcock F is closed. The reactor is then shut down.

UNLOADING OF SAMPLES

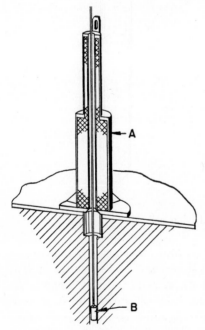

FIG. 10-13.   Unloading of samples.

Owing to the radioactivity induced in the silica cell and aluminum can and tubing, extreme care must be exercised in the removal of samples. Health Physics personnel should be present during this operation in order to monitor the beta-ray and gamma-ray activity of the materials removed from the reactor. A constant check for beta-ray activity is made on the aluminum tubing as it is drawn up by hand from the reactor. Canvas gloves are worn during these operations. After 15 min, plus M is removed from the reactor (see Fig. 10-11) and the aluminum tubing unwound from the spiral groove. Disconnect the aluminum tubing from the manometer system and suspend shield A (see Fig. 10-13) over the thimble at a height convenient to pass the aluminum wire through the hole in the center of the shield. After taking up all slack in the tubing, lower the shield to the top of the reactor and draw up sample B into the shield.

The sample is then lowered into the storage pit. Several days are required before the irradiated cell assembly may be used for subsequent experiments.

TREATMENT OF RESULTS

The slopes of the curves obtained in Experiments 2 and 3 are measured in units of cm^3 of gas evolved per min. Since the oxygen plus hydrogen gas liberated from the solution is saturated with water vapor at room temperature, a correction in pressure must be made.

Let P_t = atmospheric pressure, total pressure of gas evolved.

P_w = vapor pressure of water at the temperature of the measurements.

Then $P_g = P_t - P_w$ = pressure of oxygen + hydrogen liberated.   (10-12)

Since $P_g v = nRT$,

where v = volume of gas in cm^3, P_g = pressure in mm Hg of $H_2 + O_2$,
n = number of molecules of $O_2 + H_2$ liberated, R = gas constant
= 1.036×10^{-19} mm Hg cm^3/molecule/degree and T = temperature in °K, then

$$\frac{dv}{dt} = \frac{RT}{P_g}\frac{dn}{dt}. \tag{10-13}$$

From this,

$$\frac{1}{w}\frac{dn}{dt} = \frac{dv}{dt} \times \frac{1}{w} \times \frac{P_g}{1.036 \times 10^{-19}} \times \frac{1}{T}, \tag{10-14}$$

where w = weight of solution in grams. This equation gives the number of molecules of gas liberated per min from 1 gram of solution irradiated. The energy absorbed/gram of solution may then be calculated by dividing the rate of gas evolution by the weight of the solution, and applying Equations 10-10′ and 10-11′ to the results.

The thermal neutron flux is estimated from the dE_B in the B^{10} (n,α) Li^7 reaction by equation 10-15.

$$\left(\frac{dE}{dt}\right)_B \left(\frac{ev}{(\text{min}) \, (\text{gram sol})}\right) = E_r \left(\frac{ev}{n}\right) \times f \left(\frac{n}{(\text{cm}^2) \, (\text{sec})}\right) \times M \left(\frac{\text{mole}}{\text{liter}}\right) \times 6.02$$

$$\times 10^{23} \left(\frac{\text{molecules}}{\text{mole}}\right) \times \frac{\text{liter}}{1000 \, \text{grams}} \times \frac{60 \, \text{sec}}{\text{min}} \times \sigma \, (\text{cm}^2), \tag{10-15}$$

where: $E_r = 2.34 \times 10^6$ ev/B^{10} (n,α) Li^7 reaction; $\sigma = 7.37 \times 10^{-22}$ cm^2, thermal cross section for natural boron; M = moles/liter of boric acid (H_3BO_3), f = thermal neutron flux in neutrons/(cm^2) (sec). After insertion of these constants into Equation 10-15, one obtains Equation 10-16 for 0.025 M boric acid.

$$f\left(\frac{n}{(\text{cm}^2)\,(\text{sec})}\right) = 0.64 \times 10^{-6}\left(\frac{dE}{dt}\right)_B\left(\frac{\text{ev}}{(\text{min})\,(\text{gram sol})}\right). \quad (10\text{-}16)$$

Sample calculations of gamma-ray energy absorbed per gram of water and of the neutron flux of CP-5 are given in Table 10-3.

TABLE 10-3. MEASUREMENT OF GAMMA-RAY AND THERMAL NEUTRON FLUX IN CP-5

Solution number	(2)	(3)
Vertical thimble number	25	25
Concentration of KI, M	0.0001	0.0001
Concentration of H_3BO_3, M	—	0.025
Weight of sample, grams	63.14	61.40
Temperature, °C	29.5	29.5
Pressure (atmospheric), mm Hg	746	746
Pressure of water vapor at 29.5°, mm Hg	30.8	30.8
P_g, pressure of gases evolved, mm Hg	715.2	715.2
(dv/dt) obs., cm³/min	0.328	2.01
(dv/dt), (cm³/min) (gram sol)	0.0052	0.0328
T, °K	302.7	302.7
dn/dt, molecules gas/(min) (gram sol)	0.0119×10^{19}	0.0749×10^{19}
$(dE/dt)_\gamma$, ev/(min) (gram sol) (Equation 10-10')	3.17×10^{19}	—
$(dE/dt)_B$, ev/(min) (gram sol) (Equation 10-11')	—	3.25×10^{19}
f, neutrons/(cm²)(sec)	—	2.08×10^{13}

PROBLEMS

1. What is the gamma-ray flux in thimble 25 in units of ev/(liter) (min)?
2. Calculate the neutron flux in the thimble used for Experiment 3.
3. Calculate the per cent burnup of B^{10} during irradiation and the per cent attenuation of a neutron beam in passing through the cell containing 0.25 M boric acid.

A HIGH LEVEL GAMMA IRRADIATION FACILITY *

Chemical irradiation experiments have been made both in reactors and in special gamma-ray facilities such as that shown in Fig. 10-14. The gamma rays originate in the fission products of spent fuel elements from the Materials Testing Reactor, which are located in the irradiation rack on the floor of a canal and covered by sufficient water (17 ft) to protect personnel from the radiation. The water serves also as a coolant for the fuel elements and as a transparent medium for observation. It is continuously demineralized by recirculation through a mixed-bed ion-exchange unit. By maintaining the canal water at a minimum conductivity of 200,000 ohm-cm (800,000 is common in practice) and at a pH of about 7, corrosion of the fuel elements and underwater equipment

---

* This material is a condensation by J. B. Hoag, with the counsel of H. Gladys Swope of the ANL Chemical Engineering Division, of an ANL leaflet describing this facility. It was designed by Phillip Fineman and others of the ANL Chemical Engineering Division.

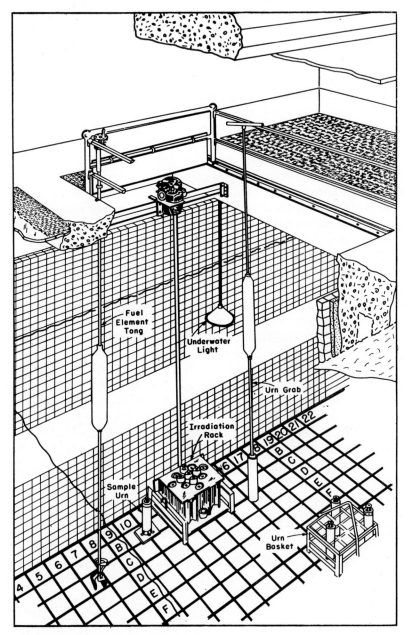

Fig. 10-14.   The Argonne high-level gamma irradiation facility.

is kept to a minimum. The ion-exchange unit also removes small amounts of radioactive materials introduced from the fuel-element cladding. White-glazed ceramic tile on the walls and white paint on the floor improve the visibility and minimize the dissolution of minerals from concrete. The 12 spent-fuel elements, which are about 2 ft long (active portion) and 3 in. square, are placed vertically in individual cadmium-lined aluminum compartments in the irradiation rack. The irradiation samples are sealed in thin-walled ($\frac{1}{16}$-in.) aluminum urns having internal dimensions of $4\frac{1}{8}$ in. diameter $\times$ 28 in. in length, weighted at the bottom to overcome the buoyancy of the water. They are placed in spaces between the fuel elements and are rotated slowly at 2 rpm to insure symmetrical exposure to the gamma rays. Samples may also be placed outside the rack for weaker gamma intensities. A twin-hook 15-ton bridge crane is used, primarily for handling the fuel element carrier, and a 1-ton monorail crane, attached to the underside of the trolley of the larger crane, is used for all other equipment.

A gamma flux of 1 to 3 million roentgens/hr is maintained. The flux decreases with time from, for example, 2.3×10^6 r/hr to 8.5×10^5 r/hr in 72 days. Four fuel elements are replaced every six weeks (with a minimum dose rate of 1×10^6 r/hr in the sample ports surrounded by four fuel elements). The important gamma energies for experiments in this facility range from 0.22 to 2.5 Mev; the average energy is approximately 0.75 Mev. There is a very low neutron background, $\sim$250 neutrons/(cm^2)(sec) probably from the interaction of gamma rays with the naturally occurring deuterium in the canal water.

The quantitative measurement of the intensity and the total radiation dosage given to the material under irradiation are important for evaluation of the effects of the rays. Chemical dosimetry may be used, where chemical indicators, such as ferrous sulfate, ferrous-and-cupric sulfate, or ceric sulfate, are exposed to the radiation. Routinely, 0.001 M ferrous sulfate plus 0.001 M sodium chloride in 0.8 N sulfuric acid is used. With new fuel elements a check is made using ferrous-cupric solution. Changes in their spectral characteristics are measured.

Glass dosimetry could be used but is not useful for accurate work. Here, optical changes in glasses of special composition are measured spectrophotometrically and correlated with the dosage. The glasses are "activated"—made more sensitive to ionizing radiations—by incorporating compounds of silver or cobalt in the base glass melt. Silver-activated phosphate glass and cobalt-activated silicate glass have been tried. Ion chambers may of course be used to measure the gamma intensity.

Irradiations are made at an ambient temperature of about 75°F. However, a temperature rise may occur in the sample during irradiation. The samples and their packages must be able to withstand this temperature rise.

Chapter 11

A METALLURGY HOT LABORATORY

By WILLIAM F. MURPHY, Metallurgy Department,
International School of Nuclear Science and Engineering[*]

INTRODUCTION

The purpose of this chapter is to describe some of the facilities needed to carry out experiments on highly radioactive metals and alloys.

The properties of metals and alloys change as a result of irradiation in nuclear reactors. The metallurgist and the metallurgical engineer are interested in studying these changes. The radioactivity of irradiated metallic materials introduces a new and hazardous factor into such studies. Sometimes the level of radioactivity of the irradiated specimens is low, so that no special handling facilities other than tongs are needed. More often special equipment and shielding are required.

Laboratories designed for work with radioactive materials are generally called *hot laboratories*. The special shielding facilities which enclose the highly radioactive material are *hot cells* or *caves*. Master-slave manipulators are used for handling the radioactive specimens and for operating equipment in the caves.

The building housing the hot laboratory for metallurgical investigations at the Argonne National Laboratory has two single-cell caves for high levels of radiation, and one three-cell cave for intermediate levels of radiation. A vault

[*] As part of the Metallurgy Laboratory Program of the International School of Nuclear Science and Engineering, the students are introduced to the techniques employed in handling, examining, and testing metallic materials which have been irradiated in a reactor.

Experiments offered to the students include: (1) tensile tests on irradiated and unirradiated carbon steel, (2) impact tests on carbon steel to determine the effect of irradiation on the transition temperature, and (3) the effect of irradiation on the electrical resistivity of ordered and disordered copper-gold alloy. The techniques involved in the use of the CP-5 reactor as a tool for irradiating metals and alloys have been an integral part of the experiments.

Acknowledgement is made to F. L. Brown, W. B. Doe, and E. W. Rylander for their assistance in preparing this manuscript.

for storage of radioactive specimens and storage areas for equipment and shielded casks are also available. Other facilities include a machine shop, a general workshop, and a general laboratory for work on unirradiated materials. The building also contains a photographic dark room, a radiation safety laboratory, and offices.

Single-Cell Caves

The two single-cell caves are similar in construction. The floor space inside each cave is 6 ft from front to back, and 10 ft wide. The inside height is 12.5 ft. Part of the height is a requirement of the upright portion of the slave ends of the manipulators. The 3-ft-thick walls on the front and sides are made of an aggregate of magnetite (an iron ore) and concrete. The specific gravity of the

Fig. 11-1. Front of a single-cell cave.

aggregate is 3.2. These walls provide adequate protection from 10,000 curies of 1-Mev gamma radiation. There are two large windows in the front wall and a smaller window in each side wall. Access doors are at the rear of the cave. The roof is a steel pan about 3 ft deep, filled with magnetite. The roof shielding is required because of the offices on the upper floor of the building. The over-all weight of each cave is about 210 tons. The inside of the caves is lined with sheet steel; the outside is painted concrete.

The general appearance of the front and back of a single-cell cave is shown in Figs. 11-1 and 11-2. Since these photographs were made, the area in back of each of the caves has been enclosed. The enclosures, which are called isolation rooms, are used for decontamination of equipment.

The two front windows on each cave are 36 in. wide, 30 in. high and 36 in. thick. The side windows are smaller. They are essentially tanks filled with 80 per cent stabilized zinc bromide solution (specific gravity, 2.5). The solution is stabilized by means of a chemical such as hydroxylamine hydrochloride. The two side walls and the top and bottom of the tank are steel. The glass walls consist of two laminations of 1-in.-thick glass plates. Two plates are required

FIG. 11-2.   Rear of a single-cell cave.

for strength, especially in the larger windows. This arrangement is also desirable as a safeguard in case one pane of the lamination should be damaged. A non-browning, radiation-resistant glass is used inside of the cave. The steel part of the tank is stepped so that there is no straight path at the boundary between the concrete and the steel through which radiation could escape from the cave. Each window is provided with a thermal expansion tank for the zinc bromide solution.

The access doors at the rear of each cave are made of laminated steel and are 14 in. thick. Details may be seen in Fig. 11-2. Each of the two sections weighs

10.5 tons. They ride on an overhead track. The doors are opened and closed by means of a chain-and-sprocket arrangement. A handwheel crank, not shown in the figure, is now used for moving the doors. The doors are constructed so that they have a tongue and groove overlap when closed. The doorway is 6 ft wide and 7 ft high when the doors are completely open.

Various small openings into the caves are provided on the front and side walls. When not in use, these ports are closed with plugs. The plugs are generally steel tubes filled with magnetite and/or lead shot. Spirally grooved solid-aluminum plugs are sometimes used to conduct water or air lines or electric

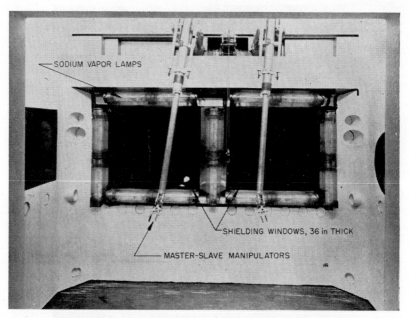

FIG. 11-3. Interior of a single-cell cave.

wiring into the caves. Small tools and other items can be introduced through these ports while radioactive material is exposed in the cave. A special lead-shielded port on either side of each cave provides a means of introducing and removing radioactive samples without opening the doors.

There are two sources of general illumination in the caves. The fluorescent lights located over the doorway on the rear wall of the cave interior provide ordinary lighting. In the event of an electric power failure these lights are automatically connected to an emergency electric system. Sodium vapor lights are the chief source of illumination. They are not on the auxiliary power system. These lamps are arranged as a frame around the two front windows on the inside of the cave (see Fig. 11-3). The monochromatic sodium light tends to eliminate the chromatic fringe effect which is evident with ordinary lighting.

Each cave has its own ventilation system, which operates continuously while the cave is in use. The system automatically connects to the emergency electric circuit in the event of a power failure. Air is drawn into the cave through any available opening and is exhausted through filters to the atmosphere outside of the building. The ventilation system is designed to maintain a pressure inside which is less than the pressure outside of the cave. Preliminary glass-fiber filters on each side and over the doorway on the inside of the cave remove a large portion of the air-borne dust. Before the exhaust gases are discharged to the outside atmosphere, they are drawn through a high-efficiency paper filter. This filter is capable of removing 99.9+ per cent of particles 0.3 micron and larger in diameter.

Utilities, such as water, compressed air, and electricity (both 110 and 220 volts a.c.) are available on the panels below the windows on the front and sides of each cave.

Each of the two high-level caves has a pair of ANL Model 6A mechanical master-slave manipulators (Figs. 11-1 and 11-3). The manipulators extend into the cave through a slot above the front window. The carriage, on which the manipulators ride, is located in the slot. It is capable of being moved the entire width of the cave. Telescoping shielding blocks move with the carriage so that the part of the slot not occupied by the manipulators is adequately closed to radiation. On the inside of the cave above the front windows and below the slot, there is a slight overhang which provides a certain amount of shielding against direct radiation to the slot.

Individual manipulators are provided with an electrically operated indexing feature. This permits the slave hand to be extended with reference to the master hand from the fully retracted position to a distance of 24 in. In the fully retracted position the slave hand is 15 in. from the inside of the window when the slave arm is vertical. This indexing movement plus the side motion and the natural swing of the manipulators enables a total area of a little over 40 ft^2 to be covered. The manipulators can reach only to about 2 ft from the floor. This is seldom a hardship because most work is done on tables and benches at a height just below the level of the sodium vapor lights under the windows. Each manipulator has a lifting capacity of about 10 lb. The operator using these manipulators has some sense of feeling with respect to the functioning of the slave hands. The Model 6 manipulators will be replaced by the newer Model 8.

There is a 1000-lb-capacity boom crane mounted between the manipulators and on the same carriage. It can be seen in Figs. 11-1 and 11-3. The crane has a mechanical indexing feature which enables it to be extended into or retracted from the cave. It is used chiefly for lifting covers from shielded casks and for moving equipment in the cave.

The Three-Cell Cave

The three-cell cave was specifically designed for the preparation, examination, and photography of highly radioactive metallographic specimens. Each of the three cells is 7 ft wide, 6 ft deep, and 12.5 ft high. The outer walls are 2-ft-thick, high-density concrete. Sheet steel covers the concrete both inside and outside the cave. These walls are designed to shield 100 curies of 1-Mev gamma radiation. The roof of the cave consists of a steel pan filled with magnetite.

Each cell has a front window which is 58 in. wide and 30 in. high. The win-

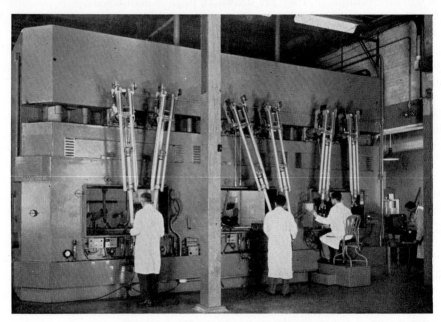

Fig. 11-4.   Front of a three-cell cave.

dows in this cave are a few inches thicker than the walls to provide comparable shielding. These are zinc bromide windows as previously described. The location of the windows and the general appearance of the front of the cave may be seen in Fig. 11-4. Each end cell has a smaller window on the side.

The access door to each cell is at the rear of the cave. The doors, which are steel shells filled with magnetite, move on overhead I-beams. A handwheel drive moves the door directly back out of the doorway. The opening to each cell is 5 ft wide and 8 ft high. The rear of the cave is shown in Fig. 11-5.

The partitions between the cells are in three vertical sections. Each section is made of laminated steel and is 8 in. thick. The lower section, which extends from the floor to a height of 4 ft, is fixed in position. The middle section is about

3 ft high. It can be moved out through the back wall of the cave by means of a screw mechanism. The upper portion of the partition was designed so that it could be raised into the roof. With the partitions removed, two pairs of manipulators can be of mutual assistance to each other and equipment can be transferred from one cell to another without opening the cave.

Each cell is equipped with a pair of ANL Model 8 mechanical master-slave manipulators (see Fig. 11-6). Their general movements are about the same as for the ANL Model 6A manipulators, but the detailed structure is different. The indexing feature of these manipulators involves a rotation rather than a transla-

Fig. 11-5.   Rear of a three-cell cave.

tion as with ANL Model 6A. The slave arm pivots on the end of the tube through the cave wall about a horizontal axis parallel to the front wall of the cave. Each pair of manipulators can be moved sideways on a carriage in the slot in the cave wall. An accordion-type folding shielding system is provided in the slot in which the manipulators move. There is no crane associated with these manipulators.

Utilities are available on the outside of the walls as for the high-level cave. There are ports in the front and side walls. The special shielded port for the introduction of radioactive samples can be seen in Fig. 11-5, lower right.

Lighting and ventilation are generally similar to those of the high-level caves. The ventilation pattern is such that a pressure gradient is established between the cells. The lowest pressure is in the cell used for grinding specimens

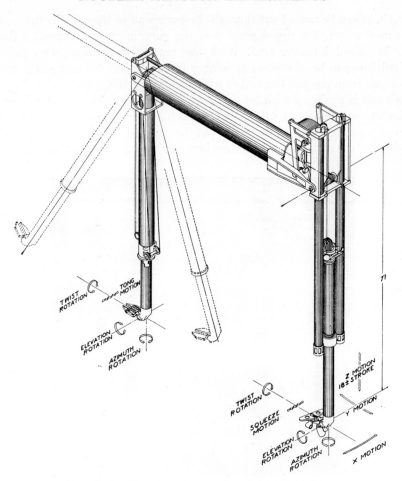

FIG. 11-6. Diagram of a master-slave manipulator.

and the highest pressure is in the cell used for examination of specimens. Air-intake vents are provided just above the front windows.

STORAGE AREA

The storage room has specific areas for slightly radioactive equipment (with fixed contamination), and for shielded storage casks, and a vault for radioactive specimens. The area is shown in Fig. 11-7. The vault consists of a series of steel tubes, 8 ft long and 4 or 6 in. in diameter, imbedded vertically in concrete. Each tube has a screw cap and a lock. The 4-in.-diameter tubes will hold four storage drawers one above the other. The storage drawers consist of steel tubes with a 6-in. lead shielding plug on the top end. There is also a pull bar on the

Fig. 11-7.   Storage area.

top end of each drawer. The bottom is closed but the side wall is partially cut away for insertion of specimens. The over-all length of a drawer is about 19 in. Specimens to be stored in a drawer are usually placed in a metal can about 9 in. high and 3 in. in diameter.

General Handling Equipment

Radioactive specimens are generally received in heavy lead-shielded containers which may weigh several tons. These casks are unloaded from the shipping truck at the receiving dock with a 10-ton electric crane. The casks are transported from the loading dock to the storage area on dollies. A battery powered Moto-Truc Grip-All tractor is used to push or pull the loaded dollies. Large containers may be pushed directly into one of the single-cell caves for unloading and examination of the contents.

If the contents are too large for the vault, they may be stored in the shielded container in which they were received. Otherwise they would be placed in cans and put in the storage drawers previously described. These transfer operations are performed in the caves.

A transfer cask is used to move a loaded drawer from the cave to the storage vault. The transfer cask on its dolly is aligned with the special shielded port, against the cave wall. The gate which is on the end of the transfer cask nearest the cave is opened. A grappling rod is pushed through the cask into the cave.

The drawer is grasped and drawn into the transfer cask. The gate is then closed. The radioactive material is now shielded on all sides by 6 in. of lead. A pin secures the drawer to the cask. The cask is taken to the storage area near the vault. A 5-ton electric crane raises the cask by its yoke. The cask swings into a vertical position so that the shielded end of the drawer is up and it is lowered over an open vault tube. A grappling rod is attached to the drawer and the gate is opened. The retaining pin is removed and the drawer is lowered into the vault. The grappling rod and cask are removed and the cover to the storage hole is locked in place. A reverse process takes the specimens from the vault to any of the caves.

EQUIPMENT FOR EXAMINATION OF SPECIMENS

Most of the equipment used for examination of radioactive specimens has been specially designed or modified for remote control or manipulator operation.

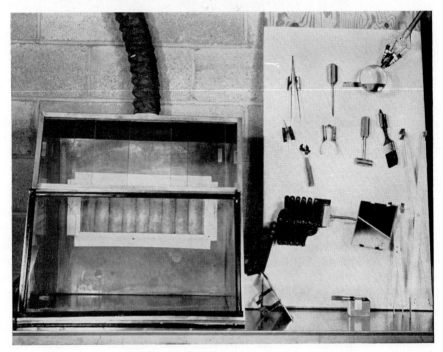

FIG. 11-8. Equipment for cave use.

Some small hand tools are shown in Fig. 11-8. The hood on the left in Fig. 11-8 is used as an additional means for confining contamination inside the caves when granular or powder materials are involved in the examination.

For initial visual examination, hand magnifiers are used inside the caves and binoculars and telescopes from outside. Identification, corrosion, and obvious dimensional changes are thus noted. Sometimes photographs are taken directly through the cave windows. One of the high-level caves is equipped with low-magnification periscopic optical systems for visual examination and photography of small specimens. More modern viewing equipment with a larger field of view is available in the examination cell of the metallography cave. Fig. 11-9 shows the Bausch & Lomb low-magnification periscopic stereocamera

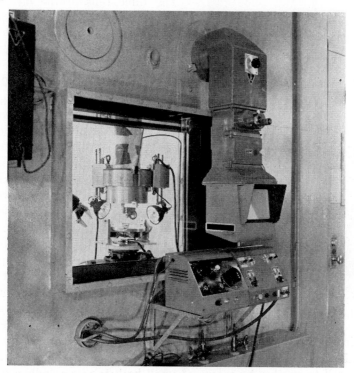

FIG. 11-9.   Binocular microscope and stereocamera.

and viewer of the metallography cave. The specimen stage for the camera is motorized and has a remotely adjustable lighting system.

Some types of equipment are shown in Figs. 11-10 to 11-13. A remotely operable analytical balance for weight and density determinations is shown in Fig. 11-10. Density measurements are made by the method of weight loss on immersion in a liquid. Manipulators are used for all operations. A milling operation is shown in Fig. 11-11. The milling area can be enclosed and ventilated with an inert atmosphere. A trough and a can for chip collection are provided. Mechanical linkages to some of the controls are extended through ports in the front wall of the cave.

Measurements of hardness, tensile strength, impact energy, fatigue strength, electrical resistance, some magnetic properties, and many kinds of linear dimensions, including surface roughness and spacing in channels between plates, have all been made in the single-cell caves. Machining operations such as drilling, milling, sawing, punching, shearing, and lathe work have also been carried out to a limited extent.

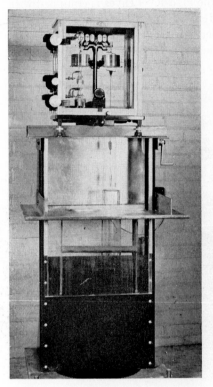

The three cells of the metallography cave are each used for special operations. The cell on the extreme left (Fig. 11-4) is used for mounting and grinding the specimens. The middle cell is used for polishing and etching. Fig. 11-12 shows a view of the cell. Three polishing benches with pantographic heads are visible. A device for electrolytically etching the samples is located in front of the center polishing bench. A washing jar is located in the right front corner of the cell. Various controls are on the outside wall below the window. They govern the speed of the polishing wheels, operation of the etching equipment, the washing operation, and other necessary remote operations. The cell on the right (Fig. 11-4) is used for the examination of the metallographic specimens. This cell contains a Tukon hardness tester, a bench microscope, and the previously mentioned stereocamera. Periscopic systems are used with these items and operations are by remote control. Radioactive specimens are moved from one cell to another by means of small baskets on an endless tape. This conveyor belt system runs the length of the three cells just inside the cave below the front windows.

FIG. 11-10. Analytical balance.

A Bausch & Lomb Metallograph is connected to the third cell but is actually located outside of it. It is used for examining and photographing irradiated polished and etched specimens. High- and low-magnification lens systems are available. Intense ordinary light or polarized light may be used for illumination. The specimens are automatically transported through the cave wall and placed on the microscope stage. Adequate shielding is provided around the stage so that there is no radiation hazard. The Metallograph is shown in Fig. 11-13.

The equipment which has been briefly mentioned is indicative of the types of operations carried out in both the single-cell and three-cell caves. A complete listing of equipment would be much more extensive.

FIG. 11-11.   Milling operation in cave.

RADIATION SAFETY

There are three general areas of radiation safety: (1) monitoring procedures, (2) control of the spread of contamination, and (3) waste disposal. Monitoring procedures involve several techniques. Every person working in the hot laboratory is given a pocket electrostatic dosimeter and a film badge. The dosimeter can be checked by the wearer as often as desired. Film badges are examined once a week. In addition, detectors for radioactive material on hands and feet are located at the exits to the cave area. Portable beta-gamma radiation detectors are also available for checking equipment and clothing. Monitoring of the air in the caves and the cave area may be either periodic or continued. A "carpet sweeper" type of floor monitor for beta-gamma radiation is very useful. Although these caves are not generally used for high-alpha-emitting materials, equipment is available for monitoring such activity.

Control of the spread of contamination begins with the setting up of equipment in the caves. Efforts to localize contamination begin at this point. Con-

Fig. 11-12.   Polishing and etching cell.

Fig. 11-13.   Metallograph for irradiated specimens.

sideration must be given to the nature of the specimens. For example, a powdery corrosion product on a specimen requires special handling to avoid the spread of contamination. Such a specimen would be washed in a manner to confine the loose radioactive material to a small volume. Working surfaces and exposed surfaces of equipment are usually covered with strippable coatings. Polyethylene sheeting, industrial tape, and plastic coatings, either sprayed or painted, are used to protect surfaces against contamination.

The manipulators are used for initial cleanup and decontamination after an experiment has been completed and the radioactive specimens have been put into storage. They are used to wipe down surfaces with paper napkins wet with water or alcohol. Shielded containers for the disposal of cleaning materials, both solid and liquid, should be available. If the activity remains high in the cave after this preliminary cleaning, personnel entering the cave must wear gas masks or supplied air masks. Toe rubbers or canvas boots for the feet and other protective clothing must be worn in the cave during cleaning operations. Protective clothing is monitored in the isolation room with portable instruments.

The radioactive waste material is collected in suitable shielded containers. These containers are emptied periodically or on demand, depending on the rate of accumulation of waste and the level of radioactivity involved.

Members of the Radiation Safety Group supervise all decontamination operations and make periodic checks of floors, cave structures, and equipment. They locate and have removed exposed sources of hazardous radiation.

Hot-laboratory operations, including the design and use of building facilities and equipment, are a highly cooperative enterprise. The engineers and scientists who design and make equipment must cooperate with the user with regard to utility for remote control and contamination control. The operators of caves and equipment must cooperate with members of the Radiation Safety Group to minimize the contamination problem. The complexity of operating procedures demands that all personnel be carefully and adequately trained in hot-laboratory techniques. Radiation and other hazards should be maintained at a minimum to safeguard personnel and prevent possible interference with experiments.

Chapter 12

SEPARATIONS PROCESSES

By K. A. Varteressian (Chairman), M. Ader, W. J. Mayer, and D. M. Macdonnell
of the Chemical Engineering Department, International School of Nuclear Science and
Engineering; and J. V. Natale, D. P. Krause, R. P. Larsen, L. E. Ross and F. B. Gast
of the Chemical Engineering Division, Argonne National Laboratory

URANIUM DISSOLUTION

INTRODUCTION

Aqueous processing of irradiated nuclear fuel or blanket materials for purposes of decontamination and recovery usually begins with dissolution of the fuel or blanket material. In most cases, such materials are metallic or oxidic. However, in the case of a reactor, such as the Oak Ridge Homogeneous Reactor Experiment, in which the fuel, uranyl sulfate, is already in aqueous solution, a dissolution step is obviously unnecessary. Since fuel and blanket elements are normally clad in a corrosion-resistant material (e.g., aluminum, zirconium, stainless steel) the first step in dissolution involves removal of the cladding.

Removal of cladding or canning may be mechanical or chemical. The former, if feasible, is preferred because of its simplicity and the reduction of chemical and waste-disposal costs. If mechanical removal is impossible, chemical means are employed and these take one of three forms: (1) the cladding is dissolved separately and disposed of, and then the fuel is dissolved; (2) the cladding is ruptured and the fuel is dissolved out; or (3) the cladding and fuel are dissolved together. The method chosen will depend on the particular fuel element–cladding combination being considered, on chemical and waste-disposal problems, and on the recovery process to be employed. For example, a fuel element consisting of metallic uranium clad with a thin aluminum jacket can be treated with caustic to dissolve the aluminum but leave the uranium unaffected. The caustic solution containing dissolved aluminum is then removed from the dissolver and the uranium is dissolved in nitric acid. If the uranium and aluminum are alloyed so that such a separation cannot be made, a dilute solution of mercuric nitrate in nitric acid may dissolve both metals simultaneously. If a solvent extraction process is to follow, in which a salting agent is required for efficient uranium extraction (e.g., using hexone as solvent), the presence of aluminum nitrate derived from the fuel element is not a disadvantage. In all cases of dissolution, the chemical system employed must be compatible with materials of construction and with waste treatment and waste-storage facilities.

Factors to Be Considered

Many factors enter into consideration in carrying out dissolutions of fuel and blanket materials. Among these may be mentioned the following:

1. Temperature Control. The dissolver must be designed to remove large quantities of heat released by the exothermic process of metal dissolution. Because such reactions tend to increase in rate with increase in temperature, control of temperature is essential in preventing too rapid or violent reactions. Heat transfer and removal are effected by (a) the liquid environment surrounding the metal, and (b) a cooling jacket or coil outside the dissolver or cooling coils inside the dissolver. Usually a reflux condenser is placed above the dissolver to aid in temperature control, but primarily to prevent loss of water and acid due to vaporization.

2. Explosive Reactions. It is known that alloys of uranium and zirconium in which zirconium is present in concentrations up to 50 atom per cent can react explosively when dissolved in nitric acid.*

One of the products of dissolution, namely hydrogen gas, must be considered from the standpoint of forming explosive mixtures with oxygen. For example, hydrogen is formed in the caustic dissolution of aluminum cladding and in the hydrofluoric acid dissolution of zirconium-uranium fuel elements. The precautions to be taken are those normally taken—dilution of the hydrogen with an inert gas, maintaining the hydrogen concentration outside the range of explosive mixture with oxygen, grounding of equipment to prevent ignition by sparks, etc. Oftentimes, the problem may be circumvented by addition of suitable (oxidizing) reagents to the dissolver solution so that hydrogen gas is not formed.

3. Criticality. Fuel elements containing fissionable isotopes should be processed in amounts considered to be safe from the standpoint of not exceeding the critical mass. This is especially true of enriched materials. A simple method of avoiding a potential hazard in this connection is the use of safe geometrical designs for processing equipment.

4. Dissolution Rate. In addition to the effect of temperature in controlling reaction rates, acid concentration, surface area, and the previous history of the metal are important in determining rates of dissolution. The surface area is

---

* This reaction, its causes, and methods of prevention have been studied and are discussed in R. P. Larsen, R. S. Shor, H. M. Feder, and D. S. Flikkema, "A Study of the Explosive Properties of Uranium-Zirconium Alloys," ANL-5135 (July 1954).

usually fixed in that the fuel elements are of a particular design. However, the number of fuel elements charged into a dissolver will affect the total solid area available to the dissolving solution. In general, higher acid concentrations will cause faster rates of dissolution. The metallurgical treatment (e.g., as cast vs. rolled metal, annealing and quenching rates and temperatures, etc.) undergone by fuel materials will affect not only the rate but sometimes also the method of dissolution. For example, in the experiment below, when cast, uranium metal will dissolve in nitric acid more rapidly and evenly than rolled uranium. The rolled uranium will be attacked primarily in a direction perpendicular to the rolling. A honeycomb network is produced and can be seen visually when a thin slice of uranium is incompletely dissolved. The cause of this mode of attack is believed to be the stringing out of the inclusions or impurities by the rolling treatment and the preferential attack by the acid along the boundaries containing these impurities.

The conditions chosen for dissolution will of course be determined to a large degree by the capacity and processing rate of the entire separations plant.

5. Acidity. The acid employed in dissolution must be compatible with the materials of construction, as well as able to dissolve the fuel element in question. Thus, hydrochloric acid does not find much use in dissolution procedures, although special equipment can be constructed which will withstand its corrosive action. In aqueous processes, it is also desirable that the dissolution yield solutions with no insoluble residues that must be specially handled. Of course, the acid chosen should yield metal salts which are compatible with the processing steps to follow.

The ratio of acid to metal employed in a dissolution will depend on the rates of dissolution desired (see above) and on the final acidity desired in the dissolver solution which serves as feed for the subsequent schemes for precipitation, solvent extraction, ion exchange, etc., which follow. For example, both high-acid and acid-deficient feeds can be employed in solvent extraction processes. Acidity may be reduced by simply dissolving more metal. One of the reasons for making a particular choice of acid conditions is to effect an increase or decrease in concentration of specific fission-product species, thereby improving fission-product decontamination.

6. Dissolution in the Presence of Excess Metal. Advantages may be gained by the presence of excess metal during dissolutions rather than by dissolving to completion. In the case of uranium dissolution, the rate of reaction diminishes considerably when the concentrations of metal and acid become small, thereby necessitating long periods of time to effect complete dissolution. In order to obtain quantitatively plutonium in the tri-, tetra-, or hexavalent oxidation states, appropriate reducing or oxidizing agents may be added to the dissolver solution.

A practical consideration that deserves mention is the possibility of metal salts, such as uranyl nitrate, solidifying or freezing in tanks and transfer lines after concentrated solutions have cooled down.

7. Clarification, Scavenging. If the dissolver solution is not clear owing to the presence of insoluble residues or colloidal aggregates, the solution may be subjected to a clarification step prior to further processing. At times, a scavenging or head-end step follows dissolution. This effects a decontamination of troublesome fission-product species as well as clarification of the solution.

8. Off-Gas Processing. Mention has already been made of the problem of hydrogen gas evolution during dissolution (see Section 2 above). Serious from the viewpoint of air pollution and contamination are the release of nitric oxide and nitrogen dioxide, in the case of nitric acid dissolutions, and small amounts of volatile radioactive fission products such as iodine-131. These gases may be completely absorbed by water or caustic absorption towers. In the case of the oxides of nitrogen, a worthwhile economy may result in the recovery of by-product nitric acid. Iodine may also be removed by the use of silver or silver nitrate–containing absorbers. The tolerance of other volatile fission-product elements is such as to permit release to the atmosphere.

EXPERIMENT 12-1

URANIUM DISSOLUTION

This experiment illustrates a method of dissolving uranium metal and collecting off-gases that are evolved. Uranium metal is dissolved in nitric acid to yield a solution of uranyl nitrate. Two types of uranium metal are employed—cast and rolled—in order to demonstrate different modes and rates of acid attack. By introducing oxygen into the dissolving flask to oxidize nitric oxide to nitrogen dioxide, and by absorbing the nitrogen dioxide in water to form nitric acid, the approach to the limiting theoretical equation

$$U + 2HNO_3 + 1.5O_2 \rightarrow UO_2(NO_3)_2 + H_2O \qquad (12\text{-}1)$$

can be shown. This experiment is to be compared with one in which the oxides of nitrogen are not caught and in which 4.5 to 5.5 moles of acid per mole of uranium are consumed according to the equations

$$U + 4HNO_3 \rightarrow UO_2(NO_3)_2 + 2H_2O + 2NO, \qquad (12\text{-}2)$$

$$U + 8HNO_3 \rightarrow UO_2(NO_3)_2 + 4H_2O + 6NO_2. \qquad (12\text{-}3)$$

The experimental procedure is given below.

Uranium Dissolution Procedure

1. Weigh a uranium slice of about 100 grams on a triple-beam balance.
2. *Carefully* place the uranium metal inside a 3-necked flask with long forceps.

3. Set up dissolution and absorption apparatus as shown in Figs. 12-1 and 12-2.

4. Determine the acidity of the 10 M nitric acid stock solution by micro-titration with standard sodium hydroxide.

5. Fill the dropping funnel to its top (about 500 ml) with distilled water. Determine the number of drops per ml. This can be used as a check on the flow rate of water down the absorption column.

6. Place the dropping funnel on top of the absorption column and adjust the flow rate to approximately 1.0 to 1.5 ml/min, catching water in a 50-ml graduated mixing cylinder.

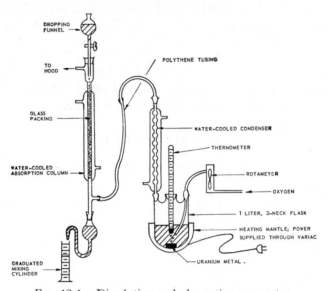

FIG. 12-1. Dissolution and absorption apparatus.

7. Adjust the flow rate of oxygen gas into the dissolver to 100 to 150 ml/min by means of the needle valve on the oxygen tank and the valve on the rotameter.

8. Turn on the cooling water for the condenser and the absorption column.

9. Add 300 ml of 10 M nitric acid to the flask through the center neck of the flask. Replace the thermometer and begin heating the flask to 100° ± 2°C. Replace the graduated mixing cylinder.

10. Readjust the oxygen and absorber water flow rates as needed to prevent escape of brown NO_2 fumes at the top of the absorption column.

11. Allow the reaction to continue at 100°C for 3 to 3¼ hr, collecting approximately 50-ml fractions of nitric acid. Note the volume of the fractions. At the end of this interval, with oxygen and absorber water continuing to flow, stop the reaction by removing the heating

mantle and cooling the flask to room temperature with an ice bath.

12. Shut off the oxygen and absorber water. Disassemble the apparatus and pour the contents of the dissolver into a 500-ml graduated mixing cylinder. Wash out the dissolver with several milliliters of distilled water. Mix contents and note the volume.

13. Remove the residual uranium metal, wash with distilled water and acetone, and let dry a few minutes. Note the appearance of the metal and the nature of acid attack. Weigh on a triple-beam balance. Calculate the weight of the uranium dissolved.

14. By means of the pH meter and microtitration with standard sodium hydroxide, determine the acid in fractions collected.

15. Discard solutions in the containers provided.

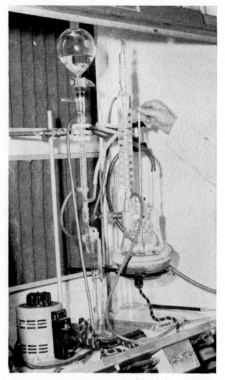

Fig. 12-2. Photograph of the dissolution and absorption apparatus.

Calculations

Original weight of uranium metal _____ grams
Final weight of uranium metal _____ grams
Weight of uranium dissolved _____ grams

A. Millimoles uranium dissolved: $\dfrac{\text{grams}}{0.238 \text{ g./m } M.}$ = _____

B. Millimoles acid added: (300 ml)(_____ m M/ml) = _____

C. Millimoles acid remaining in dissolver:
   (_____ ml)(_____ m M/ml) = _____

D. Millimoles acid consumed in dissolver: $B\text{-}C$ = _____

E. Mole ratio of (acid consumed/U dissolved): D/A = _____

F. Millimoles acid collected:

(continued on next page)

DATA SHEET 12-1 (Cont.)

Fraction	Volume	Molarity	Millimoles Acid
1.			
2.			
3.			
4.			
5.			
Total			

G. Calculated mole ratio of (acid consumed/U dissolved), assuming acid collected is returned to dissolver: $\dfrac{B - (C + F)}{A}$ = _____

EXPERIMENT 12-2

DETERMINATION OF ACID IN URANIUM (VI) SOLUTIONS

In the absence of uranyl salts, the determination of acidity by titration with a standard base is a rapid, simple, and accurate analysis. The equivalence point corresponds to the largest change in the hydrogen-ion concentration per unit volume of titrant added. The changes in hydrogen-ion concentration are ordinarily detected potentiometrically, by means of a pH meter, or with an indicating dye.

In contrast, determination of acidity in solutions containing uranyl salts is slow, quite complicated, and comparatively inaccurate. In addition to the neutralization reaction of hydrogen and hydroxide ions combining to form water, reactions which interfere with the determination of the equivalence point occur between the uranium (VI) ions and the aqueous components. Several of these reactions are:

$$UO_2^{++} + HOH \rightleftarrows UO_2(OH)^+ + H^+, \qquad (12\text{-}4)$$

$$UO_2^{++} + OH^- \rightleftarrows UO_2(OH)^+, \qquad (12\text{-}5)$$

$$2Na^+ + 2UO_2^{++} + 3OH^- \rightleftarrows Na_2U_2O_7 + 3H^+. \qquad (12\text{-}6)$$

Unless steps are taken to prevent the above reactions, the titration of an acid in the presence of a uranyl salt is useless. In practice, when a plot of pH vs. ml of standard base is made, there is no apparent break in the curve to indicate the equivalence point.

The reactions represented by Equations 12-4, 12-5, and 12-6 can be minimized by the addition of a reagent which will tie up the uranyl ion. Reagents which have been used for this purpose are oxalate, fluoride, ferrocyanide, and others. Oxalate is used in the procedure given here.

$$UO_2^{++} + C_2O_4^= \rightleftarrows UO_2C_2O_4. \qquad (12\text{-}7)$$

The use of excess oxalate and ice temperatures enhances the size and sharpness of the break. In practice it has been shown that the inflection point of this break is within ± 5 per cent of the equivalence point.

Hydrogen Ion Determination—Potentiometric: Reagents

NaOH − 0.100 N—standardized

$K_2C_2O_4$ solution—saturated

Buffer solution—pH 4

Standardization of Beckman Model H-2 pH Meter

1. Allow the instrument to warm up for at least half an hour with the switch at START position and the temperature control at 0°C.
2. Fill the titration cup holder with ice.
3. Pour some of the buffer solution into the titration cup and place in the holder.
4. Immerse the glass and calomel electrodes in the buffer solution and switch on the motor which makes the stirrer revolve.
5. Turn switch on the instrument to 0-8 pH setting and adjust, with the knob to the left of the pH switch, to pH 4.

Microtitration Procedure

1. Fill the titration cup holder with a mixture of crushed ice and water. Insert the glass titration cup, making sure there is good contact with the ice water.
2. Pipet an aliquot of the sample, about 0.05 milliequivalents of acid, into the cup. Add water until the volume is about 1 ml.
3. Immerse the electrodes and turn on the stirrer motor. Be sure the electrodes do not strike the sides of the cup.
4. Using the 0-8 pH scale, add saturated potassium oxalate solution until a pH of 4.0-4.2 is attained.
5. Note the initial burette and meter readings.
6. Add base in 0.010 ml increments, noting the burette and meter readings after equilibrium has been attained. These additions are continued until the break, i.e., maximum change in pH per addition of base, has been passed. The titration should be continued for several increments beyond the break.

Calculation

1. Subtract each pH reading from the succeeding one.
2. The largest change is denoted by the letter A, the preceding one by B, and the succeeding one by C.
3. The end point falls within the region A. The increment of base x which must be added to the smaller of the two burette readings encompassing the change A is calculated using the interpolation formula

$$x = \frac{(A - B)\,\Delta V}{2A - (B + C)}, \tag{12-8}$$

where ΔV is the incremental volume of base added.

4. The normality of the sample is then calculated from:

$$N = \frac{(\text{Burette reading, in.})(N_{\text{Base}})(\text{conversion factor, ml/in.})}{(\text{Sample size, ml})}.$$ (12-8a)

LIQUID-LIQUID PARTITION

INTRODUCTION

Separation of two or more components of a liquid solution is one of the more common of chemical-engineering problems. The usual procedures are crystallization, evaporation, and distillation, in which separation is accomplished by taking advantage of the differing solubilities or volatilities of the components. However, it is often possible to accomplish the desired separation by bringing the liquid in contact with a second liquid which selectively removes one or more of the components. The latter separation is referred to as *solvent* or *liquid extraction* and is rapidly becoming one of the more important unit operations in chemical engineering.

THE DISTRIBUTION LAW

The fundamental principle underlying the unit operation of solvent extraction is the distribution law, which can be stated: If to a system of two liquid layers made up of two immiscible or slightly miscible components, there is added a quantity of a third substance soluble in both layers, then the substance is found to distribute or divide itself between the two layers in a definite manner (M. Berthelot, 1872). The law can be deduced simply and explicitly by the application of the concepts of thermodynamics to phase equilibria, which would lead to the conclusion that the chemical potential of any substance must be the same in two phases in equilibrium. In layer 1 the chemical potential of the solute may be written

$$\mu_1 = \mu_1^0 + RT \ln a_1,$$ (12-9)

and in layer 2 it is

$$\mu_2 = \mu_2^0 + RT \ln a_2,$$ (12-10)

where a_1 and a_2 are the activities in the two layers. At equilibrium, the two values of the potential are equal, and since μ_1^0 and μ_2^0 are constants, at definite temperature and pressure, it follows that

$$\frac{a_1}{a_2} = \text{constant } (K').$$ (12-11)

This is the exact expression of the distribution or partition law; but for practical purposes it is put into an approximate form. If the solutions are dilute and behave ideally, in the sense that either Henry's law or Raoult's law applies, the activities may be replaced by the concentrations, so that

$$\frac{c_1}{c_2} = K, \qquad (12\text{-}12)$$

at a definite temperature, where K is the "distribution" coefficient. Equilibrium data for such systems are usually reported in terms of distribution coefficients. The last expression for the distribution law is only an approximation based on the assumptions of dilute solutions and ideal behavior.

In spite of the theoretical limitations, many substances have been found to obey the distribution law in a reasonably satisfactory manner, provided the solute has the same molecular weight in both solvents.

EXPERIMENT 12-3

LIQUID-LIQUID PARTITION

Purpose

1. To determine the distribution ratio $E_A{}^o$ of uranyl nitrate as a function of nitric acid concentration employing 20 vol per cent tri-n-butyl phosphate (TBP) in carbon tetrachloride as the organic phase.

2. To determine the distribution ratio $E_A{}^o$ of plutonium (IV) nitrate as a function of uranyl nitrate concentration with a constant starting aqueous concentration of 3 M nitric acid and employing 20 vol per cent tri-n-butyl phosphate in carbon tetrachloride as the organic phase.

3. To determine the distribution ratio $E_A{}^o$ of gross fission products as a function of uranyl nitrate concentration, employing 20 vol per cent tri-n-butyl phosphate in carbon tetrachloride as the organic phase, and to demonstrate the irreversibility of $E_A{}^o$ values encountered with fission-product species.

Apparatus. Three 60-ml separatory funnels, spectrophotometer, and accessory equipment for uranium analysis. Four 5-ml mixing cylinders, assorted micropipets, equipment for plutonium analysis by lanthanum fluoride, alpha counter, four graduated centrifuge tubes, equipment for scintillation counting, well-type crystal scintillation counter.

Materials

1. Solutions of the following concentrations for uranium distribution:
   (a) 1.5 M uranyl nitrate—3 M HNO$_3$
   (b) 1.0 M uranyl nitrate—1.0 M HNO$_3$
   (c) 1.0 M uranyl nitrate—0.5 M HNO$_3$
   (d) 20 vol per cent tri-n-butyl phosphate in carbon tetrachloride
2. Solutions of the following concentrations for the plutonium distribution:
   (a) 3.0 M HNO$_3$—1.5 M uranyl nitrate

   (b) 3.0 M HNO$_3$—0.75 M uranyl nitrate
   (c) 3.0 M HNO$_3$—0.38 M uranyl nitrate
   (d) 3.0 M HNO$_3$—0.0 M uranyl nitrate
   (e) Plutonium stock solution containing approximately 1mg/ml (7.1 × 10^7 cpm/ml at 50 per cent geometry)
   (f) 20 vol per cent tri-n-butyl phosphate in carbon tetrachloride
3. Solutions of the following concentrations for the fission product distribution:
   (a) 3.0 M HNO$_3$—1.5 M uranyl nitrate
   (b) 3.0 M HNO$_3$—0.75 M uranyl nitrate
   (c) 3.0 M HNO$_3$—0.38 M uranyl nitrate
   (d) 3.0 M HNO$_3$—0.0 M uranyl nitrate
   (e) Fission-product stock solution containing 6 × 10^7 cpm/ml of gamma activity
   (f) 20 vol per cent tri-n-butyl phosphate in carbon tetrachloride

Procedure: Uranyl Nitrate Distribution. Take 15 ml of 1.5 M uranyl nitrate— 3 M nitric acid solution and contact it with 30 ml of 20 per cent TBP in CCl$_4$ in a 60-ml separatory funnel. Shake well for 2 min. Allow the phases to disengage. Separate the phases by allowing the organic phase to drain from a separatory funnel. Do not drain the aqueous phase from the funnel. Analyze each phase for U concentration, using 10-λ sample size for the organic and 3-λ for the aqueous. To the uranyl nitrate solution remaining in the separatory funnel, add a fresh 30-ml volume of 20 per cent TBP in CCl$_4$. Repeat the above procedure and analyze each phase, using 10-λ samples for both organic and aqueous phases. Repeat the procedure again, using 30 ml of fresh 20 per cent TBP in CCl$_4$. Use 25-λ and 2-ml for sample sizes of the organic and aqueous phases, respectively. Repeat, using 15 ml of fresh 20 per cent TBP in CCl$_4$. Use 1 ml and 5 ml for the organic and aqueous samples.

This procedure is given in tabular form as follows:

DATA SHEET 12-2

15 ml of 1.5 M uranyl nitrate—3 M HNO$_3$						
	Volume of Organic	Sample Size, Organic	Sample Size, Aqueous	M Organic	M Aqueous	$E_A{}^O$
1st extraction	30 ml	10 λ	3 λ			
2nd extraction	30 ml	10 λ	10 λ			
3rd extraction	30 ml	25 λ	2 ml			
4th extraction	15 ml	500 λ or 1 ml	5 ml			

Complete the following table, using the same procedure as above but starting with 15 ml of 1.0 M uranyl nitrate—1 M HNO_3.

DATA SHEET 12-3

	Volume of Organic	Sample Size, Organic	Sample Size, Aqueous	M Organic	M Aqueous	$E_A{}^o$
1st extraction	15 ml	5 λ	3 λ			
2nd extraction	15 ml	10 λ	5 λ			
3rd extraction	15 ml	10 λ	10 λ			
4th extraction	15 ml	10 λ	25 λ			
5th extraction	15 ml	50 λ	100 λ			

Complete the following table, using the same procedure as above but starting with 15 ml of 1.0 M uranyl nitrate—0.5 M HNO_3.

DATA SHEET 12-4

	Volume of Organic	Sample Size, Organic	Sample Size, Aqueous	M Organic	M Aqueous	$E_A{}^o$
1st extraction	15 ml	10 λ	3 λ			
2nd extraction	30 ml	10 λ	10 λ			
3rd extraction	30 ml	25 λ	25 λ			
4th extraction	30 ml	100 λ	100 λ			

Plot the organic uranium concentration as ordinate against the aqueous uranium concentration as abscissa on rectangular coordinate paper for each of the initial nitric acid concentrations.

Plutonium Distribution. To each of four 10-ml mixing cylinders containing 5.0 ml of 20 vol percent TBP in CCl_4, add 5.0 ml of each of the following:

(a) 1.5 M $UO_2(NO_3)_2$—3 M HNO_3
(b) 0.75 M $UO_2(NO_3)_2$—3 M HNO_3
(c) 0.38 M $UO_2(NO_3)_2$—3 M HNO_3
(d) 0.0 M $UO_2(NO_3)_2$—3 M HNO_3

Add 25 λ of Pu stock solution to each mixing cylinder. Each ml of stock solution contains 7.1×10^7 cpm/ml. Shake each for 2 min. CAUTION: Be sure to cover the stoppers of the mixing cylinders with Kleenex, and wear rubber gloves. Using 100-λ samples from each phase, determine Pu concentration using the lanthanum fluoride method. Calculate $E_A{}^o$ (organic to aqueous distribution ratio) for each solution. Plot $E_A{}^o$ values as ordinate against uranium concentration as abscissa on rectangular coordinate paper.

Mixed Fission-Product Distribution. To 2 ml of each 1.5 M $UO_2(NO_3)_2$—3 M HNO_3, 0.75 M $UO_2(NO_3)_2$—3 M HNO_3, 0.38 M $UO_2(NO_3)_2$—3 M HNO_3, and 0 M $UO_2(NO_3)_2$—3 M HNO_3 add 2 ml of 20 per cent TBP in CCl_4 in 15-ml centrifuge cones (glass stoppered). Add 50 λ of mixed fission product solution, each ml of which contains 5.6×10^7 cpm of gamma activity. Shake each for 2 min. CAUTION: Be sure to cover stoppers of centrifuge cones with Kleenex, and wear rubber gloves. Using 50-λ samples for the aqueous and 500-λ samples for the organic phase, determine the fission product concentrations by scintillation counting, using the well-type crystal counter. Calculate $E_A{}^o$ for each solution. Draw off the organic phase from each solution with a transfer pipet and place in centrifuge cones. Care must be taken not to contaminate the organic phase with any aqueous solution. To this organic phase add an equal volume of fresh aqueous solution of the same concentration of uranyl nitrate and nitric acid that was originally used. Using a 100-λ sample and a 500-λ sample for the aqueous and organic phases respectively, redetermine $E_A{}^o$ for these solutions. Plot on semilog paper $E_A{}^o$ as ordinate against uranyl nitrate concentration as abscissa for the original solutions and also for the back-extracted solutions.

EXPERIMENT 12-4

ANALYTICAL PROCEDURES: A. DETERMINATION OF URANIUM BY THIOCYANATE-ACETONE

Uranium forms a colored complex with thiocyanate ion which can be made the basis for a quantitative method for the determination of uranium. In aqueous solution, the color is unstable and subject to numerous interferences. However, by the use of a mixed acetone-water system the color is stabilized and anionic interferences from ions, such as fluosilicate and sulfate, are eliminated. Cationic interferences can be eliminated by an ether extraction of the uranium. Under properly controlled conditions, the method is capable of ±1 per cent accuracy and precision.*

Special Equipment

Beckman Model B Spectrophotometer. Matched 1-cm, glass-stoppered, quartz or Corex absorption cells

---

* C. E. Crouthamel and C. E. Johnson, "Spectrophotometric Determination of Uranium by Thiocyanate Method in Acetone Medium," Anal. Chem., **24,** 1780 (1952).

Reagents

C.P. ammonium thiocyanate

C.P. acetone

SnCl$_2$: 10 grams reagent-grade SnCl$_2 \cdot$2H$_2$O diluted to 100 ml with concentrated HCl

HCl, concentrated

H$_2$SO$_4$, concentrated

HNO$_3$, concentrated

3 M Al (NO$_3$)$_3$ solution

Standard uranium solutions

Diethyl ether

Preparation of Solutions: 1. Acetone-Thiocyanate. The acetone-thiocyanate solution must be prepared fresh daily from recrystallized ammonium thiocyanate and kept cold during use. Dissolve 57 grams of recrystallized ammonium thiocyanate in acetone and dilute with acetone to 250 ml to make a 3 M solution. Place solution in an ice bath and keep cold. Be careful to keep solution bottle tightly stoppered in order to reduce the evaporation of the acetone.

Recrystallization of Ammonium Thiocyanate. Ammonium thiocyanate as received from the manufacturer is often wet, thereby giving essentially a saturated solution. It is known that solutions of ammonium thiocyanate are unstable, and therefore it becomes necessary to recrystallize and dry the reagent before use. The recrystallization is carried out from methyl alcohol as follows:

PROCEDURE	NOTES
1. Saturate reagent-grade methanol with reagent-grade ammonium thiocyanate at 50° to 60°C. Stir for 1 hr at this temperature.	
2. Filter the solution while hot through a coarse-grade, 3-in., sintered-glass filter.	This step serves to remove any insoluble material which would contaminate the final product.
3. Cool the filtered solution in an ice bath at about 0°C.	
4. Filter the crystals, using suction, on a coarse-grade, 3-in., sintered-glass funnel.	The methanol at this point may be re-saturated. However, do not use methanol for more than two recrystallizations.
5. Dry the crystals by drawing air through the mass.	Only long enough to remove the mother liquor.
6. Further dry the crystals by passing dry nitrogen *up* through the mass by attaching rubber tubing from the dry nitrogen source to the bottom tube of the funnel.	See sketch of the apparatus, Fig. 12-3.
7. Store the dried crystals in a container through which there is a constant flow of dry nitrogen.	See Fig. 12-3.

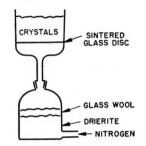

APPARATUS FOR DRYING CRYSTALS ON FUNNEL

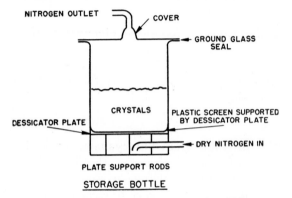

STORAGE BOTTLE

Fig. 12-3. Drying and storing ammonium thiocyanate.

Preparation of Solutions: 2. Stannous Chloride. Ten-gram reagent-grade stannous chloride dihydrate is dissolved in 10 ml concentrated HCl and diluted to 100 ml with concentrated HCl.

Preparation of Solutions: 3. Aluminum Nitrate. Add sufficient C.P. $Al(NO_3)_3 \cdot 9H_2O$ to water to give a saturated solution (about 3.0 M). Filter through a sintered-glass filter (medium) before use.

Care of Absorption Cells. Extreme precautions must be taken to keep the absorption cells clear. After extended use of the cells, there is a tendency for the windows to become clouded with a deposit of unknown composition which is extremely difficult to remove. Before use the cells should be carefully checked for matching as follows: Fill both cells with distilled water and place in the carrier as usual. The machine is set at the proper wave length (375 mμ) and the per cent transmission for the first cell is adjusted to 100 by means of the slit-width control. The second cell is then moved into the light beam. If the cells are properly matched, the transmission should also be 100 ± 0.5 per cent. If the cells do not match within the above limits, remove the water and fill the cells with hot HNO_3–H_2SO_4 solution for 5 min. Then recheck the matching characteristics as above. This procedure should be repeated until the cells match. If this cleaning procedure is unsuccessful, the cells should not be used together as a pair.

Only lens tissue should be used to wipe off the outside of the cells.

Do not allow the acetone-thiocyanate solution to stand in the cells after completion of a set of samples. Immediately pour the liquid out of the cells and rinse twice with acetone. Then rinse with distilled H_2O and finally fill with distilled H_2O. *Do not let the cells stand empty!*

Adjustment of the Oxidation State. Since the uranyl ion is the species which complexes with thiocyanate and also is the species which is extracted by ether, care must be taken to oxidize some samples prior to color formation or extraction. Uranium solutions in nitric acid in general do not require oxidation, since the uranous ion is not stable in this medium. However, some samples, such as those associated with a dissolution in a HCl–ethyl acetate mixture have the uranium in the $(+4)$ state and require oxidation. For solutions which do not require extraction prior to color development, the oxidation may be simply carried out with bromine water. Pipet the required sample into a 25-ml volumetric flask, and add bromine water until the color of the bromine persists. Remove the excess bromine by heating the flask on a sand bath.

For samples which require extraction from interfering cations, the oxidation is carried out by adding the appropriate amount of $Al(NO_3)_3$ and HNO_3 plus 1 drop of 1 M $Cr_2O_7^=$ solution and heating for one hour at 80-90°C on a water bath. Before extraction, the excess $Cr_2O_7^=$ is destroyed by the addition of Fe^{++} ion until the color of the $Cr_2O_7^=$ disappears. Bromine water should not be used for oxidation of samples to be extracted since halides interfere with the extraction of uranium by ether.

Calculations. The calculation makes use of the proportionality of concentration and optical density and requires the preparation of only the two standards described in the procedure. From the measured optical density and the known concentration of the standard, a factor may be determined, which factor, multiplied by the optical density of the unknown and the appropriate dilution factor, gives the concentration of the unknown in moles of uranium per liter.

EXAMPLE

$$\text{OD standard} = 0.570$$

$$\text{Conc. standard in 25 ml} = 15.0 \times 10^{-5}\ M$$

Therefore, $\dfrac{15.0 \times 10^{-5}}{(0.570 - \text{OD blank})} \times (\text{OD sample-blank}) \times \text{dilution factor}$

$$= \text{Conc. U, } M/l \text{ in sample.}$$

Procedures. Add thiocyanate-acetone solution to only *one* sample at a time, since these solutions are not too stable.

The reagent blank and samples are read against distilled water to avoid frequent preparation of the reagent blank due to its instability. The value obtained for the blank is then subtracted from the observed optical density of the sample and standards prior to calculation of the uranium molarity.

PROCEDURE FOR PURE URANYL
NITRATE SOLUTION

NOTES

1. (a) Pipet aliquot directly into a 25-ml volumetric flask.
   (b) Dilute to about 5 ml with water.

Sample sizes should be chosen to give between 0.4 and 0.9 mg U.
To avoid reduction of uranium by $SnCl_2$ in conc. HCl.

2. Add 20 drops of 10 per cent $SnCl_2$ solution.

The stannous ion reduces Fe^{+++} to Fe^{++}, which does not give a color with thiocyanate.

Mix well!

3. Pipet 15 ml of acetone-thiocyanate solution into the flask.

The 15 ml of acetone-thiocyanate solution must be accurately measured with a pipet. A precipitate may form in the flask at this step, but will redissolve upon the addition of water.

4. Make up to volume with H_2O.

Mix well!

5. Transfer the solution to a glass-stoppered quartz or Corex absorption cell.

Rinse the cell three times with the solution before final filling.

6. Read the optical density at wave length 375 mμ at sensitivity setting 3, with shutter control at the filter setting.

The sample should be read against distilled water. Blanks must be prepared and read every tenth sample and for each series of samples.

7. Calculate molarity as outlined under the section on calculations.

The OD reading of the blank must be subtracted from the OD reading of the standards and sample before calculation.

Standards. Two standard uranium solutions are necessary for proper control of the method. The first standard uranium solution required is a primary standard which is used to determine the proportionality between concentration and optical density. This is to be analyzed in duplicate at the beginning of each set of samples. A set consists of five samples in duplicate. In addition to the primary standard, a second standard is necessary for checking the precision and accuracy of the method. This standard should be run immediately after the calculation standard and again at the end of the set, and calculated as an unknown. Therefore, a typical set of samples should consist of the following:

1. Blank
2. Primary standard in duplicate
3. Check standard
4. Samples—maximum, five samples in duplicate
5. Check standard
6. Blank

Ether Extraction. In some cases it will be necessary to determine the uranium content of samples which contain interfering cations such as Ni^{++}, Cr^{+++} (or $Cr_2O_7^=$), or MnO_4^-, large amounts of Fe^{+++}, or others. In these cases an ether extraction of the uranium has to be made.

PROCEDURE FOR ETHER EXTRACTION

NOTES AND EXPLANATIONS

1. Pipet a suitable aliquot of the sample into a 100-ml volumetric flask.

Sample size should be chosen to give 0.4 to 0.9 mg U.

2. Add sufficient conc. HNO_3 and 3.0 M $Al(NO_3)_3$ to make the final solution to be extracted 2.0 M in $Al(NO_3)_3$, 2.0 M in HNO_3.

If the sample volume is less than 1 ml, add 4 ml $Al(NO_3)_3$ and 1 ml HNO_3. For larger sample sizes, calculate the amount of both reagents needed. Nitrate is absolutely essential, since it is $UO_2(NO_3)_2$, not the UO_2^{++} ion, which is extracted. For samples which contain fluoride, add enough $Al(NO_3)_3$ ($\frac{1}{6}$ the molar conc. of fluoride) for complexing the fluoride, plus the amount necessary to bring $Al(NO_3)_3$ conc. to 2.0 M.

3. Oxidize the sample as outlined under the section, Adjustment of Valence State.

The uranyl ion UO_2^{++} complexes with nitrate and is extracted as the nitrate complex, whereas the uranium ion U^{+4} is not extracted.

4. After oxidation of the uranium and reduction of excess dichromate, cool, and add diethyl ether so that the ether volume is twice that of the aqueous phase. Place the flask on a shaker and extract for 5 min.

The final volume of the ether plus aqueous solution should not occupy more than one-half the volume of the flask used for extraction. Sulfate and chloride ions must be absent during extraction, since they interfere with the extraction by reducing the distribution coefficient of the uranium into the organic phase.

PRECAUTION! Diethyl ether is an extremely volatile and flammable liquid. Handle only in a hood, making certain there are no flames burning in the area.

5. Allow the phases to separate, and decant the ether phase into a 100-ml round-bottomed flask containing 15 to 20 ml of water.

It is especially important that the separation of the first ether strike be handled without loss, since this ether phase contains 80 to 90 per cent of the uranium.

6. Repeat the ether extraction two more times as before (steps 4 and 5).

HNO_3 is also extracted by ether, and precipitation may occur during extraction. This may be remedied by the addition of more HNO_3.

7. Place the combined ether extracts on a steam bath in a hood and allow the ether to evaporate.

Discard the aqueous raffinate to active waste.

8. After the ether has evaporated, add 6 drops of concentrated H_2SO_4 and 1 ml of concentrated HCl to the aque-

PROCEDURE FOR ETHER EXTRACTION

NOTES AND EXPLANATIONS

ous residue, and place the flask on a sand bath.

9. Heat until the volume has been reduced to about 2 ml, and again add 1 ml of concentrated HCl.

HCl helps to remove the last traces of nitrate ion.

10. Evaporate the sample to fumes of H_2SO_4.

11. By means of a transfer pipet, transfer the cooled solution to a 25-ml volumetric flask. Carefully rinse the flask with small portions of H_2O, taking care to keep the volume of the sample plus washing to less than 9 ml.

12. Proceed to develop the color as outlined for pure uranyl nitrate solution, with the exception that 6 drops of concentrated H_2SO_4 must be added to the standards and blank.

Sulfate causes a slight reduction in the optical density of the uranium-thiocyanate complex, so H_2SO_4 is added to the blank and standards to compensate for this reduction.

13. Calculate as outlined.

Analysis of Dilute Uranium Solutions. There may be occasion when uranium analysis on dilute, highly radioactive samples is required and where a fluorometric determination does not give the required accuracy. In these cases the pretreatment of the samples, i.e., oxidation or extraction, is the same as outlined, but the optical density readings may be made in 2-cm or 5-cm absorption cells. Proper adjustments of the uranium concentration in the standards should be made to compensate for the increased light absorption due to the longer light path. For a rough guide the concentration of a standard for 2-cm cells should be half that when using 1-cm cells; for 5-cm cells the ratio would be 1:5.

Operation of Beckman Model B Spectrophotometer. The Beckman Model B spectrophotometer is a prism instrument having a wave length range from 325 mμ to 1000 mμ. The range is covered by the use of two phototubes, blue-sensitive and red-sensitive. The blue-sensitive tube is used for wave lengths from 325 to 700 mμ, while the red-sensitive is for wave lengths from 625 to 1000 mμ. Provision is made for rapid interchange of the phototube. See the Beckman Instruments Bulletin No. 291 for a complete description of the instrument.

The instrument has seven operating controls, as follows:

1. Power and lamp switches
2. Sensitivity multiplier control
3. Dark current control
4. Wave-length selector
5. Slit-width adjustment control
6. Cell-carriage positioning knob
7. Shutter control

OPERATING PROCEDURE

NOTES

1. Plug in a constant-voltage supply and turn power and lamp switches on.

The sensitivity multiplier should be in a standby position and shutter control should be at shutter setting before turning power and lamp switches on.

2. Allow instrument to warm up for 30 min.

3. Use the wave-length selector control to set the wave length at the desired value.

For the uranium-thiocyanate method, the wave length used is 375 mμ. The blue-sensitive phototube is used.

4. Insert the cell carrier and cells containing blank and sample solution in the cell compartment.

5. Close the light-tight cover to the cell compartment and move the cell containing reagent blank into the light path by means of the cell-carriage positioning knob.

The shutter *must* be in closed-shutter position whenever the cover is opened, to prevent any large quantity of light from striking the phototube.

6. Turn the sensitivity multiplier control to position 3.

Sensitivity setting 3 is the setting used for the uranium-thiocyanate method.

7. Adjust the dark current by means of the dark current control so that the meter reads 0 per cent transmittance (∞ on the optical density scale).

8. Move the shutter control to FILTER position.

The shutter control has three positions: FILTER, SHUTTER, and OPEN. The filter position is used for wave lengths from 325 to 400 mμ.

9. Adjust the meter to 100 per cent transmittance (0 optical density) with the slit-width control.

10. Recheck the dark current and 0 optical density by moving the shutter control alternately to SHUTTER and FILTER position. Adjust if necessary.

11. When the machine is standardized on the blank, move the shutter control to SHUTTER.

12. Move the cell containing the sample into the light path.

The shutter control must be in the closed position whenever a new cell is moved into the light path.

13. Move the shutter control to FILTER position.

14. Read and record the optical density of the sample.

For most precise and accurate readings, the middle third of the meter scale is preferred, i.e., optical density readings between 0.18 and 0.50.

15. Recheck the dark current and 0 optical density settings on the blank.

16. When the instrument is turned off, disconnect the constant-voltage transformer from the line.

The most frequent difficulty experienced when using the Model B spectrophotometer is instability of the meter needle. If the meter is unstable when the shutter is at *filter* position (open) but stable on dark current, it is usually an indication that the tungsten light source needs to be replaced. For complete servicing instructions, see the Beckman Instruments Bulletin No. 291.

EXPERIMENT 12-5

ANALYTICAL PROCEDURES: B. DETERMINATION OF PLUTONIUM BY THE LANTHANUM FLUORIDE METHOD

Plutonium (III) and (IV) may be quantitatively coprecipitated with lanthanum fluoride. When used in conjunction with a "holding oxidant," this precipitation separates plutonium (III) and (IV) from plutonium (VI); when used with a reducing agent, a complete precipitation of all plutonium is obtained. The precipitation is carried out in dilute nitric acid, using 0.5 mg of lanthanum as a carrier. The washed precipitate is slurried onto a stainless-steel planchet, ignited, fixed to the planchet with collodion, and counted.

Because alpha particles are easily absorbed, both the amount and the distribution of solids on the planchet must be carefully controlled. The amount of solid should not exceed 1 mg on a 1-in.-diameter planchet, and the spread should be as uniform as possible with respect to both density over a particular sample and area for all samples. Excessive solids or clumping of the precipitate will cause the results to be low. In many instances the problem of excessive solids can be overcome by reducing the sample size and accepting a lower count rate.

With careful work, a precision of ±3 per cent for the 95 per cent confidence level may be obtained. The assay of a plutonium solution obtained in this manner will be about 3 per cent lower than that obtained by direct plating of a weightless sample.

Since the lanthanum fluoride precipitation is not specific for plutonium but will carry other actinide elements, the method is not applicable to samples containing, for example, appreciable amounts of americium and curium. In such cases the plutonium must first be separated by solvent extraction or ion-exchange methods.

Separation of the plutonium by solvent extraction or ion exchange is also necessary when the ratio of uranium to plutonium in a solution is unusually high. The small amount of uranium which is also carried by the lanthanum fluoride may contribute an appreciable portion of the alpha count on low-counting samples. This is especially true for enriched uranium solutions. The percentage of the shorter-lived uranium 234 in enriched fuels may be as much as 200 times that found in natural uranium.

Reagents

HNO_3—1.5 N, 1 N
1 N HNO_3—1 N HF
$NH_2OH \cdot HCl$—3 M
$La(NO_3)_3$, 10 mg La/ml
HF conc. (48 per cent)
Collodion—amyl acetate, 1 to 500
Zapon

PROCEDURE: AQUEOUS SAMPLES	NOTES
1. Pipet the sample into 1 ml of 1.5 N HNO_3 in a 5-ml centrifuge cone.	The optimum counting range is 5×10^4 cpm per sample.
2. Add 3 drops of 3 M $NH_2OH \cdot HCl$ and 1 drop of $La(NO_3)_3$. Mix well with a platinum stirring wire and allow to stand for 10 min, with occasional stirring.	The La^{+3} concentration should be about 0.25 mg/ml to give quantitative carrying of the Pu.
3. Add 3 drops of conc. HF, mix well, and allow to stand for 5 min.	The free fluoride concentration should be at least 2 N to give complete Pu precipitation when aluminum is present in the sample. The quantity of HF added must be increased because of fluoride loss through complex ion formation.
4. Centrifuge 5 min at top speed. Decant the supernate to active waste.	
5. Add 1 ml of 1 N HF wash solution. Mix with platinum wire; centrifuge 3 min. Decant the supernate to active waste.	If the sample is high in uranium, two washes are advisable.
6. Add 3 drops of 1 N HNO_3. Using a transfer pipet, slurry the precipitate and transfer it to a stainless-steel disc which has been ringed with Zapon. Considerable care should be taken to see that the precipitate is evenly spread over the disc. Rinse the cone and transfer pipet once with 3 drops and once with 2 drops of 1 N HNO_3.	The steel disc must be cleaned by washing with trichloroethylene and dried with acetone. The Zapon ring is applied with a brush and should be about $\frac{1}{16}$ in.
7. Dry under a heat lamp, then ignite slowly to a dull-red heat over a micro burner.	Flaming the sample reduces the total solids on the plate. Rapid ignition of the Zapon causes flaking and possible loss of activity.
8. When the plate is cool, cover the sample with 1 to 2 drops of diluted collodion. Dry under a heat lamp and mount for counting.	The collodion film is added to fix the sample on the plate, thus reducing possible contamination of the counter.

Procedure: Organic Samples

1. Pipet sample into a 5-ml Pyrex cone, using methanol to rinse the pipet. If the sample plus rinsings equal 1 ml, add 1 drop of 16 N HNO_3. If the sample plus rinsings is small, add 1 ml of 1.5 N HNO_3 and enough methanol to maintain one phase.

2. Follow regular procedure, starting at step 2. If upon addition of the aqueous reagents in steps 2 and 3 there is a phase separation, add more methanol.

Calculation

$$\text{cpm/ml} = \text{cpm} \times \text{dilution factor}$$
$$1 \text{ mg plutonium-239} = 7.1 \times 10^7 \text{ cpm at 50 percent geometry}$$

EXPERIMENT 12-6

ANALYTICAL PROCEDURES: C. DETERMINATION OF GROSS GAMMA ACTIVITY

With the exception of strontium-89 and -90 and yttrium-90, each of the common long-lived fission products has a characteristic gamma ray which is coincident with beta emission. The energies of these gamma rays vary from 0.15 Mev for cerium-141 to 0.75 Mev for zirconium-95. The conversion of this spectrum of gamma rays into recorded counts constitutes a gross gamma activity determination.

Gamma-ray assays are carried out in a well-type scintillation counter. Samples are pipetted into small glass tubes, diluted to a standard height, and placed in the well of sodium iodide–thallium activated crystal (see Fig. 12-4). The photons which are intercepted by the crystal are converted to pulses of visible light, which are detected photoelectrically, amplified, and registered. Results are reported as cpm/ml or cpm/mg of a particular macro constituent of the solution, e.g., uranium. The simultaneous detection of hard beta activity is prevented by the use of a lead absorber between the sample and the detector.

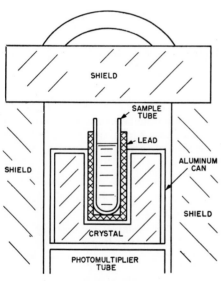

FIG. 12-4. Scintillation assembly.

The counting efficiency for a 1-in.-thick crystal is not the same for all gamma rays. For a crystal of this size it varies from about 50 per cent at 0.75 Mev to 100 per cent at 0.15 Mev. Any attempt to make an exact correlation between the number of counts and the number of disintegrations in a sample of mixed fission products is therefore invalid.

The counting rate for a particular sample is of course a function of the height to which it has been diluted in the sample tube. Between 0 and 6 mm there is less than 1 per cent change in the counting rate, but a dilution to 31 mm—the standard height—reduces the rate 19 per cent. Centrifuged or filtered precipitates such as those obtained in a fission-product analyses may be assayed in the scintillation counter by carrying out the final centrifugation in the sample tube or forcing the filter paper and its contents to the bottom of the tube. After multiplying this count by 0.81, a comparison may be made with the gross gamma activity of the original solution.

Procedure

1. Pipet a sample containing from 10^4 to 10^5 cpm into a standard gamma tube.
2. Place the tube in the height gauge and add solvent (either aqueous or organic) until the plane of the top of the gauge is tangent to the bottom of the meniscus.
3. Stir the contents of the tube thoroughly with a small glass stirring rod.
4. Drain the stirring rod for a moment against the inside of the tube and discard it in the active waste container.
5. Seal the tube with a cork and submit it to the counting room for a gamma assay.

Calculation

$$\text{cpm/ml} = \text{cpm} \times \text{dilution factor}$$

STEPWISE COUNTERCURRENT SOLVENT EXTRACTION

INTRODUCTION

Solvent extraction deals with three major problems when employed as a unit operation for a separations process. These problems are: (1) obtaining equilibrium data or distribution coefficients, (2) deciding on the type of contact and, (3) calculating the results. Equilibrium data are usually obtained in the laboratory (Exper. 12-3) or may be obtained from the literature. A discussion of the type of equipment to be used as the best mode of contact of the two liquid phases is beyond the scope of this experiment, but the standard works should be consulted.* By using stepwise countercurrent extraction, with separatory funnels as the method of contact, the calculation of the result of any specified system is primarily, it will be shown, a matter of stoichiometry with the aid of equilibrium data. Because equilibrium data are frequently difficult to express algebraically, the computations are apt to involve time-consuming trial and error unless a graphical procedure is followed. The graphical method makes use of the X-Y diagram which gives the equilibrium and operating concentrations in the two-phase system.

CONSTRUCTION OF THE X-Y DIAGRAM

If equilibrium data are obtained they may be plotted on an X-Y diagram to represent the relation between the concentrations of a given solute in the two phases in equilibrium with each other (see Fig. 12-5). Likewise, if the

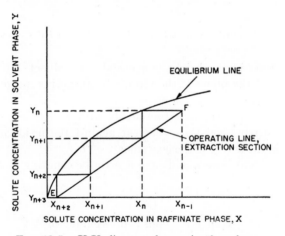

FIG. 12-5. X-Y diagram for a simple column.

system is carried out in more than one stage or more than one contact in which equilibrium has been established, a material balance may be calculated around any stage or an entire extraction section. For example, a material balance around the n-th stage in an extraction section may be represented by the following equation:

$$GY_{n+1} + LX_{n-1} = GY_n + LX_n, \qquad (12\text{-}13)$$

or

$$Y_{n+1} = \frac{L}{G}(X_n - X_{n-1}) + Y_n, \qquad (12\text{-}14)$$

---

* R. E. Treybal, "Liquid Extraction," 1st ed., McGraw-Hill Book Co., Inc., New York (1951); J. H. Perry (Ed.), "Chemical Engineers Handbook," 3rd ed., McGraw-Hill Book Co., Inc., New York (1950).

where G = volume or flow rate of extracting solvent,*

    Y_{n+1} = concentration of solute in extracting solvent in the $n + 1$ stage,

    Y_n = concentration of solute in extracting solvent in the n stage,

    L = volume or flow rate of raffinate,

    X_{n-1} = concentration of solute in raffinate in the $n - 1$ stage,

    X_n = concentration of solute in raffinate in the n stage.

If the line represented by this equation considering X_n and Y_{n+1} as variables, be drawn on the X-Y plot (see Fig. 12-5), then any point on this line has as its coordinates the composition of the raffinate leaving a stage (in this case the n-th stage) and the extract entering this stage from the stage succeeding. This line is known as the *operating line* and is based solely on the stoichiometry of the process. Fig. 12-5 also represents the construction for a three-stage countercurrent extraction effecting the reduction of the raffinate concentration from X_{n-1} to X_{n+2}; Y_{n+3} is 0, since pure extractant is used. The line EF representing Equation 12-14 is the operating line and drawn with a slope L/G.

If the initial and desired final raffinate concentrations X_{n-1} and X_{n+2} are specified, then the number of equilibrium stages required, using a given solvent ratio L/G, is obtained by stepping off the intervals after first drawing the equilibrium curve and then drawing the operating line EF through E with a slope of L/G. The point E has the coordinates Y_{n+3}, X_{n+2}, where Y_{n+3} is the solute concentration in the fresh solvent (0 in the diagram) and X_{n+2} is the final raffinate concentration.

If the number of equilibrium stages is specified, then the calculation of the required solvent ratio for a specified X_{n+2} (or loss in the raffinate) is necessarily carried out by trial and error, but is not time-consuming.

The Concept of Scrubbing†

It is feasible in many types of solvent extraction processes to scrub the product stream and thus effect a better separation of some constituents. Suppose that a column has been decided upon for the contacting equipment. Preliminary distribution data have been obtained and flow rates have also been decided. We can diagram the column with the corresponding countercurrent flow as shown in Fig. 12-6A. This would be considered a typical extraction column. However, if the product of this column should still contain a constituent or constituents that we wish to separate, it would be possible to pass this product into a second column and to scrub or back-extract constituents that would

---

* As used here, the symbols G and L imply constant volumes. Sometimes it is preferable to use weights and weight concentrations throughout.

"Feed solution" = The original solution containing substances which are to be separated from each other.

"Raffinate solution" = The solution left from the solvent treatment of a feed solution.

† "Scrubbing" = Transferring of impurities from a solvent phase into an aqueous phase by liquid-liquid contact.

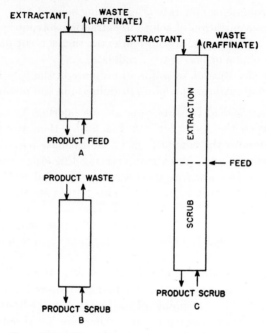

FIG. 12-6. Simple and compound columns.

contaminate the product. A better separation would therefore be effected at the expense of a greater volume of waste. This type of column is shown in Fig. 12-6B. It is possible to combine these two columns as well as their functions as shown in Fig. 12-6C. The column in this instance is referred to as a *compound column* and is divided into two sections, sometimes designated as the *extraction section* and the *scrub section*. The number of stages in each section depends on

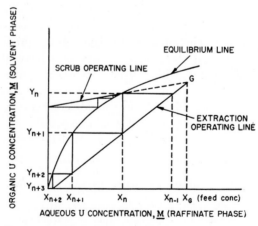

FIG. 12-7. X-Y diagram for compound column.

the loss to be tolerated and the amount of decontamination to be accomplished.

The scrub operating line is represented on an X-Y diagram in the same manner as the extraction operating line. If a material balance of the product is taken around the entire column—i.e., the concentrations in the waste, feed, scrub, and extractant streams are known—then the concentration in the product stream can be calculated. Starting with this point on the ordinate of the X-Y diagram, the line drawn with a slope of the flow ratios (aqueous scrub flow rate/extractant flow rate) is designated the *scrub operating line*. The intersection of the scrub and extraction operating lines represents the feed concentration read on the abscissa (see Fig. 12-7). It must be remembered that the scrub operating line as drawn here represents the result of the stoichiometry of the principal constituent extracted and does not represent the back extraction of minor constituents.

STAGE EFFICIENCY

If it can be assumed that the two phases leaving each stage of the contacting equipment are essentially at steady state and equilibrium, then the number of equilibrium stages will be equal to the actual number of stages. If equilibrium cannot be assumed, because of inadequate contact of the phases, then an "over-all stage efficiency" may be introduced. This is defined as the ratio of the calculated number of equilibrium stages to the number of actual stages or contacts required. Thus, with an over-all efficiency of 50 per cent, the concentration X_{n-1} would be reduced to X_{n+2} in six stages, whereas Fig. 12-7 shows that only three equilibrium stages would be required. The stage efficiency depends on so many factors that the concept is employed only as an approximate basis for calculation when data on the system of interest are available.

EXPERIMENT 12-7

STEPWISE COUNTERCURRENT SOLVENT EXTRACTION

Purpose. The aims of this experiment are (1) to extract uranyl nitrate into an organic phase under stepwise countercurrent conditions and (2) to construct an X-Y diagram from the stoichiometry of the operation.

Apparatus. The experiment calls for five 125-ml separatory funnels and ten 50-ml graduates, as well as the spectrophotometer and accessory equipment for uranium analysis.

Materials. Solutions of the following compositions are needed:

0.5 M $UO_2(NO_3)_2$, 1.0 M HNO_3—feed solution, designated AF
20 vol per cent tri-n-butyl phosphate in carbon tetrachloride—extractant, designated AX
1.0 M HNO_3—scrub solution, designated AS

Procedure. Place the five separatory funnels in a funnel rack. Three separatory funnels will represent three extraction stages and two funnels will represent scrub stages. The conditions under which the uranyl nitrate will be extracted are as follows:

	Volume	Ratio of Volume to Feed Volume	Composition
AF	20 ml	1	0.5 M uranyl nitrate, 1.0 M HNO$_3$
AS	10 ml	0.5	1.0 M HNO$_3$
AX	50 ml	2.5	20 vol per cent TBP in CCl$_4$

To start the process, place 50 ml of extractant AX and 10 ml of scrub solution AS in each separatory funnel by means of volumetric pipets. Place 20 ml of feed solution AF in the feed stage (first extraction stage). Stopper all funnels and shake for 2 min. Allow the phases to settle, and separate the phases from each stage into two different 50-ml graduated mixing cylinders. This procedure is best explained by a diagram shown in Fig. 12-8.

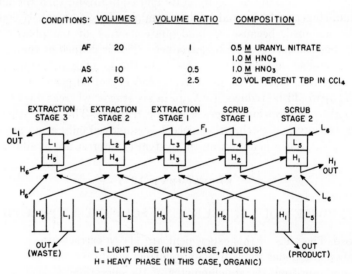

FIG. 12-8. Diagram of stepwise countercurrent extraction (first equilibration).

After the phases are separated in the mixing cylinders, the arrows above the mixing cylinders indicate how the phases should be recombined. Starting with the separatory funnel representing scrub stage 2, the heavy phase is discarded and the heavy phase from the scrub stage 1, H$_2$, is combined with 10 ml of fresh scrub solution. The separatory funnel representing scrub stage 1 receives the light phase L$_5$ from scrub stage 2 and the heavy phase from the first extraction stage H$_3$. The first extraction stage receives the light phase from scrub stage 1, L_4 and the heavy phase H_4 from extraction stage 2. In addition, this stage will receive 20 ml of fresh feed solution. Extraction stage 2 receives the light phase L_3 from extraction stage 1 and the heavy phase H_5 from extraction stage 3. Extraction stage 3 receives the light phase L_2 from extraction stage 2

Extraction Stage 3	Extraction Stage 2	Extraction Stage 1	Scrub Stage 1	Scrub Stage 2
$\boxed{L_1} + H_5$	$L_2 + H_4$	$L_3 + \enclose{circle}{F_1} + H_3$	$L_4 + H_2$	$L_5 + \boxed{H_1}$
$\boxed{L_2} + \enclose{circle}{H_6}$	$L_3 + F_1 + H_5$	$L_4 + \enclose{circle}{F_2} + H_4$	$L_5 + H_3$	$\enclose{circle}{L_6} + \boxed{H_2}$
$\boxed{L_3 + F_1} + \enclose{circle}{H_7}$	$L_4 + F_2 + H_6$	$L_5 + \enclose{circle}{F_3} + H_5$	$L_6 + H_4$	$\enclose{circle}{L_7} + \boxed{H_3}$
		1st Throughput *		
$\boxed{L_4 + F_2} + \enclose{circle}{H_8}$	$L_5 + F_2 + H_7$	$L_6 + \enclose{circle}{F_4} + H_6$	$L_7 + H_5$	$\enclose{circle}{L_8} + \boxed{H_4}$
$\boxed{L_5 + F_3} + \enclose{circle}{H_9}$	$L_6 + F_4 + H_8$	$L_7 + \enclose{circle}{F_5} + H_7$	$L_8 + H_6$	$\enclose{circle}{L_9} + \boxed{H_5}$
$\boxed{L_6 + F_4} + \enclose{circle}{H_{10}}$	$L_7 + F_5 + H_9$	$L_8 + \enclose{circle}{F_6} + H_8$	$L_9 + H_7$	$\enclose{circle}{L_{10}} + \boxed{H_6}$
		2nd Throughput		
$\boxed{L_7 + F_5} + \enclose{circle}{H_{11}}$	$L_8 + F_6 + H_{10}$	$L_9 + \enclose{circle}{F_7} + H_9$	$L_{10} + H_8$	$\enclose{circle}{L_{11}} + \boxed{H_7}$
$\boxed{L_8 + F_6} + \enclose{circle}{H_{12}}$	$L_9 + F_7 + H_{11}$	$L_{10} + \enclose{circle}{F_8} + H_{10}$	$L_{11} + H_9$	$\enclose{circle}{L_{12}} + \boxed{H_8}$
$\boxed{L_9 + F_7} + \enclose{circle}{H_{13}}$	$L_{10} + F_8 + H_{12}$	$L_{11} + \enclose{circle}{F_9} + H_{11}$	$L_{12} + H_{10}$	$\enclose{circle}{L_{13}} + \boxed{H_9}$
		3rd Throughput		
$\boxed{L_{10} + F_8} + \enclose{circle}{H_{14}}$	$L_{11} + F_9 + H_{13}$	$L_{12} + \enclose{circle}{F_{10}} + H_{12}$	$L_{13} + H_{11}$	$\enclose{circle}{L_{14}} + \boxed{H_{10}}$
$\boxed{L_{11} + F_9} + \enclose{circle}{H_{15}}$	$L_{12} + F_{10} + H_{14}$	$L_{13} + \enclose{circle}{F_{11}} + H_{13}$	$L_{14} + H_{12}$	$\enclose{circle}{L_{15}} + \boxed{H_{11}}$
$\boxed{L_{12} + F_{10}} + \enclose{circle}{H_{16}}$	$L_{13} + F_{11} + H_{15}$	$L_{14} + \enclose{circle}{F_{12}} + H_{14}$	$L_{15} + H_{13}$	$\enclose{circle}{L_{16}} + \boxed{H_{12}}$
		4th Throughput		

○ indicates material introduced into the system before equilibration.

□ indicates material removed from the system after equilibration.

* A throughput may be defined in this experiment as the number of equilibrations necessary for the feed to be moved from the first extraction stage to the point where it is removed from the last extraction stage.

FIG. 12-9. Chart of equilibrations in stepwise countercurrent extraction.

and 50 ml of fresh extractant. The light phase L_1 from extraction stage I is discarded. All the funnels are stoppered and shaken again for 2 min. The phases are allowed to settle and are then separated into the mixing cylinders and the process is repeated. These manipulations succeed in moving the organic extractant from left to right, while the scrub and feed solutions move in the funnels from right to left. Succeeding equilibrations can be conveniently listed in chart form as shown in Fig. 12-9.

At the end of the fourth throughput (in some cases the third) the system should be at steady state, i.e., the uranium concentrations in the waste (L_{12} + F_{10}), the product (H_{12}), and in each stage, should be constant. The waste and product phases from the third and fourth throughputs should be analyzed for uranium concentration. These phases are listed in the diagram as L_9 + F_7, L_{12} + F_{10}, H_9 and H_{12}.

Analyze the phases of each separatory funnel (stage) after the completion of the four throughputs. The phases to be analyzed are:

Sample	Sample Size, λ	M
L_9 + F_7	250	
L_{12} + F_{10}	250	
H_9	10	
H_{12}	10	
L_{13} + F_{11}	50	
L_{14} + F_{12}	10	
L_{15}	10	
L_{16}	25	
H_{16}	100	
H_{15}	25	
H_{14}	10	
H_{13}	10	

From the uranium analyses of the stage samples, construct an equilibrium diagram by plotting uranium concentration in the extractant phase as ordinate against uranium concentration in the aqueous as abscissa. (Use data from distribution experiment, 1.0 M HNO_3 system, if more points are needed to define equilibrium curve. In general, however, this is not to be recommended.)

Determine the uranium loss for this system (this is a function of the uranium concentration in sample L_{12} + F_{10}). Construct the operating line for the extraction section of the operation.

From the uranium concentration in the product and volume ratios of scrub and extractant solutions, construct the scrub operating line.

Step off the stages necessary to reduce the uranium concentration in the feed stage to the loss obtained in the process. Does the number of stages correspond to the number of stages actually used?

CONTINUOUS COUNTERCURRENT SOLVENT EXTRACTION
IN PULSE COLUMNS

INTRODUCTION

A description of solvent extraction columns is given and the general type of equipment to be used in the continuous-countercurrent extraction experiment is discussed below. Salient features of design and operation are pointed out which may be of value at some future time, either in research or production. In the design and construction of the unit, consideration is given to the limited amount of time available to each student for column operation. The flowsheet has been designed to permit introduction of variables during the course of operation, and also to allow the student to observe visually the changes that result. With this in mind, the unit has been assembled so as to be as simple as possible, and yet have the degree of flexibility necessary for use as an experimental tool.

EQUIPMENT

The laboratory-scale experimental unit (see Figs. 12-10, 12-11, and 12-12) consists primarily of Pyrex glass pipes containing perforated plate and packed sections, accompanying pumps, tanks, samplers, controllers, and stainless-steel piping and tubing. The perforated plate and packed sections of the glass columns are of ¾-in.-i.d. and 6 ft in length. Each disengaging section (top and bottom) consists of a piece of Pyrex glass pipe and tee, the diameter of each section being 1 in. and the length 18 in. The structural supports for the glass columns, piping, sampling devices, tanks, flow-rate measuring equipment, interface control pump, and pulsing pumps were made of Unistrut (Series P-1000 and 4000).*

Countercurrent flow of the liquid phases through the plates and packing is employed simultaneously with the pulsing of the column contents.

Column A: Extraction and Scrubbing. Column A (see Fig. 12-10) is in the nature of a compound tower in which uranyl nitrate is extracted into the solvent and the solvent is scrubbed with aqueous nitric acid to remove fission products. The extraction section is 2 ft in length and the scrub section is 4 ft long. These sections are connected by a glass pipe tee which serves as the feed entry point. The over-all length of the plate portion is 6 ft and consists of 48 plates, each one mounted rigidly on a ⅛-in.-diameter support rod at 1½-in.

---

* Unistrut Products Company, Bulletin No. 700.

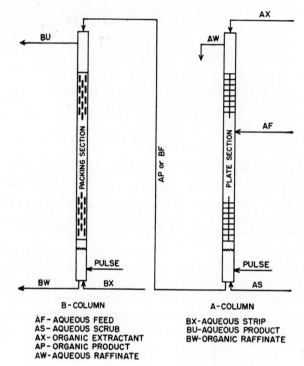

B-COLUMN

AF - AQUEOUS FEED
AS - AQUEOUS SCRUB
AX - ORGANIC EXTRACTANT
AP - ORGANIC PRODUCT
AW - AQUEOUS RAFFINATE

A-COLUMN

BX - AQUEOUS STRIP
BU - AQUEOUS PRODUCT
BW - ORGANIC RAFFINATE

FIG. 12-10.   Flow pattern in pulse columns.

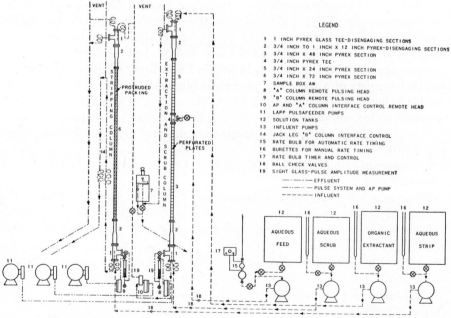

LEGEND

1   1 INCH PYREX GLASS TEE-DISENGAGING SECTIONS
2   3/4 INCH TO 1 INCH X 12 INCH PYREX-DISENGAGING SECTIONS
3   3/4 INCH X 48 INCH PYREX SECTION
4   3/4 INCH PYREX TEE
5   3/4 INCH X 24 INCH PYREX SECTION
6   3/4 INCH X 72 INCH PYREX SECTION
7   SAMPLE BOX AW
8   "A" COLUMN REMOTE PULSING HEAD
9   "B" COLUMN REMOTE PULSING HEAD
10   AP AND "A" COLUMN INTERFACE CONTROL REMOTE HEAD
11   LAPP PULSAFEEDER PUMPS
12   SOLUTION TANKS
13   INFLUENT PUMPS
14   JACK LEG "B" COLUMN INTERFACE CONTROL
15   RATE BULB FOR AUTOMATIC RATE TIMING
16   BURETTES FOR MANUAL RATE TIMING
17   RATE BULB TIMER AND CONTROL
18   BALL CHECK VALVES
19   SIGHT GLASS-PULSE AMPLITUDE MEASUREMENT
        ————·—— EFFLUENT
        ——·——·— PULSE SYSTEM AND AP PUMP
        ———————— INFLUENT

FIG. 12-11. Schematic diagram of solvent extraction pulse columns.

404

intervals by means of ¼-in.-diameter tubular spacers. The plate thickness is 0.005 in., and the diameter 0.75 in.; it contains seventy-two 0.032-in.-diameter perforations. The liquid is cycled through the perforated plates by the action of the pulsing mechanism. Interface control is accomplished by means of a pump located in the solvent effluent stream (see the section, Interface Control).

Column B: Stripping.* Column B, in which uranyl nitrate is extracted or

FIG. 12-12. Pulse columns and accessory equipment.

stripped from the solvent into the aqueous phase, consists of a 6-ft section of ¾-in.-i.d. glass pipe packed with 0.24 × 0.24-in. stainless-steel 316 protruded packing.† Attached to the top and bottom of this packed section are the glass pipe disengaging sections, of 1-in. i.d. and 18 in. long. The unit is also provided with a pulsing mechanism in the event that pulsing of the countercurrent-flowing liquids is desired. Interface control involves the use of a jackleg which can be raised or lowered manually. The jackleg is attached to the effluent

* Stripping is transferring a solute from a solvent phase into an aqueous phase by liquid-liquid contact.

† Scientific Development Co., Bulletin No. 12.

solvent stream which emerges from the bottom of the column (see Interface Control for a description of jackleg).

Pumps. Pumping and metering of the influent streams is effected with two Milton Roy duplex-type pumping units. These are reciprocating, positive-displacement piston pumps.[*] The pistons are $\frac{5}{8}$ in. in diameter, and the maximum stroke length is 3 in. The motor speed is 1725 rpm and is geared down to 24 rpm for the piston speed. The motor is $\frac{1}{6}$ hp and operates on 110-volt, 60-cycle a.c. Maximum capacity of each piston is 5.7 gal/hr (theoretical) at 210 lb/in.^{2}

A step-valve arrangement with double ball checks is installed at the head of the pump. All pump parts that come into contact with the liquid being pumped are made of 18-8 stainless steel. Teflon (tetrafluoroethylene polymer) packing is used.

Interface Control. Interface control of the columns is maintained by the use of the following two methods. On column A the heavy effluent phase (solvent) is metered by a Lapp Pulsafeeder[†] pump employing a remote reagent head and check-valve assembly. The control of column B is effected by the jackleg as described below.

Installation of a Lapp Pulsafeeder pump on column A with a remote head enables one to accurately meter and pump the heavy phase to column B. Also, if desired, the unit permits the pumping of radioactive solutions behind protective shielding and controlled ventilation while the Pulsafeeder power unit can work in an open area. The remote head is connected to the pump by means of a hydraulic line. The Pulsafeeder pump employed is a combination piston-diaphragm pump and has positive displacement. The piston size is 1 in. in diameter and its maximum stroke length is 1 in. The machine is supplied with a device for the adjustment of the desired stroke length. At 58 strokes/min, the pump delivers 11.9 gal/hr at a discharge pressure of 250 lb/in.^{2} The remote head and check-valve assembly are constructed of 18-8 stainless steel with a diaphragm made of Kel-F (trifluorochloroethylene polymer). The over-all diameter of the remote head is 6 in.

The jackleg mechanism controlling the interface on column B is constructed partly of $\frac{3}{8}$-in. stainless-steel tubing and partly of $\frac{3}{8}$-in. coiled polyethylene tubing. The jackleg is actually the heavy phase (solvent) effluent line connected to the bottom of the column and rising parallel to it and having a pipe tee (vent and spillover point) at the top. In operation, the coiled polyethylene tubing provides the flexibility for raising and lowering the spillover point. The principle of operation involves the balancing of the total column head against the total head of the jackleg. In this manner the interface can be controlled at will.

Although the present installation employs manual adjustments on the inter-

* Milton Roy Controlled Volume Pumps, Bulletin No. 251, and Catalog No. 146.
† Lapp Pulsafeeder, Bulletin No. 300.

face control mechanisms, the devices can be readily adapted to utilize instrumentation for automatic operation via pneumatic or electronic circuits.

Pulsing. The pulsing of the liquid in columns A and B when desired is done by means of Lapp Pulsafeeder pumping units employing reagent heads remotely located from the power units and connected to the columns by hydraulic lines. The pumps are of the same description as appears under the preceding heading, Interface Control, except that the remote head has a diameter of 8 in. and does not utilize a check-valve assembly.

In column A the action of the pulsing unit causes the countercurrent-flowing streams to reciprocate through the plate perforations, thereby effecting the breakup of the dispersed stream (solvent) into minute droplets. Provisions have been made to vary both the frequency and the amplitude of these pulses so that comparisons of column efficiency can be made under various conditions. (Owing to limited time, no provisions have been made to vary other obvious variables, such as plate spacing, number of perforations, thickness of plate, etc.). To prevent the pulsing from interfering with the influent and effluent streams, appropriate check valves are used in these lines. Column B can be pulsed similarly through the protruded packing. The pulsing units used consist of Lapp Pulsafeeder pumps (with an adjustment for varying the stroke length or amplitude) and Graham variable-speed power-transmission units (as the variable frequency control for the pumps). Both of these adjustments are performed manually.

The pulse amplitude for each column is measured by means of a centimeter scale affixed to a sight glass which is externally mounted.

The pulse frequency is determined by means of a scale on the Graham variable-speed power-transmission unit.

Flow-Rate Measurement. Measurement of the influent-stream flow rate on the present equipment consists of the determination of an average rate rather than an instantaneous rate. The methods employed are (1) burette and stopwatch method, and (2) an automatic system, namely, a calibrated bulb and timer arrangement.*

The burette and stop-watch method involves filling a burette to the desired volume, momentarily turning the tank valve off, feeding from the burette, and then timing the measured volume pumped. The burette is located on the suction side of the pump.

In the calibrated bulb flow-timer system, the operation is completely automatic except for initial starting of the flow-rate measurement by means of a contact switch. The instrument consists essentially of three parts: (1) a bulb of calibrated volume with an electrode at each end, (2) an electric circuit actuated through the two electrodes and consisting of three or less relays, pilot lights, a switch, and a reset-type timing device, and (3) a solenoid valve. The

---

* L. F. Coleman, "Calibrated Bulb Flow-Meter," Argonne National Laboratory (June 19, 1953).

flow rate is determined by the time consumed for the liquid level to pass from one electrode to the other in the calibrated bulb. Knowing the time and the volume pumped, one can easily obtain the rate.

The bulb flow-timer device is readily adaptable to the measurement of conductive and nonconductive liquids. Slight modification of the system is required in the latter case, namely, the use of a secondary conductive liquid.

Sampling. Two approaches in obtaining samples of the effluent streams are used in the solvent extraction unit provided for the laboratory course.

The first method involves the use of standard $\frac{1}{4}$-in. stainless-steel needle valves, positioned properly in the effluent stream to insure a representative quantity of material. In this instance, sampling is a matter of bleeding the normal liquid holdup of the valve into a reservoir, and then taking the desired sample from the downstream line. Such methods of sampling are effective where the effluent stream is of a level of radioactivity which is noninjurious to the health of the worker.

The second sampling method consists of an enclosure (steel box) containing two hypodermic needles, a glass vial with a Buna-N-type rubber diaphragm top and externally mounted syringe, valves, and vent and liquid carrying lines. These components are assembled in such a fashion that sampling of the aqueous raffinate is effected with a minimum of effort and time. In an application, where the stream of liquid contained in a tank is highly radioactive owing to gamma, beta, and alpha activity, the sampler is modified for remote sampling. Also, shielding is added to the steel box, a separate sample vial, shielded carrier, and screw mechanism for inserting on the needles is provided, and a bulb or tank for sample recycle is installed.

Some general considerations in regard to sampling methods for solvent extraction equipment are: (1) extreme precautions to minimize radioactive contamination; (2) representative sampling; (3) size of sample—minimum exposure to radioactivity; (4) nature of radioactivity; (5) salt concentration of the liquid in regard to clogging sample lines; (6) sample containers, sample shielding, and laboratory analyst's technique of removing sample for analysis.

Solution Composition: Influent. The influent streams to be pumped through the solvent extraction equipment are the feed, scrub, solvent, and strip solutions.

Feed solution is prepared by the dissolution of uranyl nitrate hexahydrate crystals (Mallinckrodt) in distilled water and 68.5 per cent (15.3 M) nitric acid to yield a solution of composition 0.1 M uranyl nitrate and 3.0 M nitric acid. Trace amounts of fission products may be added if desired.

Scrub solution is made by adding 68.5 per cent (15.3 M) nitric acid to distilled water to give a concentration of 3.0 M.

The *solvent stream* is composed of the solvent, *n*-tributyl phosphate, and the diluent, carbon tetrachloride. Tributyl phosphate (TBP) is purchased with the specification that it be butanol free. The carbon tetrachloride is technical-grade material. Solvent makeup of 0.4 M or 10.8 per cent by volume of TBP involves mixing of the 10.8 per cent by volume of the solvent with 89.2 per cent by volume of the diluent. The mixture is then washed with a ⅕ vol of 0.1 M sodium hydroxide to eliminate mono- and dibutyl phosphates. After phase separation, the sodium hydroxide wash is followed by two ⅕-vol distilled water washes.

The *strip solution* used in column B is laboratory-distilled water.

General Operation of Equipment and Some Flowsheet Variables

Purpose. The aims of the following procedures are (*a*) to acquaint the reader with the construction and operation of laboratory-type extraction columns (perforated plate column and packed column, both with pulsing), (*b*) to indicate a method of separating uranyl nitrate from fission products, and (*c*) to study the effect of several variables on column performance.

Equipment. This comprises two pulse columns—one with perforated plate, of the compound type; the other with packing, of the simple type—and accessories.

Materials. The following materials are needed: for feed (AF)—0.1 M uranyl nitrate, 10^3 cpm/ml cesium activity, and 3 M nitric acid in aqueous solution; as solvent (AX)—0.4 M *n*-tributyl phosphate in carbon tetrachloride solution; as scrub (AS)—3 M nitric acid in aqueous solution; as strip (BX)—distilled water.

Procedure

1. Inspect and become familiar with the mechanical construction and facilities of the extractor and accessories.
2. Run the perforated-plate column as a compound extraction and scrub column (column A). Run the packed column as a strip column (column B) using suitable feed, solvent, scrub, and strip ratios.
3. Fill the compound column with scrub solution and the simple column with water. Then, pump solvent into the compound column until an interface is established at the lower end (aqueous phase continuous).
4. Adjust the scrub and solvent rates to specified values, and at the same time, keep the interface level constant by pumping the solvent from the bottom of the compound column to the top of the simple column.
5. Next, pump in at the specified rates the feed to the compound column and the strip to the simple column, and establish the interface in the latter by means of the jackleg. Check and adjust the interfaces, rates, pulse amplitudes, and pulse frequencies for both columns. Take a set of samples of all the effluent streams.
6. Repeat, taking terminal samples from the simple column, every 2 min for 10 min, after which increase intervals between samples to 10 min for 30 min.

7. Continue running the columns under these conditions for 1 hr subsequent to the removal of the above-mentioned samples and take a set of terminal samples of both the aqueous and the organic phase from each column.

8. Observe the phase contacting patterns, and study the effect of one or more of the following variables, on the performance of the columns, as time permits: (a) throughput, (b) flow-rate ratio, (c) amplitude of pulse and (d) frequency of pulse.

In studying any one of these variables, the others should be kept constant at their average values. The variables studied should then be set at least at three different levels and the effect on column performance studied for that variable at each level. Care must be exercised in bringing the contents of the columns to steady-state conditions each time a change is made in the value of the variable. Terminal samples are withdrawn only after steady-state conditions are approached within the columns.

For example, when studying the effect of pulse amplitude on column performance, the other variables such as throughput, feed composition, pulse frequency, etc., are all kept constant at their average values. The pulse amplitude is then set at a minimum value and the columns are run under these conditions for approximately one hour. At this time, terminal samples are withdrawn. The pulse amplitude is then set at an intermediate value and the run is continued for another hour, after which terminal samples are again withdrawn for analysis. This procedure is repeated a third time for the maximum value of pulse amplitude. The other variables will be studied in a similar manner.

The final step carried out in this experiment is the "scrub-out" or shutdown procedure in which almost all uranium (and fission products, if present) are removed from the columns. This is accomplished by discontinuing the pumping of the aqueous feed stream (AF) while maintaining the flow of all other streams (i.e., AX, AS, BX) until the uranium color has been removed from both columns. Oftentimes, the discontinuance of the AF stream will cause hydraulic instability in the columns, which is made evident in local flooding or loss of interface position. It may be avoided by maintaining the combined aqueous flow rate (AF + AS) by substituting AS solution for AF during the shutdown procedure.

EXPERIMENT 12-8

CONTINUOUS COUNTERCURRENT SOLVENT EXTRACTION IN PULSE COLUMNS

Purpose. The aims of the present experiment are (a) to demonstrate startup, steady-state conditions, and scrub-out operations, and (b) to demonstrate the effects of certain variables on column performance—namely, (1) pulse amplitude, (2) pulse frequency, (3) flow-rate ratios, and (4) throughput.

Solution Compositions. Solutions AF, AS, AX, and BX have the following compositions: AF (aqueous feed)—0.1 M $UO_2(NO_3)_2$, 3.0 M HNO_3; AS (aqueous scrub)—3.0 M HNO_3; AX (organic extractant)—0.4 M TBP in CCl_4, (10.8 per cent TBP by vol); BX (aqueous strip)—distilled H_2O.

Feed Composition. The feed solution is prepared on the following basis, per liter of solution: 50.2 grams of $UO_2(NO_3)_2 \cdot 6H_2O$ and 0.20 liter of concentrated nitric acid (68.5 per cent). Dissolve and dilute to a volume of 1 liter with distilled water.

Flow Rates

AF (aqueous feed) . . . 60 ml/min	AS (aqueous scrub) . . 10 ml/min
AX (organic extractant) 50 ml/min	BX (aqueous strip) . . 50 ml/min

Procedure of Experiment

PART I

Startup operations and the attainment of steady-state conditions.

PART II

(a) Vary amplitude from an average value of 1.6 cm to 1.1 and 2.1.
(b) Vary frequency from an average value of 65 cpm to 40 and 90.
(c) Vary flow-rate ratios of the solvent to feed, of scrub to feed, and of strip to feed from their average values.
(d) Vary throughput from the average value (100 per cent) to 50 per cent and 150 per cent.

PART III

Scrub-out operations and shutdown.

Operational Instructions

1. STARTUP

(a) Adjust flow rates (AX, AS, BX), establish interfaces, and set pulse at 1.6 cm and 65 cpm.
(b) Operate unit at mechanical equilibrium (steady conditions) after interfaces, flow rates, and pulse are set.
(c) Pump in feed and adjust flow rate.

2. FLOW RATES (INFLUENT)

(a) Check and record all influent flow rates every 15 min during startup period. Make necessary adjustments.

(b) Check and record all influent flow rates every one-half hr after the startup period.

3. SAMPLING

(a) Take terminal samples from column B during the attainment of steady-state conditions (BU, BW).

(b) Take terminal samples after steady-state conditions are reached (AW, AP, BU, BW).

(c) Take terminal samples after steady-state conditions are reached upon introduction of any variable (AW, AP, BU, BW).

4. PULSE MEASUREMENTS

(a) Check and record pulse measurements during the startup period.

(b) Check and record pulse measurements after each period (change in variable) of operation.

5. SHUTDOWN

Turn off the feed pump. Continue pumping all other influent streams until final traces of uranium color are removed from the columns. Next, turn off all pumps except the AP pump. Adjust the latter and the jackleg so that the interface levels are kept constant. When no more organic phase trickles down column A, shut down the entire unit, making sure that the proper interface level is kept in each column.

Data Sheets. The data may be recorded conveniently in Data Sheets 12-5 to 12-9.

DATA SHEET 12-5

| | Col. A—¾-in. i.d. | | Col. B—¾-in. i.d. | | |
| | PULSE MEASUREMENTS Date_____ | | | | |
Time	Displ.* (cms)	Freq. (cycles/min)	Displ.* (cms)	Freq. (cycles/min)	Remarks

* Maximum linear displacement in ¾-in. i.d.

DATA SHEET 12-6

INFLUENT STREAM DATA **AF** Bulb Vol. = 53.5 ml						
Date	Time	Timer Reading (min)	Bulb Rate (ml/min)	Diff. Rate + −	Remarks	Initials

DATA SHEET 12-7

(One sheet each for AS, AX, and BX)

INFLUENT STREAM DATA					
Date	Time	Burette Rate (ml/min)	Diff. Rate + −	Remarks	Initials

DATA SHEET 12-8

(One sheet each for AP, AW, BU and BW)

EFFLUENT STREAM DATA			
Date and Time	Type Sample	S#	Initials

DATA SHEET 12-9

OPERATION LOG		
Date	Time	Log Remarks

BIBLIOGRAPHY FOR EXPERIMENT 12-8

G. Sege, F. W. Woodfield, "Pulse Column Variables," Chem. Eng. Progress, **50**, 396-402 (1954).

J. D. Thornton, "Recent Developments in Pulsed Column Techniques," Amer. Inst. Chem. Eng., **13**, 39 (1954).

Z. S. Morello and N. Poffenberger, "Commercial Extraction Equipment," Ind. Eng. & Chem., **42**, 1021 (1950).

W. M. Harty, "The Design Philosophy of Remote Operation and Maintenance of Separations Facilities," Amer. Inst. Chem. Eng., **13**, 115 (1954).

E. H. Hoffing and F. J. Lockhart, "A Correlation of Flooding Velocities in Packed Columns," Chem. Eng. Progress, **50**, 94 (1954).

M. W. Davis, T. E. Hicks, and T. Vermeulen, "Mixer-Settler Extraction Equipment," Chem. Eng. Progress, **50**, 188 (1954).

B. V. Coplan, J. K. Davidson, and E. L. Zebroski, "The Pump-Mix Mixer-Settler—A New Liquid-Liquid Extractor," Chem. Eng. Progress, **50**, 403 (1954).

G. H. Beyer and R. B. Edwards, "Flooding Characteristics of a Pulse Extraction Column," Iowa State College, 553 (1954).

W. A. Burns and W. F. Johnson, "Plate Design for Pulse Columns," U. S. Patent 2,662,001 (Dec. 8, 1953).

H. L. Shulman, C. F. Ulrich, and N. Wells, "Performance of Packed Columns: Part I. Total, Static, and Operating Hold-Ups," New York Operations 6096 (1954).

H. L. Shulman, C. F. Ulrich, A. Z. Prouix, and J. O. Zimmerman, "Performance of Packed Columns: Part II. Wetted Areas, Effective Interfacial Areas, etc.," New York Operations 6097 (1954).

R. T. Schenck, "Remote Control for Continuous Liquid Extraction," AECD-2610 (1949).

R. M. Cohen and G. H. Beyer, "Performance of a Pulse Extraction Column," Iowa State College, 294 (1952).

EXPERIMENT 12-9

BATCH DISTILLATION WITH AND WITHOUT RECTIFICATION

INTRODUCTION

The unit operation of distillation, which is used to separate the constituents of solutions on the basis of differences in their volatilities, is little used in spent-fuel processing—primarily because few of the substances encountered in such work are volatile at moderate temperatures or without decomposition.

There are, however, some instances and possibilities in which this unit opera-

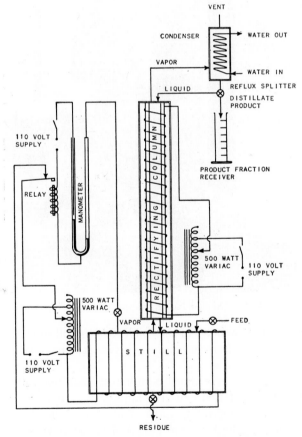

FIG. 12-13. Simplified sketch of a batch fractional distillation unit

tion is or may be used. Among these, mention may be made of the purification of solvents, the recovery of acids, and the separation of various volatile substances of interest in the atomic-energy field, such as uranium hexafluoride.

Two of the more common types of batch distillation are simple distillation and distillation with rectification. In the first type, the vapors evolving from the still are directly condensed without further treatment; in the second type, the vapors leaving the still flow countercurrently to part of the condensate in a

Fig. 12-14. Hooded batch fractional distillation unit.

rectifying section; the remainder of the condensate is collected as product. The latter type is particularly useful when the substances to be separated have close volatilities.

The primary aim of this experiment is to become familiar with the operation of a batch fractional distillation unit. The apparatus is used to recover the acid from an aqueous waste containing nitric acid and cesium-137 activity. The water and the acid are collected separately and the activity is concentrated in the still residue.

APPARATUS AND MATERIALS

The distillation unit consists of (1) a 3-liter distillation flask with a 500-watt electric heating mantle, (2) a 42-in.-long, 1 in.-diameter rectifying section with two jackets and a heating coil wound around the inner jacket for adiabatic operation, (3) a condenser with a magnetically energized valve for adjusting reflux, and (4) a control panel including a product receiver (see Figs. 12-13 through 12-16).*

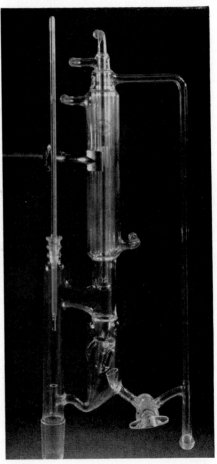

The rectifying section of each of the four units is differently packed in order to show variations in the degree of fractionation due to differences in the pattern of vapor-liquid interfacial contact. The first of these rectifying sections contains no packing. The second contains 6 × 6-mm glass rings. The third contains 0.16 × 0.16-in. protruded stainless-steel packing. The fourth contains 1-turn 3/16-in. glass helices. The result obtained with each of these units may then be compared as to the degree of separation achieved.

The material to be fractionated in each unit consists of 1200 ml of 8.0 M HNO_3 containing approximately 1×10^3 cpm/ml of cesium-137 activity. These concentrations are quite arbitrary; they are used here for convenience. For the determination of acidity, a pH meter or standard NaOH and phenolphthalein indicator are used.

Procedure

1. Inspect the equipment and be familiar with its various parts and their functions.

FIG. 12-15. Condenser and reflux regulator of distillation unit.

2. Charge the still with 1.2 liters of 8 M HNO_3 and add the required volume of cesium-137 concentrate to make a solution of 1×10^3 cpm/ml activity. Stir

*Unit purchased from Scientific Development Company, State College, Pa. Condenser and reflux regulator purchased from H. S. Martin & Co., Evanston, Ill.

and take a 5-ml sample for analysis. Add boil-easers to the flask and connect the latter to the column.

3. Run tap water through the condenser at the rate of about 0.5 liter/min. Turn the heat on for the heating coil around the inner jacket, and adjust it by means of the Variac so that a temperature of 100°C is indicated by the jacket thermometer.

4. Turn on the heat for both the lower and upper halves of the Glas-Col mantle. Adjust the heat input to 100 watts and increase power input to 500

GLASS HELICES	GLASS RASCHIG RINGS	PROTRUDED PACKING
one turn	6 × 6 mm	0.16 × 0.16 inch
3⁄16 inch I.D.	(approx ¼ inch)	stainless steel

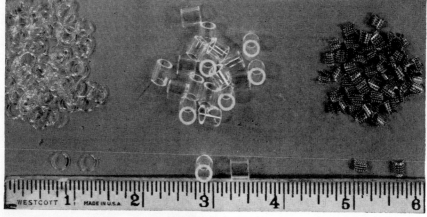

FIG. 12-16. Various packings for rectifying section of distillation unit.

watts in steps of 100 watts each minute. Continue heating until the contents of the still begin to boil. At this time disconnect the heat to the upper mantle of the still.

5. Set the Flexopulse timer to maximum reflux (120:1). As the vapors reach the condenser, adjust the pressure regulator to a boil-up rate of 0.75 liter/hr (7 to 11 cm of H_2O, except for the column with no packing). Thereafter adjust the power input to the mantle and the water flow to the condenser, so that the heat input is slightly greater than that required for the specified boil-up, and the heat removal is slightly greater than that needed to keep the temperature of the condenser water somewhat below its boiling point. (These may be approximated, visually, from the time intervals between heat-on and heat-off, and the height to which the vapors rise in the condenser, respectively.)

6. Five minutes after the condensate reaches the bottom of the rectifying column, adjust the timer to 2:1 overflow-to-product reflux, except in the case of the column with no packing, in which case use the minimum reflux possible with the apparatus (1:120). The heat input to the jacket is so manipulated as

to keep the rectifying section jacket temperature at 100°C. Collect the distillate in portions approximately equal to 5 vol per cent of the charge (60 ml), until the temperature of the condensate begins to rise sharply. At this point collect the distillate in 10-ml portions. During this time note the condensate temperature and volume frequently, and increase the jacket heat to keep its temperature at the average of the temperature of the condensate and that of the residue in the still. For the column with no packing, this temperature adjustment should be made and kept up, from the start to the end of distillate collection. Then there will be no need to collect the intermediate distillate in smaller portions.

7. When the temperature rise of the condensate becomes negligible, resume distillate collection in portions approximately equal to 5 vol per cent of the charge (60 ml). Continue distilling until 75 vol per cent of the charge is collected (900 ml). Towards the end of distillation, the appearance of brown fumes of NO_2 in the condenser and receiver is to be expected.

8. Close the product take-off stopcock, turn off the heats to the still and jacket of the unit, and let it cool off. After the still is *thoroughly* cool, disconnect it from the column, stir its contents and take a 5-ml sample for analysis (acid content and cesium-137 activity). CAUTION: The activity of the solution at this point is approximately 4×10^3 cpm/ml. Be careful not to spill or spatter any of the solution on yourself. Avoid undue exposure to the solution. This step should be completed in not more than 5 min.

9. Make a cesium-137 activity balance for the contents of the still before and after the distillation, and see how close the concentration factor is to 4. Use the same technique and apparatus as in Experiment 12-6 for the measurement of activity due to cesium-137.

10. Plot cumulative mole per cent overhead as abscissa vs. distillate temperature and vs. distillate composition (mole per cent H_2O) as ordinates. Compare the calculated values for zero holdup with the experimental values for finite holdup, on the same graph. Only alternate samples need be analyzed for acid, and the experimental points may be plotted at their average values. Under the circumstances, the comparison of calculated with experimental compositions of the distillate may be made, strictly speaking, only with the column which has no packing and the column which has 0.16 × 0.16-in. protruded packing. This is because it is known that the former contains no ideal stages in the rectifying column (no countercurrent contact between vapor and liquid) and the latter contains the equivalent of around thirty theoretical stages.

For the column with the protruded packing, the calculated data of Table 12-1 may be used for the comparison. For the column with no packing, on the other hand, a similar table is to be calculated from the equilibrium data in Table 12-2 by means of the Rayleigh equation for simple distillation, as shown in Data Sheet 12-12.

To do this, calculate from data in Table 12-2, values of $100y_D$ (mole per cent

TABLE 12-1. CALCULATED VALUES OF CUMULATIVE MOLE PER CENT OVERHEAD
AND DISTILLATE AND RESIDUE COMPOSITIONS[a]

(Batch Distillation with Rectification)

Charge—8.0 M HNO$_3$ Reflux ratio, overflow/product—2:1
Number of theoretical plates in rectifying   Holdup in rectifying column—0
    column—30

Cumulative Mole % of Charge Overhead	Temperature of Distillate, °C	Composition, Mole % H$_2$O	
		In Distillate, $100y_D$	In Residue, $100x_R$
0	—	—	83.7
18.5	100	Approx. 100	80.0
34.9	100	Approx. 100	75.0
45.5	100	Approx. 100	70.0
49.3	100	Approx. 100	67.5
53.6	106.5	90	65.0
56.8	117.3	80	63.6
61.5	119.7	70	62.4
63.0	121.9	61.8	61.8
100.0	121.9	61.8	61.8

[a] Calculations by W. J. Mecham.

TABLE 12-2. LIQUID-VAPOR EQUILIBRIUM FOR NITRIC ACID AND WATER[a]

(Total Pressure = 760 mm Hg)

Temperature, °C	Mole Per Cent HNO$_3$	
	In Liquid	In Vapor
100.0	0	0
106.5	8.36	0.627
112.0	12.3	1.76
118.5	22.1	6.60
121.6	30.8	16.6
121.9	38.3	38.3
121.0	40.2	60.2
118.0	46.5	75.9
112.0	53.0	89.1
99.0	61.5	92.1
86.0	100	100

[a] Data from J. H. Perry (Ed.) "Chemical Engineers' Handbook," 2nd ed., McGraw-Hill Book Co., New York (1941).

water in distillate) and $100x_R$ (mole per cent water in residue). Then, for each x_R, calculate its $1/(y_D - x_R)$ value, and plot these vs. the corresponding x_R values. From this plot, the values of the integral

$$\int_{(x_R)_0}^{x_R} dx_R/(y_D - x_R) = \ln \frac{R}{R_0} \tag{12-15}$$

DISTILLATE VOLUME AND TEMPERATURE DATA

Barometer, mm Hg _____   Room Temperature _____ °C   Date _____

Volume of charge _____ ml   Column height _____ cm
Volume of total distillate _____ ml   Column packing _____
Volume of final residue _____ ml   No. of theoretical plates _____
Boil-up rate _____ ml/hr   Reflux ratio,* O/P _____
Pressure drop _____ cm of H₂O

  * The ratio of moles returned to rectifying column to moles taken as product, per unit time.

| Time | Temperature, °C | | | Total Amount Distilled | |
	Residue	Jacket	Condensate	Volume, ml	Volume % of Charge

CUMULATIVE MOLE PER CENT OVERHEAD AND DISTILLATE COMPOSITION DATA

Date _____

Gram moles of charge = 59.0; (49.4 H₂O + 9.6 HNO₃)

DISTILLATE FRACTION

Time	ml Collected	HNO₃ Molarity	Gram Moles Collected*	Mole % H₂O*	Temp., °C	Cumulative Mole % of Charge Overhead*

* See Table 12-3 for densities of aqueous solutions of nitric acid.

CALCULATED VALUES OF CUMULATIVE MOLE PER CENT OVERHEAD AND DISTILLATE AND RESIDUE COMPOSITIONS[a]

(Batch Distillation Without Rectification)

Charge—8.0 M HNO$_3$

Number of theoretical plates in rectifying column—0

Reflux ratio, overflow/product—0:1

Holdup in rectifying column—0

Mole Per Cent H$_2$O in Residue, $100x_R$	Mole Per Cent H$_2$O in Distillate, $100y_D$	$y_D - x_R$	$1/(y_D - x_R)$	$\int_{(x_R)_0}^{x_R} dx_R/(y_D - x_R)$	Cumulative Mole % Overhead, $100\left(1 - \dfrac{R}{R_0}\right)$

[a] Obtained by graphical integration using the Rayleigh equation for simple distillation.

TABLE 12-3. MOLARITY, PERCENTAGE, AND DENSITY OF AQUEOUS SOLUTIONS OF NITRIC ACID AT 20°C[a]

Moles HNO$_3$/liter	Per Cent HNO$_3$	Density, grams/ml
0.159	1	1.004
0.320	2	1.009
0.484	3	1.015
0.648	4	1.020
0.815	5	1.026
0.983	6	1.031
1.152	7	1.037
2.032	12	1.066
3.150	18	1.103
4.150	23	1.134
5.200	28	1.167
6.065	32	1.193
7.220	37	1.227
8.160	41	1.253
9.140	45	1.278
10.15	49	1.304
11.17	53	1.328
12.22	57	1.351
13.01	60	1.367
14.07	64	1.387
15.16	68	1.405
15.30	68.5	1.407

[a] Data from "Handbook of Chemistry and Physics," 35th ed., Chemical Rubber Publishing Company, Cleveland (1953-1954).

(where $R_0 = 59.0$, R stands for total moles of residue at the beginning and at the end of a given distillation, and $(x_R)_0 = 0.837$ is the mole fraction H_2O in the initial charge) may easily be calculated for various values of x_R. The cumulative mole per cent of the charge taken overhead will then be equal to

$$100 \left(1 - \frac{R}{R_0} \right),$$

against which the values of $100y_D$ and $100x_R$ may finally be plotted.

ION EXCHANGE*

INTRODUCTION

Ion exchange is the exchange of anions or cations in a solution with ions of negative or positive charge, respectively, on an exchange resin. These resins may be considered to consist of two main parts: (a) the immobile and insoluble resin radical and (b) the mobile and soluble exchange ion. Thus, if these two parts are represented by R and I, respectively, a cation-exchange resin would be one in which R is negatively charged and I is positively charged, i.e. R^-I^+; an anion-exchange resin, on the other hand, would be one in which R is positively charged and I is negatively charged, i.e. R^+I^-. In ordinary exchange resins R is usually a complex organic radical of either negative or positive charge, whereas I may be a hydrogen ion (H^+) in cation-exchange resins, or a hydroxyl ion (OH^-), in anion-exchange resins. Other ions may be substituted for (H^+) and (OH^-), such as (NH_4^+) and (Cl^-) respectively.

In a separation by ion exchange, there are ordinarily two principal steps. The first step is one of adsorption in which the mobile ions of the solution and of the resin exchange places. Thus, the ion originally in the solution is adsorbed in the resin, and the ion originally in the resin is taken into the solution. For example, with a substance M^+X^- in solution:

$$\underset{\text{In resin}}{[R^-NH_4^+]} + \underset{\text{In solution}}{[M^+ + X^-]} = \underset{\text{In resin}}{[M^+R^-]} + \underset{\text{In solution}}{[NH_4^+ + X^-]}. \qquad (12\text{-}16)$$

The second step consists of elution in which the ion adsorbed in the resin, M^+, is now desorbed into a solution. The solution used for elution is called the *eluent*. The latter supplies a mobile ion to the resin, which in turn gives up the adsorbed ion to the eluent. For example, with an eluent H^+Y^- in solution:

$$\underset{\text{In resin}}{[M^+R^-]} + \underset{\text{In eluent}}{[H^+ + Y^-]} = \underset{\text{In resin}}{[R^-H^+]} + \underset{\text{In eluent}}{[M^+ + Y^-]}. \qquad (12\text{-}17)$$

This type of exchange takes place, to a smaller or greater degree, with the different cations or anions in a given solution, depending on their affinity for

* F. C. Nachod (Ed.), "Ion Exchange: Theory and Application," Academic Press, Inc., New York (1949); R. Kunin and R. J. Myers, "Ion Exchange Resins," John Wiley & Sons, Inc., New York (1950).

adsorption on the resin. As a result, both in the adsorption and elution (desorption) steps, there is a certain selectivity for different ions, whereby separation of various ions is possible after repeated adsorptions and desorptions in the resin, in both of the steps mentioned above.

A cation-exchange column containing Dowex 50W resin is used to separate nickel (II) and cobalt (II) from each other by means of elution with pH-adjusted citric acid.* The separation closely resembles that employed in separating members of the lanthanide and actinide series and offers the advantage that the separation can actually be seen taking place on the resin in the column, the green nickel band moving down the column ahead of the pink cobalt band. The effect of variables such as flow rate, resin particle size, and pH can be studied by different teams of students and the data obtained compared.

As a demonstration experiment, the instructors will set up an anion-exchange column containing Dowex-1 (100-200 mesh) to separate nickel (II), cobalt (II), and iron (III). Use is made of the difference in stability of the chloride complexes of nickel, cobalt, and iron.† Nickelous ion does not form a chloride complex and is not adsorbed; cobaltous and ferric ion form strong anionic complexes with chloride and may be separated by virtue of the difference in their stabilities. Thus, elution with 7 M hydrochloric acid serves to wash nickel out of the column; elution with 5 M hydrochloric acid desorbs the cobalt; and elution with 1 M hydrochloric acid desorbs the iron.

EXPERIMENT 12-10

ION EXCHANGE

Purpose. The purpose of this experiment is to become familiar with the elements of ion-exchange techniques, such as preparation of small resin columns, back-washing, adsorption, elution, washing, etc., used in separations processes. The separation of nickel ions from cobalt ions by means of a cation-exchange resin is used as the illustration.

Nickel-Cobalt Separation Procedure

1. Prepare a resin column of 25-cm height, as in Fig. 12-17, by making a slurry of the Dowex 50W resin (either 20-50 mesh or 50-100 mesh) in water and pouring directly into the 1.2-cm-diameter glass column partially filled with water (see Experimental Notes, 1, below). Open the column stopcock during the filling so that the excess water can run out, but do not allow the liquid level to fall below the resin level. The column is backwashed, i.e., water is forced up through the column to insure the removal of channels and air pockets in the

* T. H. Roberts, B. E. Willeford, Jr., and R. A. Alberty, "An Ion Experiment for Physical Chemistry," J. Chem. Educ., **29**, 545 (1952).

† K. A. Kraus and G. E. Moore, "Anion Exchange Studies: VI." "The Divalent Transition Elements Manganese to Zinc in Hydrochloric Acid." J. Chem. Soc., **75**, 1460 (1953).

resin bed and the removal of cracked resin particles by flotation. The liquid level should not be allowed to fall below the resin level in any of the subsequent steps.

2. Precondition the resin column by washing with several column volumes of 3 M ammonium thiocyanate followed by several column volumes of water. This may be followed by washing the column successively with 6 M hydrochloric acid, water, 3 M ammonium chloride to convert the resin to the ammonium form, and water to remove the ammonium chloride (Note 2, below).

3. Pipet directly on top of the resin 4.00 ml of the stock solution containing 50 mg/ml each of nickel (II) and cobalt (II) as chlorides. By means of the stopcock control, allow the solution to flow down the resin at a very slow flowrate, about 0.5 ml/min, in order to adsorb the nickel and cobalt on the uppermost part of the column. Discard displaced water.

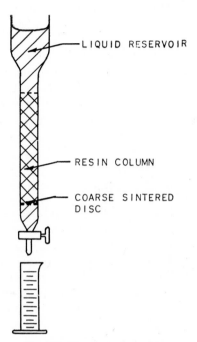

LIQUID RESERVOIR

RESIN COLUMN

COARSE SINTERED DISC

4. Wash the column with 50 ml of water to remove the ammonium chloride formed in the previous step. Discard washings.

5. Place a 100-ml graduated mixing cylinder under the column.

6. Five per cent citric acid with pH adjusted to 3.24 (or 3.28) with concentrated

Fig. 12-17. A resin column.

ammonium hydroxide is next passed through the resin at about 3 ml/min (Note 3, below). About 500 to 600 ml of this solution is used to elute the nickel and cobalt.

Collection of effluent fractions for analyses is made as follows. The effluent is caught in the 100-ml cylinder without sample removal until green color (nickel) begins to appear in the effluent. At this point, begin collection of a 1-ml fraction in a small graduated centrifuge cone after every 9 ml has been caught in the large cylinder. After the nickel is removed from the column and pink color (cobalt) begins to appear in the effluent, collect a 2-ml fraction in the graduated centrifuge cone after every 23 ml has been caught in the large cylinder. All volumes should be noted on the data sheet (Note 4, below).

The following is given as an example. Assume nickel begins to appear in the effluent after 84 ml of the citric acid solution has been passed through the resin. Collect a 1-ml fraction in a centrifuge cone labeled No. 1. The total volume of effluent collected is 85 ml. Collect 9 ml in the large cylinder and then another 1-ml fraction in a centrifuge cone labeled No. 2. The total volume of effluent collected is now 95 ml, etc. If cobalt appears in the effluent after 163 ml has been collected, collect a 2-ml fraction in a centrifuge cone, label appropriately, collect another 23 ml in the large cylinder, and then another 2-ml fraction in a centrifuge cone, etc. The total volumes of effluent collected for these fractions are 165 ml and 190 ml, respectively.

7. Wash the resin with about 100 ml of 3 M ammonium chloride followed by water until all ammonium chloride is removed (Note 5, below).

8. Determine the nickel and cobalt concentrations in the fractions collected by means of the spectrophotometric analyses of the nickelic dimethylglyoxime and cobaltous thiocyanate complexes, respectively (Note 6, below). Analyze only every other fraction of the nickel fractions except where more analyses are needed to establish the peak of the elution curve. Plot the data obtained on a graph of effluent volume vs. mg/ml of cation. Where the elution curves for the nickel and cobalt overlap, determination of both constituents in several fractions must be made to establish the ends of the curves.

Experimental Notes

1. Dowex 50W is a light-colored form of Dowex 50, with essentially similar properties. Dowex 50, also known as Nalcite HCR, is obtained by sulformation of a copolymer consisting of styrene and divinylbenzene. The divinylbenzene forms cross-linkages between the chains of polymerized styrene. The more divinylbenzene, i.e., the greater the cross-linkages, the denser is the network and the less the swelling of the resin.

The relation between mesh size and millimeter openings of some standard screens is:

Mesh Size	Opening, mm
10	2.00
20	0.85
40	0.36
50	0.29
70	0.21
80	0.17
100	0.14
200	0.074

2. The ammonium thiocyanate wash removes iron which is found in Dowex 50. The hydrochloric acid removes other impurities and any iron remaining from the previous treatment. (The anion resin, Dowex 1, a quaternary ammonium type salt, is usually washed with concentrated hydrochloric acid prior to use.)

3. The eluent is prepared by dissolving 50 grams of citric acid monohydrate and 1 gram of phenol in water and diluting to 1 liter with water. Concentrated (15 M) aqueous ammonia is added to give a pH of 3.24 (approximately 14 ml). The phenol is added to inhibit mold formation and has no effect on the elution.

4. This sampling procedure permits one to determine the concentration of

nickel or cobalt at a particular volume of effluent. If one collects 10- or 25-ml fractions and removes aliquots for analyses, a block diagram or histogram must be drawn on the graph of effluent volume vs. concentration.

5. The presence of chloride is detected by addition of silver nitrate solution. A white precipitate of silver chloride indicates the presence of chloride.

6. The analyses are made in a Beckman Model B spectrophotometer employing 1-cm Pyrex or Corex cells. The use of stoppered cells is advised for the cobalt determination to prevent creeping of the acetone-thiocyanate solution to the outside of the cells. Calculations can be made in a manner similar to that described on page 107 of the instruments booklet, or concentrations may be read from a standard curve of optical density vs. concentration.

DATA SHEET 12-13

ION-EXCHANGE ELUTION

Resin: Dowex 50W (NH$_4$R), 8 per cent cross-linkage, _____ mesh
Resin column: 25 × 1.2 cm
Adsorption: 4.00-ml solution containing 50 mg/ml each of Ni and Co as chlorides
Elution: 5 per cent citric acid, pH _____, 3 ml/min

Fraction	Vol. of Fraction (ml)	Total Vol. of Effluent (ml)	Nickel Analysis				Cobalt Analysis			
			Sample Size (ml)	Optical Density	mg	mg/ml	Sample Size (ml)	Optical Density	mg	mg/ml
1										
2										
⋮										
20										

Spectrophotometric Determination of Nickel: Reagents

Sulfuric acid, concentrated
Potassium citrate, 45 per cent by weight
Bromine water, saturated
Ammonium hydroxide, concentrated
Dimethylglyoxime, 1 per cent in ethyl alcohol

Procedure*

1. Pipet an aliquot containing nickel (0.015 to 0.15 mg) into a 25-ml volumetric flask.

* E. B. Sandell, "Colorimetric Determination of Traces of Metal," Interscience Publishers, Inc., New York (1950).

2. Add about 10 ml water.
3. Add 10 drops concentrated sulfuric acid.
4. Add 1 ml (about 15 to 20 drops) 45 per cent potassium citrate solution (Note 1, below).
5. Add 10 drops of a solution of water saturated with bromine (Note 2, below).
6. Cool in an ice bath about 2 min.
7. Add concentrated aqueous ammonia dropwise until the solution is ammoniacal (about 1 ml after bromine color disappears).
8. Add 10 drops 1 per cent dimethylglyoxime in ethyl alcohol (Note 3, below).
9. Dilute to 25.00 ml with water, mix, and pour into a 1-cm spectrophotometric cell. Read at 520 mμ in a Beckman Model B spectrophotometer against a solution blank containing all the above reagents except nickel (Note 4, below).

Notes

1. Citrate is added to complex any iron (III) that may be present and to remove it as an interference.
2. Bromine is added to oxidize Ni (II) to Ni (III), the latter forming the wine-colored complex whose intensity is measured. Excess bromine is removed (and the solution decolorized) after making the solution ammoniacal.
3. If a red-colored precipitate appears on adding dimethylglyoxime, the oxidation to Ni (III) has not been effected, or too large an amount of nickel has been taken. The sample is therefore discarded.
4. Water may be used as the reagent blank if the latter is measured against water at 520 mμ and a correction, if any, is added to the sample readings. Color intensity should be measured within 15 min after development, since intensity increases with time.

Spectrophotometric Determination of Cobalt: Reagents

Stannous chloride: 20 grams reagent-grade $SnCl_2 \cdot 2H_2O$ dissolved in 40 ml HCl. Let stand 30 min and dilute to 100 ml with H_2O. Add a piece of tin foil.

3 M ammonium thiocyanate in acetone, prepared fresh daily (Note 1, below).

6 M hydrochloric acid.

Procedure*

1. Pipet an aliquot containing cobalt (0.05 to 0.50 mg) into a 25-ml volumetric flask.

* E. B. Sandell, *ibid*.

2. Add 2 ml 6 M hydrochloric acid.
3. Add 2 or 3 drops stannous chloride reagent (Note 2, below).
4. Add 15.00 ml of 3 M ammonium thiocyanate in acetone.
5. Dilute to 25.00 ml with water, mix, and pour into a 1-cm spectrophotometric cell. Read at 625 mμ in a Beckman Model B spectrophotometer against a solution blank containing all the above reagents except cobalt (Note 3, below).

Notes

1. The thiocyanate-in-acetone reagent is prepared fresh daily, since it deteriorates on standing.
2. Added to remove any possible iron interference by reducing iron(III) to iron(II), the latter forming no colored complex with thiocyanate.
3. Water is usually used as the reagent blank if a series of samples is being analyzed, since the solutions deteriorate on standing. In this case the reagent blank is measured against water at 625 mμ and a correction, if any, is added to the sample readings. The use of stoppered cells is advised to prevent creeping of the acetone-thiocyanate solution to the outside of the cells.

Appendices

APPENDIX 1

SOME ABBREVIATIONS FOR THE LITERATURE*

AECD	Declassified reports, U. S. Atomic Energy Commission, Oak Ridge, Tenn.
AECU	Unclassified reports, U. S. Atomic Energy Commission, Oak Ridge, Tenn.
ACCO	American Cyanamid Company, Watertown, Mass.
Acta Crys.	Acta Crystallographica.
ADD	Abstracts of Declassified Documents. Predecessor of NSA (July 1948).
ACRH	Argonne Cancer Research Hospital, Chicago, Ill.
AEP	Monsanto Chemical Company, St. Louis, Mo.
ALO	AEC, Albuquerque Operations Office, Albuquerque, N. M.
Am. J. Phys.	American Journal of Physics.
AMF	American Machine & Foundry Co., Greenwich, Conn.
Anal. Chem.	Analytical Chemistry.
ANL	Argonne National Laboratory, Lemont, Ill.
ANP	Aircraft Nuclear Propulsion Project, Oak Ridge, Tenn.
APAE	Alco Products, Inc., American Locomotive Co., Schenectady, N. Y.
APDA	Atomic Power Development Associates, Detroit, Mich.
APEX	General Electric Company, ANP Project, Cincinnati, Ohio.
BAW	Babcock & Wilcox, New York, N. Y.
BDX	Bendix Aviation Corp., Detroit, Mich.
BMI	Battelle Memorial Institute, Columbus, Ohio.
BNL	Brookhaven National Lab., Upton, Long Island, N. Y.
BRB	Bridgeport Brass Company, Bridgeport, Conn.
BSC	Bethlehem Steel Company, Quincy, Mass.
Can. J. Chem.	Canadian Journal of Chemistry.
Can. J. Phys.	Canadian Journal of Physics.
Can. J. Research	Canadian Journal of Research.
CERD	Combustion Engineering, Inc., Windsor, Conn.
COO	AEC, Chicago Operations Office, Lemont, Ill.
CU	Columbia University, New York, N. Y.
DLWK	Duquesne Light Co., Walter Kidde Nuclear Laboratories, Pittsburgh, Pa.
DOW	Dow Chemical Company, Detroit, Mich.
DP	E. I. du Pont de Nemours & Co., Aiken, S. C.

*The unclassified Atomic Energy Project reports are sold by the Office of Technical Services, Department of Commerce, Washington 25, D. C.

430

FWE	Foreign Weapons Effects, AEC, Oak Ridge, Tenn.
GAT	Goodyear Atomic Corp., Portsmouth, Ohio.
GEAP	General Electric Company, Schenectady, N. Y.
GEL	General Electric Co., General Engineering Laboratory, Schenectady, N. Y.
HEC	Hooker Electrochemical Co., Niagara Falls, N. Y.
HO	AEC, Hanford Operations Office, Richland, Wash.
HW	General Electric Co., Hanford Works, Richland, Wash.
IDO	AEC, Idaho Operations Office, Idaho Falls, Idaho.
Ind. Eng. Chem.	Industrial and Engineering Chemistry.
ISC	Iowa State College, Ames, Iowa.
J. Amer. Chem. Soc.	Journal of the American Chemical Society.
J. Appl. Phys.	Journal of Applied Physics.
J. Biol. Chem.	Journal of Biological Chemistry.
J. Chem. Ed.	Journal of Chemical Education.
J. Chem. Phys.	Journal of Chemical Physics.
J. Chem. Soc.	Journal of the Chemical Society (London).
K	Union Carbide Nuclear Co. (K-25 Plant), Oak Ridge, Tenn.
KAPL	Knolls Atomic Power Lab. (General Electric Co.), Schenectady, N. Y.
KLX	The Vitro Corporation of America, New York, N. Y.
KLXS	The Vitro Corporation of America (Study Group), New York, N. Y.
KY	Union Carbide Nuclear Co. (C-31 Plant), Paducah, Ky.
LA&LAMS	Los Alamos Scientific Lab., Los Alamos, N. M.
MCW	Mallinckrodt Chemical Works, St. Louis, Mo.
MDDC	Predecessor of AECD (March 1948).
MIT	Massachusetts Institute of Technology, Cambridge, Mass.
MLM	Mound Laboratory, Miamisburg, Ohio.
NAA-SR	North American Aviation, Inc., Canoga Park, Calif.
NBL	New Brunswick Laboratory, New Brunswick, N. J.
NBS	National Bureau of Standards, Washington, D. C.
NDA	Nuclear Development Corp. of America, White Plains, N. Y.
NEA	Foster Wheeler-Pioneer Service & Engineering Co., New York, N. Y.
NLCO	National Lead Company of Ohio, Cincinnati, Ohio.
NMI	Nuclear Metals, Inc., Cambridge, Mass.
NNES	National Nuclear Energy Series, McGraw-Hill Book Co., Inc., New York, N. Y.
NNSD	Newport News Shipbuilding & Dry Dock Co., Newport News, Va.
NP	"Non-Project" research and development reports.
NPG	Commonwealth Edison Company (Nuclear Power Group), Chicago, Ill.
NSA	Nuclear Science Abstracts, Superintendent of Documents, U. S. Government Printing Office, Washington 25, D. C.
NYO	AEC, New York Operations Office, New York, N. Y.
Nuc. Sci. Eng.	Nuclear Science and Engineering.
ORINS	Oak Ridge Institute of Nuclear Studies, Oak Ridge, Tenn.
ORNL	Oak Ridge National Laboratory, Union Carbide Nuclear Co. (ORNL), Oak Ridge, Tenn.

ORO	AEC, Oak Ridge Operations Office, Oak Ridge, Tenn.
OTS	Office of Technical Services, Department of Commerce, Washington, D. C.
Phys. Rev.	The Physical Review.
PNG	Pacific Northwest Power Group, Richland, Wash.
PWAC	Pratt & Whitney Aircraft Div. of the United Aircraft Corp., East Hartford, Conn.
Rev. Mod. Phys.	Reviews of Modern Physics.
Rev. Sci. Instr.	Review of Scientific Instruments.
RFP	Rocky Flats Plant, Denver, Colo.
RME&RMO	Exploration Reports, AEC, Division of Raw Materials, Washington, D. C.
SAN	AEC, San Francisco Operations Office, San Francisco, Calif.
SC	Sandia Corporation, Sandia Base, Albuquerque, N. M.
SEP	Sylvania Electric Products, Inc., Boston, Mass.
SRO	AEC, Savannah River Operations Office, Aiken, S. C.
SO	AEC, Schenectady Operations Office, Schenectady, N. Y.
TEI&TEM	U. S. Geological Survey, Trace Elements Reports, Washington, D. C.
TID	AEC, Technical Information Service, Oak Ridge, Tenn.
TVA	Tennessee Valley Authority, Chattanooga, Tenn.
UCLA	University of California Medical Research Lab., Los Angeles, Calif.
UCRL	University of California Radiation Laboratory, Berkeley, Calif.
UR	University of Rochester, Rochester, N. Y.
UWFL	University of Washington Applied Fisheries Lab., Seattle, Wash.
WAPD	Westinghouse Elect. Corp., Atomic Power Division, Pittsburgh, Pa.
WASH	Atomic Energy Commission, Washington, D. C.
WEC	Westinghouse Electric Company, Industrial Atomic Power Group, Pittsburgh, Pa.
WIN	National Lead Co., Inc., Winchester, Mass.
WT	Weapon Test Reports, AEC, Oak Ridge, Tenn.
Y	Union Carbide Nuclear Company (Y-12 Plant), Oak Ridge, Tenn.

APPENDIX 2

CONVERSION OF ENERGY UNITS

```
          ┌─────────────┐
          │   Grams     │
          │     ↑       │
          │ 2.51 × 10⁷  │
          │     ↓       │
          │   Kw-hr     │
          │     ↑       │
          │   3413      │
          │     ↓       │
          │    Btu      │
          │     ↑       │
          │    252      │
          │     ↓       │
          │  Calories   │
          │  (gram)     │
          │   3.087     │
          │     ↓       │
          │   Ft-lb     │
          │     ↑       │
          │   1.356     │
          │     ↓       │
          │   Joules    │
          │     ↑       │
          │    10⁷      │
          │     ↓       │
          │    Ergs     │
          │     ↑       │
          │    672      │
          │     ↓       │
          │   Atomic    │
          │ mass units  │
          │     ↑       │
          │    931      │
          │     ↓       │
          │    Mev      │
          │     ↑       │
          │    10⁶      │
          │     ↓       │
          │     ev      │
          └─────────────┘
```

MULTIPLY:

Btu's by	To obtain
252	calories (gram)
1.055×10^{10}	ergs
778	ft-lb
1.17×10^{-11}	grams
1055	joules
2.93×10^{-4}	kw-hr
7.09×10^{12}	mass units
6.58×10^{15}	Mevs

Calories (gram) by	To obtain
3.968×10^{-3}	Btu's
4.185×10^{7}	ergs
3.0874	ft-lb
4.651×10^{-14}	grams
4.185	joules
1.1628×10^{-6}	kw-hr
2.81×10^{10}	mass units
2.62×10^{13}	Mevs

Ergs by	To obtain
9.480×10^{-11}	Btu's
2.389×10^{-8}	calories (gram)
7.3756×10^{-8}	ft-lb
1.111×10^{-21}	grams
1.000×10^{-7}	joules
2.778×10^{-14}	kw-hr
6.703×10^{2}	mass units
6.242×10^{5}	Mevs

Ft-lb by	To obtain
1.285×10^{-3}	Btu's
0.3239	calories (gram)
1.356×10^{7}	ergs
1.51×10^{-14}	grams
1.356	joules
3.766×10^{-7}	kw-hr
9.10×10^{9}	mass units
8.47×10^{12}	Mevs

MULTIPLY:

Grams by	To obtain
8.53×10^{10}	Btu's
2.15×10^{13}	calories (gram)
9.0×10^{20}	ergs
6.63×10^{13}	ft-lb
9.0×10^{13}	joules
2.50×10^{7}	kw-hr
6.02×10^{23}	mass units
5.62×10^{26}	Mevs

Joules by	To obtain
9.480×10^{-4}	Btu's
0.2389	calories (gram)
1×10^{7}	ergs
0.7376	ft-lb
1.11×10^{-14}	grams
2.778×10^{-7}	kw-hr
6.703×10^{9}	mass units
6.242×10^{12}	Mevs

Kw-hr by	To obtain
3.413×10^{3}	Btu's
8.600×10^{5}	calories (gram)
3.600×10^{13}	ergs
2.655×10^{6}	ft-lb
4.00×10^{-8}	grams
3.600×10^{6}	joules
2.41×10^{16}	mass units
2.247×10^{19}	Mevs

Mass units by	To obtain
1.413×10^{-13}	Btu's
3.565×10^{-11}	calories (gram)
1.49×10^{-3}	ergs
1.10×10^{-10}	ft-lb
1.660×10^{-24}	grams
1.492×10^{-10}	joules
4.15×10^{-17}	kw-hr
931.1	Mevs

Mevs by	To obtain
1.520×10^{-16}	Btu's
3.83×10^{-14}	calories (gram)
1.602×10^{-6}	ergs
1.18×10^{-13}	ft-lb
1.78×10^{-27}	grams
1.602×10^{-13}	joules
4.45×10^{-20}	kw-hr
1.074×10^{-3}	mass units

MULTIPLY:	*by*	*To obtain*
Horsepower	2.544×10^3	Btu/hr
Horsepower	0.7457	kw
Kw	1.341	horsepower
Btu/hr	3.930×10^{-4}	horsepower
Thermal conductivity in		
Btu/lb · ft² °F/ft	4.134×10^{-3}	cal/g cm² °C/cm
Cal/g cm² °C/cm	241.9	Btu/lb ft² · °F/ft
Viscosity in		
Centipoise	2.419	lb/hr ft
lb/hr ft	0.4134	centipoise
Density		
lb/ft³	1.601×10^{-2}	g/cm³
g/cm³	62.43	lb/ft³

3.1×10^{10} fissions of U^{235} per sec give 1 watt.
1 gram U^{235} fissioned gives approximately 1 megawatt-day.
1 lb U^{235} fissioned gives 10^7 kw-hr.

APPENDIX 3

DECAY AND EXPOSURE FACTORS FOR INDIUM

From "Decay Factors for the Computation of Saturated Activities of Indium Foils," NEPA-1558, Revised by Robert G. Cochran, Pennsylvania State University Research Reactor.

In the following table the functions $e^{-\lambda t}$ and $1 - e^{-\lambda t}$ are tabulated for indium foils. The decay constant of indium is based on a half-life time of 54.0 min = 2.1393×10^{-4} sec^{-1} = 1.2836×10^{-2} min^{-1} = 7.7016×10^{-1} hr^{-1}.

In the following tables the functions $N = e^{-\lambda t}$ and $1 - N = (1 - e^{-\lambda t})$ are tabulated from 1 to 120 min by minutes, and from 1 to 10 hr by hours.

The values of the function $e^{-\lambda t}$ for times which are not tabulated (e.g., 2 hr 5 min) can be calculated according to $e^{-\lambda 125 \text{ min}} = e^{-\lambda 2 \text{ hr}} \times e^{-\lambda 5 \text{ min}} = 0.21431 \times 0.93784 = 0.20099$.

By subtracting the so calculated value $e^{-\lambda t}$ from 1, the value for $1 - e^{-\lambda t}$ is obtained.

Minutes	*N*	$1 - N$	*Minutes*	*N*	$1 - N$
1.0	98 724	01 275	16.0	81 434	18 565
2.0	97 465	02 534	17.0	80 395	19 604
3.0	96 222	03 777	18.0	79 370	20 629
4.0	94 995	05 004	19.0	78 357	21 642
5.0	93 783	06 216	20.0	77 358	22 641
6.0	92 587	07 412	21.0	76 371	23 628
7.0	91 406	08 593	22.0	75 397	24 602
8.0	90 240	09 759	23.0	74 436	25 563
9.0	89 089	10 910	24.0	73 486	26 513
10.0	87 953	12 046	25.0	72 549	27 450
11.0	86 831	13 168	26.0	71 624	28 375
12.0	85 724	14 275	27.0	70 710	29 289
13.0	84 631	15 368	28.0	69 808	30 191
14.0	83 551	16 448	29.0	68 918	31 081
15.0	82 486	17 513	30.0	68 039	31 960

Minutes	N	1 − N	Minutes	N	1 − N
31.0	67 171	32 828	76.0	37 699	62 300
32.0	66 315	33 684	77.0	37 218	62 781
33.0	65 469	34 530	78.0	36 743	63 256
34.0	64 634	35 365	79.0	36 274	63 725
35.0	63 810	36 189	80.0	35 812	64 187
36.0	62 996	37 003	81.0	35 355	64 644
37.0	62 192	37 807	82.0	34 904	65 095
38.0	61 399	38 600	83.0	34 459	65 540
39.0	60 616	39 383	84.0	34 019	65 980
40.0	59 843	40 156	85.0	33 586	66 413
41.0	59 080	40 919	86.0	33 157	66 842
42.0	58 326	41 673	87.0	32 734	67 265
43.0	57 582	42 417	88.0	32 317	67 682
44.0	56 848	43 151	89.0	31 905	68 094
45.0	56 123	43 876	90.0	31 498	68 501
46.0	55 407	44 592	91.0	31 096	68 903
47.0	54 700	45 299	92.0	30 699	69 300
48.0	54 003	45 996	93.0	30 308	69 691
49.0	53 314	46 685	94.0	29 921	70 078
50.0	52 634	47 365	95.0	29 540	70 459
51.0	51 963	48 036	96.0	29 163	70 836
52.0	51 300	48 699	97.0	28 791	71 208
53.0	50 646	49 353	98.0	28 424	71 575
54.0	50 000	49 999	99.0	28 061	71 938
55.0	49 362	50 637	100.0	27 703	72 296
56.0	48 732	51 267	101.0	27 350	72 649
57.0	48 111	51 888	102.0	27 001	72 998
58.0	47 497	52 502	103.0	26 657	73 342
59.0	46 891	53 108	104.0	26 317	73 682
60.0	46 293	53 706	105.0	25 981	74 018
61.0	45 703	54 296	106.0	25 650	74 349
62.0	45 120	54 879	107.0	25 323	74 676
63.0	44 545	55 454	108.0	25 000	74 999
64.0	43 976	56 023	109.0	24 681	75 318
65.0	43 416	56 583	110.0	24 366	75 633
66.0	42 862	57 137	111.0	24 055	75 944
67.0	42 315	57 684	112.0	24 748	76 251
68.0	41 776	58 223	113.0	23 446	76 553
69.0	41 243	58 756	114.0	23 147	76 852
70.0	40 717	59 282	115.0	22 851	77 148
71.0	40 197	59 802	116.0	22 560	77 439
72.0	39 685	60 314	117.0	22 272	77 727
73.0	39 179	60 820	118.0	21 988	78 011
74.0	38 679	61 320	119.0	21 708	78 291
75.0	38 186	61 813	120.0	21 431	78 568

Hours	N	1 − N	Hours	N	1 − N
1	46 293	53 706	6	00 984	99 015
2	21 431	78 568	7	455	544
3	09 921	90 078	8	210	789
4	04 592	95 407	9	097	902
5	02 126	97 873	10	045	954

APPENDIX 4

DECAY AND EXPOSURE FACTORS FOR GOLD

Compiled by Robert G. Cochran, Pennsylvania State University Research Reactor, from data supplied by ORNL.

For the calculation of the saturated activities of gold foils which were exposed to a certain neutron flux, the values of the functions $e^{-\lambda t}$ and $(1 - e^{-\lambda t})$ are necessary over a wide interval of time. The decay constant of gold based on a half-life time of 2.70 days $\lambda = 2.9706 \times 10^{-6}\,\text{sec}^{-1}$, $\lambda = 1.7824 \times 10^{-4}\,\text{min}^{-1}$, $\lambda = 1.0694 \times 10^{-2}\,\text{hr}^{-1}$, $\lambda = 2.5666 \times 10^{-1}\,\text{days}^{-1}$.

In the following tables the functions $N = e^{-\lambda t}$ and $(1 - N) = (1 - e^{-\lambda t})$ are tabulated from 1 to 180 min by minutes, from 1 to 48 hr by hours, and from 1 to 30 days by days.

The values of the function $e^{-\lambda t}$ for times which are not tabulated (e.g., 5 hr 36 min) can be calculated according to $e^{-\lambda 336\,\text{min}} = e^{-\lambda 5\,\text{hr}} \times e^{-\lambda 36\,\text{min}} = 0.94793 \times 0.99360 = 0.94186$.

By subtracting the so calculated value $e^{-\lambda t}$ from 1, the value for $(1 - e^{-\lambda t})$ is obtained.

Minutes	N	1 − N	Minutes	N	1 − N
1	99 982	00 017	21	99 626	00 373
2	964	035	22	608	391
3	946	053	23	590	409
4	928	071	24	573	426
5	910	089	25	555	444
6	99 893	00 106	26	99 537	00 462
7	875	124	27	519	480
8	857	142	28	502	497
9	839	160	29	484	515
10	821	178	30	466	533
11	99 804	00 195	31	99 448	00 551
12	786	213	32	431	568
13	768	231	33	413	586
14	750	249	34	395	604
15	732	267	35	378	621
16	99 715	00 284	36	99 360	00 639
17	697	302	37	342	657
18	679	320	38	324	675
19	661	338	39	307	692
20	644	355	40	289	710

Minutes	N	1 − N	Minutes	N	1 − N
41	99 271	00 728	86	98 478	01 521
42	254	745	87	461	538
43	236	763	88	443	556
44	218	781	89	426	573
45	201	798	90	408	591
46	99 183	00 816	91	98 391	01 608
47	165	834	92	373	626
48	148	851	93	356	643
49	130	869	94	338	661
50	112	887	95	320	679
51	99 095	00 904	96	98 303	01 696
52	077	922	97	285	714
53	059	940	98	268	731
54	042	957	99	250	749
55	024	975	100	233	766
56	99 006	00 993	101	98 215	01 784
57	98 989	01 010	102	198	801
58	971	028	103	180	819
59	953	046	104	163	836
60	936	063	105	145	854
61	98 918	01 081	106	98 128	01 871
62	900	099	107	110	889
63	883	116	108	093	906
64	865	134	109	075	924
65	848	151	110	058	941
66	98 830	01 169	111	98 040	01 959
67	812	187	112	023	976
68	795	204	113	006	993
69	777	222	114	97 988	02 011
70	760	239	115	971	028
71	98 742	01 257	116	97 953	02 046
72	724	275	117	936	063
73	707	292	118	918	081
74	689	310	119	901	098
75	672	327	120	883	116
76	98 654	01 345	121	97 866	02 133
77	636	363	122	848	151
78	619	380	123	831	168
79	601	398	124	814	185
80	584	415	125	796	203
81	98 566	01 433	126	97 779	02 220
82	549	450	127	761	238
83	531	468	128	744	255
84	513	486	129	726	273
85	496	503	130	709	290

Minutes	N	1 − N	Minutes	N	1 − N
131	97 692	02 307	156	97 257	02 742
132	674	325	157	240	759
133	657	342	158	223	776
134	639	360	159	205	794
135	622	377	160	188	811
136	97 605	02 394	161	97 171	02 828
137	587	412	162	153	846
138	570	429	163	136	863
139	552	447	164	119	880
140	535	464	165	101	898
141	97 518	02 481	166	97 084	02 915
142	500	499	167	067	932
143	483	516	168	049	950
144	466	533	169	032	967
145	448	551	170	015	984
146	97 431	02 568	171	96 998	03 001
147	413	586	172	980	019
148	396	603	173	963	036
149	379	620	174	946	053
150	361	638	175	928	071
151	97 344	02 655	176	96 911	03 088
152	327	672	177	894	105
153	309	690	178	877	122
154	292	707	179	859	140
155	275	724	180	842	157

Hours	N	1 − N	Hours	N	1 − N
1	98 936	01 063	19	81 611	18 388
2	97 883	02 116	20	80 743	19 256
3	96 842	03 157	21	79 884	20 115
4	95 812	04 187	22	79 035	20 964
5	94 793	05 206	23	78 194	21 805
6	93 784	06 215	24	77 362	22 637
7	92 787	07 212	25	76 539	23 460
8	91 800	08 199	26	75 725	24 274
9	90 823	09 176	27	74 919	25 080
10	89 857	10 142	28	74 122	25 877
11	88 901	11 098	29	73 334	26 665
12	87 956	12 043	30	72 554	27 445
13	87 020	12 979	31	71 782	28 217
14	86 094	13 905	32	71 019	28 980
15	85 178	14 821	33	70 263	29 736
16	84 272	15 727	34	69 516	30 483
17	83 376	16 623	35	68 776	31 223
18	82 489	17 510	36	68 045	31 954

Hours	N	1 − N	Hours	N	1 − N
37	67 321	32 678	43	63 137	36 862
38	66 605	33 394	44	62 465	37 534
39	65 896	34 103	45	61 801	38 198
40	65 195	34 804	46	61 143	38 856
41	64 502	35 497	47	60 493	39 506
42	63 815	36 184	48	59 849	40 150

Days	N	1 − N	Days	N	1 − N
1	77 362	22 637	16	01 646	98 353
2	59 849	40 150	17	01 273	98 726
3	46 301	53 698	18	00 985	99 014
4	35 819	64 180	19	762	237
5	27 711	72 288	20	589	410
6	21 438	78 561	21	00 456	99 543
7	16 585	83 414	22	352	647
8	12 830	87 169	23	273	726
9	09 926	90 073	24	211	788
10	07 679	92 320	25	163	836
11	05 940	94 059	26	00 126	99 873
12	04 595	95 404	27	097	902
13	03 555	96 444	28	075	924
14	02 750	97 249	29	058	941
15	02 127	97 872	30	045	954

APPENDIX 5

PHYSICAL AND THERMODYNAMIC PROPERTIES OF LIGHT AND HEAVY WATER

Selected from Volume 2, Section 1, "Reactor Handbook," "Light and Heavy Water Cooled Systems (ANL)," Chapter 1.3. Physical and Thermodynamic properties of Light and Heavy Water, by P. A. Lottes.

The properties of light and heavy liquid water and light-water vapor frequently used in heat transfer calculations are presented in tabular and/or graphic form. Heavy-water properties are available for relatively low temperatures only and are generally similar to those of light water. For most engineering calculations concerning heavy water at higher temperatures, the corresponding property of light water, with the exception of density, has been used, since data are not available above approximately 100°F.

The data are presented by individual property. Critical properties, constant pressure specific heat, thermal conductivity, dynamic viscosity, Prandtl number, density, and latent heat values are included when available; exception is made for specific heat of light-water vapor and latent heat of light water, because data presented in Keenan and Keyes* are the best available. In general, a tabular compilation of the physical and

* J. H. Keenan and F. G. Keyes, "Thermodynamic Properties of Steam," 1st ed., John Wiley & Sons, Inc., New York (1936).

thermodynamic properties for light and heavy liquid water are presented. Whenever possible, a graphical comparison of these properties is included. Graphs of frequently used properties of light-water vapor are included. Thermal conductivity data for heavy water are not available; consequently, thermal conductivity and the Prandtl number calculation, which includes the value of thermal conductivity, have been omitted.

A recent study by Wellman* presents a review of available data on the thermodynamic and physical properties of light liquid water in the form of tables of values; the study includes an evaluation of the accuracy of the values reported. These data were used in the preparation of this chapter with the exception that graphical data for the density and vapor pressure of light liquid water were taken from Keenan and Keyes.

The data of Kirshenbaum† for heavy water have been recalculated into units used predominately in engineering heat-transfer calculations.

Values for the properties of light water vapor were provided by Sibbitt‡ from an evaluation currently being made by Purdue University.

TABLE A5-1. CRITICAL PROPERTIES OF LIGHT WATER

Critical temperature	705.40 °F
	374.2 °C
Critical pressure	3206 psia
	218.2 atm
Critical density	19.9 lb/ft³
	0.320 g/ml

TABLE A5-2. CRITICAL PROPERTIES OF HEAVY WATER

Critical temperature	700.7 °F
	371.5 °C
Critical pressure	3212 psia
	218.6 atm
Critical density	22.7 lb/ft³
	0.363 g/ml

* E. J. Wellman, "A Survey of the Thermodynamic and Physical Properties of Water," M. S. Thesis, Purdue University (January, 1950).

† I. Kirshenbaum, "Physical Properties and Analysis of Heavy Water," 1st ed., McGraw-Hill Book Co., Inc., New York (1951).

‡ Communication from W. L. Sibbitt, School of Mechanical Engineering, Purdue University.

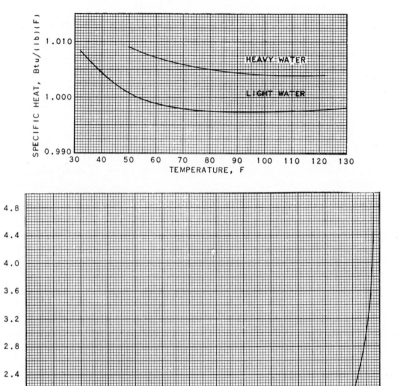

Fig. A5-1. Specific heat data for light and heavy liquid water.
(Submitted from values of Wellman and Kirshenbaum.)

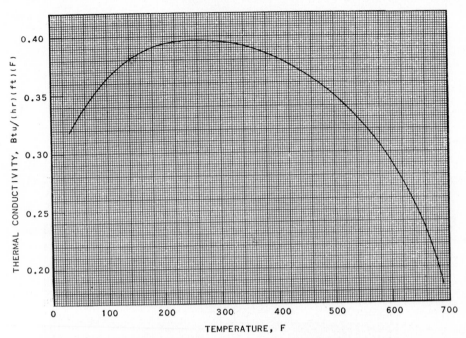

FIG. A5-2. Thermal conductivity values for light liquid water.
(Submitted from values of Wellman.)

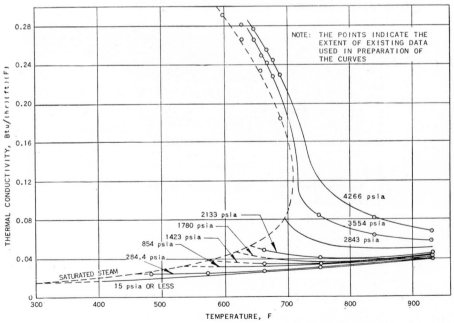

NOTE: THE POINTS INDICATE THE EXTENT OF EXISTING DATA USED IN PREPARATION OF THE CURVES

4266 psia
3554 psia
2843 psia
2133 psia
1780 psia
1423 psia
854 psia
284.4 psia
SATURATED STEAM
15 psia OR LESS

FIG. A5-3. Thermal conductivity data for light water vapor.
(Submitted from data of Keyes and Sandell and from Timroth and Vargaftig, by
W. L. Sibbitt, Purdue University, June 23, 1952.)

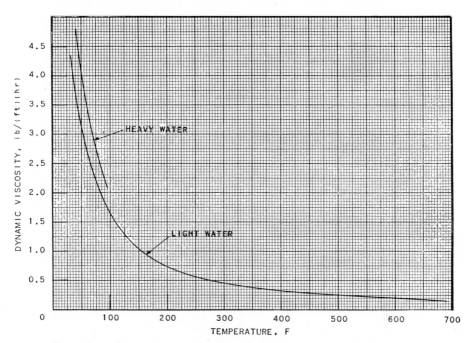

FIG. A5-4. Dynamic viscosity data for light and heavy liquid water.
(Submitted from data of Wellman and Kirshenbaum.)

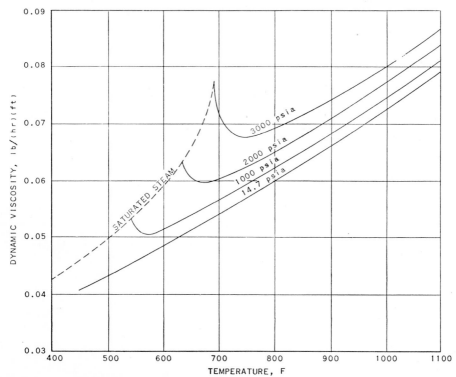

FIG. A5-5. Dynamic viscosity values for light water vapor.
(Submitted from data of Timroth by W. L. Sibbitt, Purdue University, June 23, 1952.)

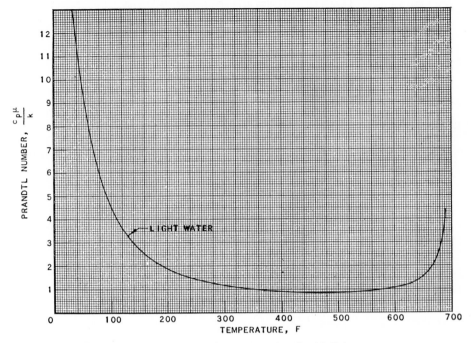

FIG. A5-6.   Prandtl number values for liquid light water.
(Submitted from values of Wellman.)

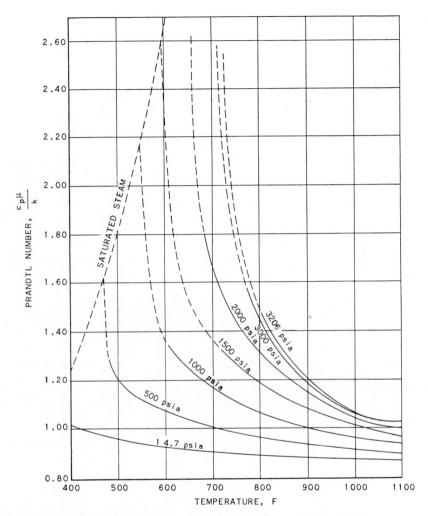

FIG. A5-7. Graphical presentation of Prandtl number value for light water vapor. (Submitted from calculations of W. L. Sibbitt, Purdue University, June 23, 1952.)

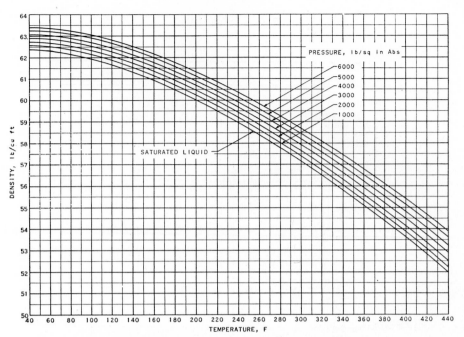

FIG. A5-8. Density values for light water (40-440°F).
(Submitted from values of Keenan and Keyes.)

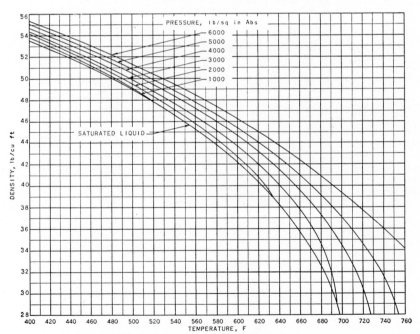

FIG. A5-9. Density for light water (400-760°F).
(Submitted from values of Keenan and Keyes.)

446

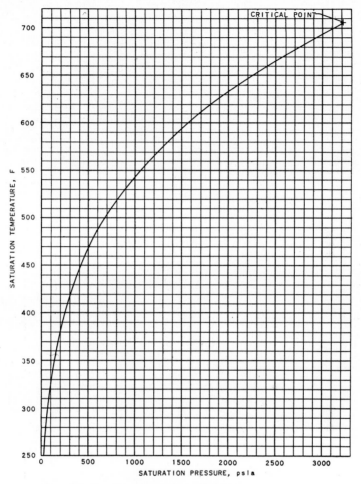

Fig. A5-10. Vapor pressure values for light water.
(Submitted from data of Keenan and Keyes.)

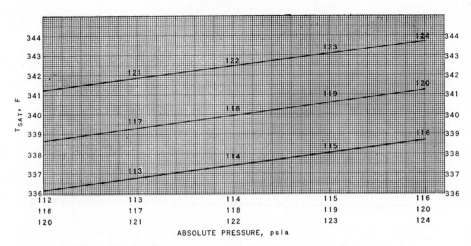

FIG. A5-11. Pressure vs. saturation temperature for water.
(Data from Keenan and Keyes.)

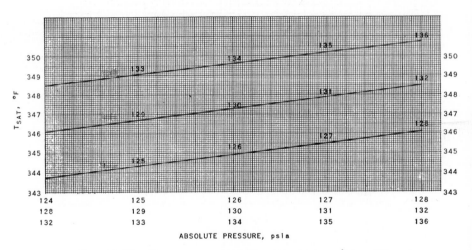

FIG. A5-12. Pressure vs. saturation temperature for water.
(Data from Keenan and Keyes.)

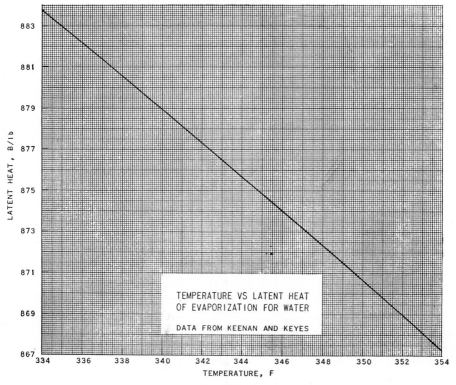

FIG. A5-13.

TABLE A5-3. ABSOLUTE DENSITY (ρ) OF LIQUID HEAVY WATER AT 1 ATM[a]

Temperature		ρ	
°F	°C	lb/ft³	gram/cm³
41	5	69.0176	1.10555
50	10	69.0444	1.10598
51.8	11	69.0450	1.10599
53.6	12	69.0450	1.10599
55.4	13	69.0438	1.10597
59	15	69.0382	1.10588
68	20	69.0063	1.10537
77	25	68.9508	1.10448
86	30	68.8746	1.10326
95	35	68.7828	1.10179
104	40	68.6723	1.10002

[a] Accuracy: 0.003%.

TABLE A5-4. VAPOR PRESSURE OF LIQUID HEAVY WATER

Temperature		Pressure	
°C	°F	Atm (absolute)	Psia
0	32	0.00480	0.0705
10	50	.01025	.1506
20	68	.0200	.2939
30	86	.0368	.5408
40	104	.0647	.9508
50	122	.1100	1.616
60	140	.1797	2.641
70	158	.2843	4.178
80	176	.4363	6.412
90	194	.6520	9.582
100	212	.9503	13.96
110	230	1.353	19.88
120	248	1.888	27.75
130	266	2.584	37.97
140	284	3.474	51.05
150	302	4.596	67.54
160	320	5.993	88.07
170	338	7.707	113.3
180	356	9.788	143.8
190	374	12.29	180.6
200	392	15.26	224.3
210	410	18.77	275.8
220	428	22.87	336.1
230	446	27.63	406.0
240	464	33.17	487.5
371.5	700.7	218.6	3212

APPENDIX 6

TRANSPORT PROPERTIES OF SODIUM-POTASSIUM ALLOY (NaK)*
(22 per cent Na, 78 per cent K, approximately the eutectic mixture)

Temp., °F	Density, ρ lb/ft^3	Viscosity, μ lb/(hr ft)	Thermal Cond., k Btu/(hr ft^2 °F/ft)	Sp. Ht., c Btu/lb °F	Prandtl No. $N_{Pr} = \mu c/k$
200	53	1.18	14.1	0.225	0.019
400	51.5	0.78	14.6	0.215	0.0115
600	49.5	0.58	15.1	0.21	0.008
800	48	0.45	15.5	0.21	0.006
1000	46.5	0.37	15.8	0.21	0.005

* From B. Lubarsky and S. J. Kaufman, "Review of Experimental Investigations of Liquid-Metal Heat Transfer," National Advisory Committee of Aeronautics, Tech. Note 3336 (March 1955); R. N. Lyon (Ed.), "Liquid Metals Handbook," Government Printing Office, NAVEXOS P-733 (Rev.) (1952); C. B. Jackson (Ed.), "Liquid Metals Handbook" (Supplement), Government Printing Office, TID 5227 (1955).

APPENDIX 7

THERMOCOUPLE CALIBRATION DATA

TABLE A7-1. CHROMEL-ALUMEL THERMOCOUPLES[a]

(Electromotive Force in Absolute Millivolts.   Temperatures in Degrees C (Int. 1948).   Reference Junctions at 0° C.)

Millivolts	.00	.10	.20	.30	.40	.50	.60	.70	.80	.90	1.00	Millivolts
						Degrees C						
−5.00	−158	−163	−168	−173	−178	−184	−190					−5.00
−4.00	−118	−122	−125	−129	−133	−137	−141	−145	−149	−154	−158	−4.00
−3.00	−84	−87	−90	−94	−97	−100	−104	−107	−111	−114	−118	−3.00
−2.00	−54	−57	−60	−63	−66	−69	−72	−75	−78	−81	−84	−2.00
−1.00	−26	−29	−32	−34	−37	−40	−43	−46	−48	−51	−54	−1.00
(−)0.00	0	−3	−5	−8	−10	−13	−16	−18	−21	−24	−26	(−)0.00
(+)0.00	0	3	5	8	10	13	15	18	20	23	25	(+)0.00
1.00	25	28	30	32	35	37	40	42	45	47	49	1.00
2.00	49	52	54	57	59	62	64	67	69	71	74	2.00
3.00	74	76	78	81	83	86	88	91	93	95	98	3.00
4.00	98	100	102	105	107	110	112	114	117	119	122	4.00
5.00	122	124	127	129	132	134	137	139	142	144	147	5.00
6.00	147	149	152	154	157	159	162	164	167	169	172	6.00
7.00	172	174	177	179	182	184	187	189	192	194	197	7.00
8.00	197	199	202	204	207	209	212	214	217	219	222	8.00
9.00	222	224	227	229	232	234	236	239	241	244	246	9.00
10.00	246	249	251	253	256	258	261	263	266	268	271	10.00
11.00	271	273	276	278	280	283	285	288	290	292	295	11.00
12.00	295	297	300	302	304	307	309	312	314	317	319	12.00
13.00	319	321	324	326	329	331	333	336	338	341	343	13.00
14.00	343	345	348	350	353	355	357	360	362	364	367	14.00
15.00	367	369	372	374	376	379	381	383	386	388	391	15.00
16.00	391	393	395	398	400	402	405	407	409	412	414	16.00
17.00	414	417	419	421	424	426	428	431	433	436	438	17.00
18.00	438	440	443	445	447	450	452	454	457	459	461	18.00
19.00	461	464	466	468	471	473	476	478	480	483	485	19.00
20.00	485	487	489	492	494	497	499	501	504	506	508	20.00
21.00	508	511	513	516	518	520	522	525	527	529	532	21.00
22.00	532	534	537	539	541	543	546	548	551	553	555	22.00
23.00	555	558	560	562	564	567	569	572	574	576	579	23.00
24.00	579	581	583	586	588	590	593	595	597	600	602	24.00
25.00	602	604	607	609	612	614	616	618	621	623	626	25.00
26.00	626	628	630	633	635	637	640	642	644	647	649	26.00
27.00	649	652	654	656	659	661	663	666	668	671	673	27.00
28.00	673	675	678	680	682	685	687	690	692	694	697	28.00
29.00	697	699	702	704	706	709	711	713	716	718	721	29.00
30.00	721	723	725	728	730	733	735	737	740	742	744	30.00
Millivolts	.00	.10	.20	.30	.40	.50	.60	.70	.80	.90	1.00	Millivolts

[a] From "Reference Tables for Thermocouples." U. S. Department of Commerce, National Bureau of Standards. Bulletin NBS Circular 561. Superintendent of Documents, Government Printing Office, Washington 25, D. C.

TABLE A7-1. CHROMEL-ALUMEL THERMOCOUPLES (*continued*)

(Electromotive Force in Absolute Millivolts. Temperatures in Degrees C (Int. 1948). Reference Junctions at 0° C.)

Millivolts	.00	.10	.20	.30	,40	.50	.60	.70	.80	.90	1.00	Millivolts
	Degrees C											
30.00	721	723	725	728	730	733	735	737	740	742	744	30.00
31.00	744	747	749	752	754	757	759	761	764	766	768	31.00
32.00	768	771	773	776	778	781	783	786	788	790	793	32.00
33.00	793	795	798	800	802	805	807	810	812	815	817	33.00
34.00	817	819	822	824	827	829	832	834	837	839	842	34.00
35.00	842	844	847	849	852	854	856	859	861	864	866	35.00
36.00	866	869	871	874	876	879	881	884	886	889	891	36.00
37.00	891	894	896	899	901	904	906	908	911	913	916	37.00
38.00	916	918	921	923	926	928	931	933	936	938	941	38.00
39.00	941	944	946	949	951	954	956	959	961	964	967	39.00
40.00	967	969	972	974	977	979	982	984	987	989	992	40.00
41.00	992	994	997	1,000	1,002	1,005	1,007	1,010	1,012	1,015	1,018	41.00
42.00	1,018	1,020	1,023	1,025	1,028	1,031	1,033	1,036	1,038	1,041	1,044	42.00
43.00	1,044	1,046	1,049	1,051	1,054	1,057	1,059	1,062	1,064	1,067	1,069	43.00
44.00	1,069	1,072	1,075	1,077	1,080	1,083	1,085	1,088	1,091	1,093	1,096	44.00
45.00	1,096	1,098	1,101	1,104	1,106	1,109	1,112	1,114	1,117	1,119	1,122	45.00
46.00	1,122	1,125	1,128	1,130	1,133	1,136	1,138	1,141	1,143	1,146	1,149	46.00
47.00	1,149	1,152	1,154	1,157	1,160	1,162	1,165	1,168	1,171	1,173	1,176	47.00
48.00	1,176	1,179	1,181	1,184	1,187	1,189	1,192	1,195	1,198	1,200	1,203	48.00
49.00	1,203	1,206	1,208	1,211	1,214	1,217	1,219	1,222	1,225	1,228	1,231	49.00
50.00	1,231	1,233	1,236	1,239	1,242	1,244	1,247	1,250	1,253	1,256	1,258	50.00
51.00	1,258	1,261	1,264	1,267	1,270	1,273	1,276	1,278	1,281	1,284	1,287	51.00
52.00	1,287	1,290	1,293	1,295	1,298	1,301	1,304	1,307	1,310	1,313	1,315	52.00
53.00	1,315	1,318	1,321	1,324	1,327	1,330	1,333	1,336	1,338	1,341	1,344	53.00
54.00	1,344	1,347	1,350	1,353	1,356	1,359	1,362	1,365	1,368	1,371	1,374	54.00
Millivolts	.00	.10	.20	.30	.40	.50	.60	.70	.80	.90	1.00	Millivolts

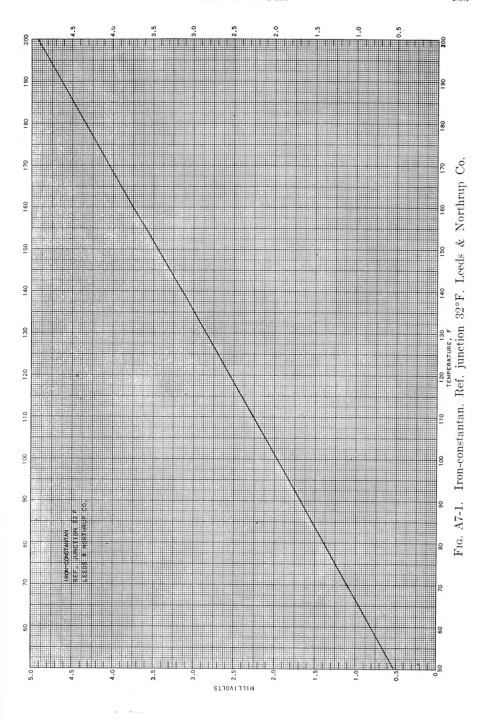

Fig. A7-1. Iron-constantan. Ref. junction 32°F. Leeds & Northrup Co.

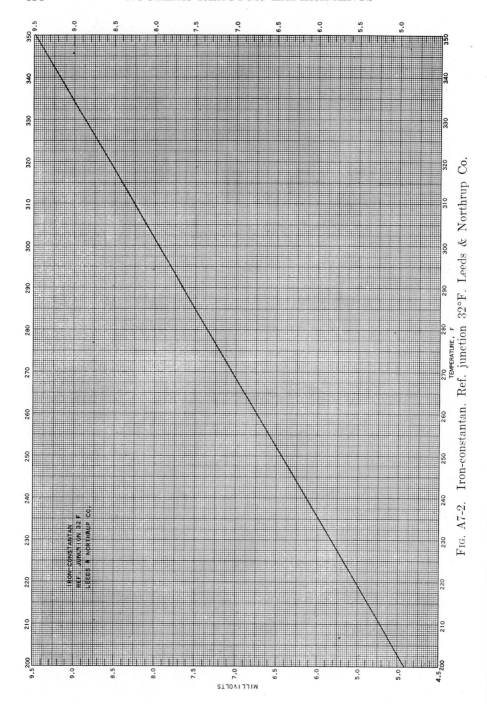

FIG. A7-2.　Iron-constantan.　Ref. junction 32°F. Leeds & Northrup Co.

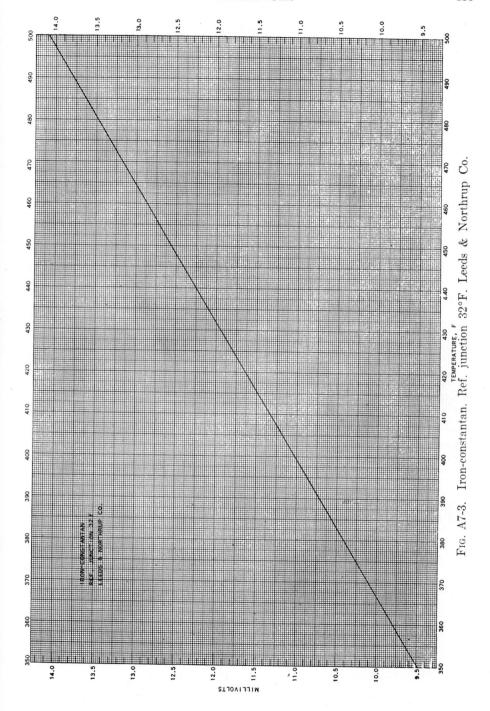

FIG. A7-3. Iron-constantan. Ref. junction 32°F. Leeds & Northrup Co.

INDEX